The Harriet Lane Home

IN MEMORY OF
THE FOUNDER OF THIS HOME
HARRIET LANE JOHNSTON
AND OF HER HUSBAND
HENRY ELLIOTT JOHNSTON
AND THEIR TWO SONS
JAMES BUCHANAN AND HENRY ELLIOTT JOHNSTON JR.
AND IN PERPETUAL WITNESS OF
THE LOVE AND SORROW OF THE WIFE AND MOTHER
WHICH QUICKENED AND DEEPENED HER DEVOTION
TO THE RELIEF OF THE SUFFERINGS OF CHILDHOOD

The Harriet Lane Home

A Model and a Gem

Edwards A. Park

John W. Littlefield

Henry M. Seidel

Lawrence S. Wissow

DEPARTMENT OF PEDIATRICS
SCHOOL OF MEDICINE, THE JOHNS HOPKINS UNIVERSITY
BALTIMORE, MARYLAND

Library of Congress Control Number: 2005935624

ISBN 0-977-37890-X

Frontispiece: front entrance of the Harriet Lane Home for Invalid Children. The formal entrance to the Harriet Lane Home led to a lawn enjoyed by staff and patients from all parts of the Johns Hopkins Hospital. Few patients arrived through this door, however. Concerned parents usually brought their children in through the dispensary building on Monument Street to the long U-shaped main corridor of the hospital. This corridor led to The Harriet Lane Home. The inscription below the illustration of the front entrance of the Home is from a marble plaque in memory of Harriet Lane Johnston. This plaque has been lost, but it was probably located originally on the left side of the corridor just after it led into the Home.

To those who have been close to us
and have provided much-needed support and encouragement
in this as well as many other endeavors

Young patients who came to the Harriet Lane Home at the Johns Hopkins Hospital received not only individualized and up-to-date medical attention but also knowledgeable and often affectionate care from nurses and nursing students. Parents sometimes brought their children to the Harriet Lane because it was close and convenient, and sometimes because they knew it was a world-class institution that was revolutionizing health care and medical education.

Contents

Preface

The history of the Harriet Lane Home, the first building on the campus of the Johns Hopkins Hospital to be entirely devoted to the care of the young, is a grand story with a remarkable cast of men and women and one that is inextricably linked with the history of pediatrics as an academic medical specialty. These men and women were, by and large, creatures of their time but they were also on the move—taking risks, leading the way, and achieving their caregiving, teaching, and scholarly goals in the context of their time. They are role models because of their successes and their failures.

When the Harriet Lane Home opened a genuinely flourishing academic pediatric environment had not yet developed in the United States. In Baltimore, the push for pediatrics as a specialty was successful by 1912, when the Home opened, but elsewhere children's hospitals were a decades-old reality. The pediatricians at the Harriet Lane Home had the advantage of knowing that there was a professional milieu outside of Baltimore that recognized that infants and children had particular needs and were not just little adults. In the late nineteenth century other U.S. cities including Philadelphia, Boston, Washington, D.C., and New York City were fortunate enough to have first-generation child specialists in their midsts.[1] Abraham Jacobi of New York City, an immigrant from Germany, was perhaps the most respected and articulate in promoting pediatrics, and he is in this regard certainly the best remembered. It was Jacobi who delineated "the content and scope of pediatrics" in 1889.[2] He said that the pediatrician must care for the well child as much as the sick child, and that this care mandated political action to help form social policy for the young. He was adamant that pediatrics does not deal with "miniature men and women."

It has its own independence assured by the knowledge that there is scarcely a tissue or an organ which behaves exactly alike in the different periods of life and that there are anomalies and diseases particular only to the infant and child.[3]

The mark of a medical specialty is the formation of a professional society to represent it and it became clear that this was necessary, too, for pediatrics. The impetus to form the new society lay as much in the helplessness engendered by debilitating infectious diseases and inadequate understanding of nutrition, public hygiene, and fluid replacement as in the participants' professional need for formalized recognition of pediatrics as a specialty.[4] The founding in 1888 of the American Pediatric Society, an elite group with membership at the time limited to one hundred, assured recognition of a specialty that would place its study "on the same elevated plane that has been established for adult life."[5] Abraham Jacobi was the society's first president.

The needs of the pediatric medical community were articulated by the founders of the Children's Hospital of Boston who stated that they had three purposes: treating the diseases of children both medically and surgically, gaining knowledge and publishing what they learned, and training young women to be nurses.[6] They validated the need in a dramatic eight-page pamphlet entitled "A Statement Made by Four Physicians in Reference to the Establishment of a Children's Hospital in the City of Boston." They saw "at the public hospitals, the central office of the dispensary, and in practice among the poor and the working people, that the children are constantly exposed to influences which invite disease in its saddest form." They noted that statisticians knew well

> the sad fatality of children in our community; medical practitioners are painfully aware that the hygienic influences which surround the children of the poorer classes are of the worst description. We desire to afford these sufferers, for darkness,... sunshine; for filth and disorder, cleanliness and system; for the rough word or neglect,... gentleness, kindly attention, encouragement; for mephitic odors, sweetness and purity.... Many, very many children sink into early graves.... We not only desire to treat these cases ... successfully, but also to give a tone to the general health of our patients which may have an influence on their future life.... Considered undesirable patients,... little sick children are entirely out of place among sick adults.... Physicians and nurses for children should have a peculiar adaptedness for the management of their young charges.

Importantly, they went on, "There is a want in our community, long felt in our medical schools, though provided for in foreign cities, namely, an opportunity to study infantile diseases ... which furnish a distinct branch of medical science, the importance of which can hardly be sufficiently recognized."[7] Happily, in time, the goals of the Children's Hospital of Boston founders were met. This helped to set the stage for the advent of the Harriet Lane Home, which Clement Smith, the historian of the Children's Hospital of Boston, considered "the birthplace of modern American pediatrics."[8]

In 1910 the Carnegie Foundation issued a scathing report by Abraham Flexner, then a member of its research staff and an 1886 graduate of The Johns Hopkins University, on the sorry state of medical education in the United States. But Flexner was not without hope. In his 1940 autobiography, he recalled that:

> The one bright spot, despite meager endowment and missing clinics, was the Johns Hopkins School of Medicine in Baltimore. It possessed ideals and men who embodied them, and from it have emanated the influences that in a half-century have lifted American medical education from the lowest status to the highest in the civilized world. All honor to Gilman, Welch, Mall, Halsted, and their colleagues and students who hitched their wagon to a star and never flinched![9]

The early history of the Harriet Lane Home can be divided into five periods based on the tenures of five men as chief of pediatrics at the Johns Hopkins Hospital and in the School of Medicine: Clemens von Pirquet, John Howland, Edwards A. Park, Francis Schwentker, and Robert Cooke. At Hopkins, John Howland's commitment to the development of new knowledge, Edwards A. Park's addition of social involvement, and Robert Cooke's activities on the national scene were part of the response to Jacobi's charge of 1889.[10] By 1956, nourished by federal funds, academic medicine began to experience an explosive expansion on all fronts. New buildings were planned as the Harriet Lane Home became outmoded and the numbers of house staff, fellows, and faculty grew. During this time, research blossomed and the primacy of technology in medicine was established.

While he was director of the Harriet Lane Home, Edwards A. Park became interested in writing its history, one that would highlight the people who inspired its growth. After retiring in 1946, Park completed a biographical narrative about Harriet Lane Johnston, the socialite active in political circles who, along with her husband, donated the funds for the establishment of the Home, and another about Clemens von Pirquet. When he received the first John Howland Award of the American Pediatric Society in 1952, Park gave a comprehensive and entertaining lecture about Howland and his career. During the rest of Park's life, he worked off and on to expand this lecture into a narrative of Howland's life and work. By 1964 Park, at the age of eighty-seven, was corresponding energetically with the surviving younger faculty of the Howland era in search of details that he could not recollect clearly or that had occurred after he had left for Yale.[11] Fortunately, all of his writings have been preserved in the Alan Mason Chesney Medical Archives of the Johns Hopkins Medical Institutions.

Before he died in 1969, Park realized that he would not finish the history of the Harriet Lane Home. He asked his close friend and colleague Helen B. Taussig, a world-renowned pediatric cardiologist at Hopkins, to edit the writings that he had drafted. He also asked her to write up his own era from 1927 to 1946.[12] She edited the foreword of this book, which tells the story of Harriet Lane and she added comments, made corrections, verified references, and trimmed the text. Unfortunately, Taussig's own busy career and advancing age prevented her from bringing the rest of Park's drafts to the same stage, or from embarking on the chronicle of his directorship that Park had requested.[13]

Until now Park's manuscripts and draft memoranda concerning Harriet Lane, Clemens von Pirquet, and John Howland have rested unpublished in the Alan Mason Chesney Medical Archives of the Johns Hopkins Medical Institutions. John Littlefield, who came to Johns Hopkins from Harvard University as Robert Cooke's successor, chafed at this situation, impatient with the passing of time because witnesses die, people forget, and younger generations don't know the past. He felt it important to collect the records of the origin and evolution of pediatrics at Johns Hopkins.

Littlefield approached Henry Seidel, who had been an intern in the last group of residents Park selected, to write chapters on Park and Francis Schwentker. Seidel spent his entire career, almost sixty years, in various capacities at Johns Hopkins. The opportunity to know Park better, as well as other major figures in the history of the Harriet Lane Home, appealed to him. "Why don't we do it together?" Seidel proposed, and together we proceeded to finish and expand the work that Park started.

Our first conversations about this project confirmed a mutual determination to write honestly about both the pleasures and the problems in the Home's history. Respect for any institution requires this and in no way do our frank observations diminish the contributions of a very humane enterprise. We wanted to include the story of the Cooke years, and felt that someone whose career was nurtured in the environment Cooke fashioned should be its author. Lawrence Wissow came to the house staff from Duke University early enough in the Littlefield directorship to make this possible. Along the way he became fully trained in both pediatrics and psychiatry and earned a perspective of the institution that complements our experience.

Thus, the authors include John Littlefield, a geneticist whose career has to a great extent been in the laboratory at Harvard and then at Johns Hopkins; Henry Seidel, initially a primary-care pediatrician and then for most of his career a teacher and student advisor at Johns Hopkins; and Lawrence Wissow, a pediatrician and psychiatrist still deep in his academic effort at Johns Hopkins. The legacy of the Harriet Lane Home is our common denominator. We include Edwards A. Park as our coauthor, not just because of his remarkable stature and leadership during his lifetime, but also because we made such extensive use of his memoranda, often verbatim and at length, and because of his urgent desire that this history of the origins of academic pediatrics in this country be completed and published. He is the sole author of the foreword of this book and is the coauthor of several other chapters. Some of Park's work required expansion and editing so headnotes are provided in chapters where Park's work overlaps with the book's authors.

The Harriet Lane Home made a remarkable contribution to the growth and development of academic pediatrics. The story told here limns the progress of splendid academic achievement while suggesting the tug-of-war between the academics in medicine and the practitioners in the community. Part history and part memoir, this volume attempts to find ways in which the past might inform the present and the future of pediatric medicine.

Henry M. Seidel
John W. Littlefield

Notes

Please note that the following abbreviations are used throughout the book, especially in the notes:

AMC=Alan Mason Chesney Medical Archives, The Johns Hopkins Medical Institutions, Baltimore, MD.

HLH-AMC=Harriet Lane Home Archive, Alan Mason Chesney Medical Archives, The Johns Hopkins Medical Institutions, Baltimore, MD.

1. Sydney A. Halpern, *American Pediatrics: The Social Dynamics of Professionalism, 1880–1980* (Berkeley and Los Angeles: University of California Press, 1988), 44–47.

2. Ibid., 50–54. The event was Abraham Jacobi's presidential address at the first meeting of the American Pediatric Society.

3. Ibid., 52.

4. Harold K. Faber and Rustin McIntosh, *History of the American Pediatric Society, 1887–1965* (New York: McGraw-Hill, 1966), 3–6.

5. Thomas Morgan Rotch, then an assistant professor of pediatrics at Harvard and later the full professor, quoted by Halpern, *American Pediatrics: The Social Dynamics of Professionalism, 1880–1980*, 49, and Faber and McIntosh, *History of the American Pediatric Society, 1887–1965*, 9.

6. Clement A. Smith, *The Children's Hospital of Boston—Built Better Than They Knew.* (Boston and Toronto: Little Brown and Company, 1983), 15.

7. Ibid., 16–17.

8. Ibid., 144.

9. Abraham Flexner, *Abraham Flexner: An Autobiography* (New York: Simon and Schuster, 1940), 85.

10. Sydney A. Halpern, *American Pediatrics: The Social Dynamics of Professionalism, 188–1980*, 52.

11. For example, on February 24, 1964 Park wrote to Katherine Dodd, a resident and then junior faculty member under Howland in the 1920s: "I have returned to the attempt to write the Harriet Lane history up to the time of my tenure of office.... The biography of Howland has never been written. I should like to write the Harriet Lane history from 1912 to 1926 around Dr. Howland, converting it into a biographical sketch of him during that period, which was the

period of his maturity and of his most important life work. . . . Whether I shall ever succeed in finishing the Harriet Lane history, I do not know, but I shall at least gather together enough material to make the task easier for someone else." Edwards Park to Katherine Dodd, February 24, 1964, RG 4, series 6, box 9, folder 5, Harriet Lane Home Archive, The Alan Mason Chesney Medical Archives, The Johns Hopkins Medical Institutions, Baltimore, MD, hereafter referred to as HLH-AMC.

12. Helen B. Taussig, April 1, 1974, HLH-AMC.

13. Ibid. "Dr. Park completed the major work on this book up to the time of his regime. This still needs editing. Dr. Park asked me to complete this study, i.e., carry it through his regime."

CHILDREN ASLEEP ON BENCH. Families frequently spent long hours in the waiting room of the Harriet Lane dispensary. Francis Schwentker, the fourth chief of the Harriet Lane Home, snapped these young sleepers as they waited their turn, c.1950.

Acknowledgments

The writing of this book, as with any book, had its measure of pleasure and pain. For us, the pleasure was markedly greater than the pain because of the many personal relationships that were renewed and developed. The pain derived from the realization of our inadequacies that we had to overcome if there was to be a reasonably successful outcome. These wonderful relationships provided balm during the learning process.

The close relatives of the men and women about whom we have written, including Sara Park (Sally) Scattergood and Charles A. (Rollo) Park, (Edwards' daughter and son), gave us invaluable insight and many delightful moments. Ann Fogg, Sally's daughter, lent her perspective as Park's grandchild during a fascinating conversation in her classroom at the Park School in Baltimore County. Helen and Harold Harrison's son, Steve, shared with us the letters from Park to his parents that revealed so much of the environment and culture of Johns Hopkins at the time. And Ann Schwentker Phillips was invariably and thoughtfully responsive as we wrote of the experience of her father, Francis.

Letters saved in family archives over the years were poignant and helpful to us. Sheila Cook Gamble provided those letters that Edwards sent to her father, James. Robert Mason, the Park family physician, shared a trove of letters as did Robert Haggerty, whose letters illuminated Edwards' relationship with the Janeway family. Charlotte Gerczak shared her beautifully written reminiscence of Miriam Brailey. In particular, we deeply appreciate Robert Cooke's permission to review his archival papers, the several hours he spent with us, and his candid responses to searching questions concerning his tenure.

Our many associates at Johns Hopkins and beyond gave us a better understanding of the events they witnessed and this enhanced our ability to write about the past. Among them were Mary Ellen Avery, Saul Brusilow, John Freeman, Emily Germain-Lee, Janet and Paul Hardy, Mildred (Polly) Hesterberg, Howard Markel, Catherine Neill, Jerriann Wilson, Jerry Winkelstein, and William Zinkham. Barton Childs, mentor and friend, offered wisdom and constant support during our many meetings. He also provided us (and thence to the Chesney Archives) with the only handwritten letter by John Howland that we discovered in our research.

Our efforts on behalf of this book were supported by a number of charitable benefactors. Sheila and Lawrence Pakula and the Louis Gross Foundation provided generous monetary support of this project. Others offered significant help as well: William MacLean and the Ross Laboratories; William Richardson and the W. K. Kellogg Foundation; and Anthony Perlman. The considerable financial support of Johns Hopkins' department of pediatrics was matched—and then some—by the constant emotional support of our chief, George Dover. He never flagged in his enthusiasm for our project.

We were the fortunate recipients of abundant technical and administrative support. The staff of the Alan Mason Chesney Archives have no peers: Nancy McCall, Gerard Shorb, Andrew Harrison, Kate Ugarte, Phoebe Letocha, and Marjorie Kehoe were generous with their time and their talents. All photographs in the book are from The Alan Mason Chesney Medical Archives of The Johns Hopkins Medical Institutions, Baltimore, Maryland, unless otherwise noted. Best efforts were made to contact the copyright holders of all photographs. In addition, Michael Henderson brought his expertise as a student of history and his fine eye for relevant material in his review of the Cooke papers and other materials in the Chesney Archives. Rebecca Proctor and Edward Chambers solved bureaucratic problems with calm and ease. Laverne Riggs patiently transcribed several hours of interviews. Francine C. Wethersby and Lynne Dwelley, always there and always pleasant, provided invaluable day-to-day support in our offices.

Any and all errors in this book are solely ours. There are fewer errors and less excess baggage because of the marvelously competent contribution of Mame Warren who strengthened our writing and helped us tell the story of The Harriet Lane Home with greater fluidity. She took over the editorship at a critical moment and helped to bring this book to fruition. Maura Burnett, a copy editor with a profound understanding of what is appropriate for the written word and also of our needs, guided us through the final steps before publication. Glen Burris supervised that process with complete professionalism. We are grateful to all.

JOHN W. LITTLEFIELD
HENRY M. SEIDEL
LAWRENCE S. WISSOW

Acknowledgments

The Harriet Lane Home

The Harriet Lane Home

A Living Monument to Harriet Lane Johnston*

BY EDWARDS A. PARK   I

THE HISTORY OF the Harriet Lane Home is divisible into several parts. It has its genesis in a romance that ended in tragedy, followed by a period between its conception and its birth when Clemens Von Pirquet of Vienna, Austria, was called to be the first professor of pediatrics at the Johns Hopkins University in 1909–1910. Next under the leadership of John Howland, 1912–1926, the Harriet Lane Home began to live and have its being. Later under Edwards A. Park, 1927–1946, the Harriet Lane Home blossomed to full maturity and fulfilled the vision entertained in its conception.[1]

Harriet Lane was born on June 30, 1831. She was the daughter of Elliot T. and Jane Buchanan Lane, James Buchanan's favorite sister. Harriet's mother died when she was seven years old and her father died two years later. Harriet, the youngest of their four children, was taken to live in Lancaster, Pennsylvania, with her uncle James Buchanan, an elderly bachelor who later became president of the United States of America from 1857 to 1861, in the period of turmoil preceding the Civil War.

---

*In a 1974 foreword to this chapter, Dr. Park's colleague Dr. Helen Taussig explained: "Dr. Edwards A. Park in the later years of his retirement undertook to write the history of the Harriet Lane Home for Invalid Children. He completed the first section and left it in almost final shape and began the section on the Howland regime. He asked me to complete the history of the Harriet Lane. In the following section, which is Part I of Dr. Park's manuscript, I have checked all available references and made a few silent emendations, chiefly in punctuation, accuracy of quotations, and elimination of repetitious lines. Otherwise the manuscript stands as he wrote it in his own delightful style." For the present book some further editing of Park's manuscript has been done for style and length.

Harriet Lane's career cannot be understood without some knowledge of her uncle, for the lives of the two were entwined. As a young girl Harriet was fashioned, so to speak, by her Uncle James. Her career sprang from his rise in the political world which, as it concerned Harriet, culminated in his becoming the ambassador of the United States to the Court of St. James in England and, following that, the president of the United States. Harriet probably would never have been known in any public way except for her uncle. It is, however, to her credit that she capitalized on their relationship to the fullest possible extent. To furnish the background of Harriet's career, a brief sketch of the life of Buchanan is necessary.

James Buchanan, born in 1791, was forty-nine years Harriet's senior. He entered politics in 1814 at the age of twenty-three years. In almost unbroken succession, he served in the Pennsylvania legislature, the lower house of Congress (interrupted by a year when he was appointed ambassador to Russia), and nine years in the United States Senate before becoming secretary of state under president James K. Polk, ambassador under President Franklin Pierce, and, finally, President of the United States.

Harriet Lane, as a small girl, is described as a hoyden with too much energy to be controlled. She attended school in Lancaster, Pennsylvania, was placed in a boarding school in Charleston, Virginia,[2] and had an ordinary finishing school education at the Convent School in Washington, D.C.[3] She received special training for her career by being brought up and moving in the political atmosphere surrounding her uncle. She is described at seventeen or eighteen years of age as a very beautiful girl with golden hair arranged simply, deep violet eyes, and an unusually beautiful mouth.

A Novel Relationship

The relation between Harriet and her uncle might have come out of a novel. At first, the attitude of the uncle was the solicitude of an elderly gentleman, not at all certain of his ability to bring up a young girl. Later his attitude changed to one of pride and complete confidence. Harriet in turn apparently worshiped her uncle, not questioning his guiding wisdom and responding to his every need, expressed or imagined, with unsurpassed devotion. If there ever was a case of Pygmalion and the statue, it was here.

The letters that passed between Buchanan and his niece show quite vividly the relation that existed between them. Buchanan's letters to Harriet were written in the formal style of the period in which he lived. Nevertheless, they are chatty, full of news about mutual friends and little events and daily happenings in his own life, and contain comments concerning the events in hers. His letters to her contain discussions of political events, prospects and plans, and are full of exhortations designed to create good behavior, accompanied quite often by reproofs. Evidently this elderly bachelor was full of a sense of duty to bring up his niece to be as nearly as possible a perfect woman in the pattern of the period. When Harriet Lane was eleven years old her uncle wrote:[4]

My dear Harriet:—

Your letter afforded me very great pleasure. There is no wish nearer my heart than that you should become an amiable and intelligent woman: and I am rejoiced to learn that you still continue at the head of your class. You can render yourself very dear to me by your conduct; and I anticipate with pleasure the months which, I trust in Heaven, we may pass together after the adjournment of Congress.... I hope to see you in good health and receive the most favorable reports of your behavior.

Buchanan wrote his niece when she was seventeen that "There is no spectacle more agreeable to me than that of a young married woman, properly sensible of the important duties of her station, and acting upon those high principles which add luster to female character."[5] In 1953 he wrote:

It is my desire to see you happily married, because, should I be called away, your situation would not be agreeable. Still you would have plenty. Whilst these are my sentiments, however, I desire that you shall exercise your own deliberate judgment in the choice of a husband. View steadily all the consequences, ask the guidance of Heaven, and make up your own mind and I shall be satisfied. A competent independence is a good thing, if it can be obtained with proper affection; though I should not care for fortune, provided the man of your choice was in a thriving and profitable business and possessed a high and fair character. I had not supposed there was any thing serious in the conversations; certainly none of your relatives can interpose any just objection. Be, however, fully persuaded in your own mind, and act after due reflection; and may God guide you![6]

As these letters abundantly make clear, the bachelor uncle had developed the devotion of a parent toward Harriet. He apparently lost no opportunity to cultivate in his niece high moral principles but at the same time was not neglectful of material objects or the development of Harriet's mind, nor was he oblivious of the material objects which he regarded as essential for permanent happiness. His ambition for her evidently did not extend beyond the conventional pattern of a marriage that was successful from the point of view of money, social position, and character, which he regarded as essential to happiness.

It is regrettable that Harriet's letters to her uncle have not been preserved but, according to her request, the Harriet Lane papers were destroyed after her death by the vote of the Harriet Lane Home trustees. Only one, written when Harriet was twenty-three, has been preserved and was published in *Life of President Buchanan* by George Ticknor Curtis:

> As regards Washington, I understand perfectly that, as far as you yourself are concerned, you wish me to do as I feel inclined, but your disinterested opinions are rather for a postponement of my visit; these I had quietly resolved to act upon. Should you have changed your mind or have any advice to give, let me know it at once, for rest assured I am always happier and better satisfied with myself when my actions are fully sanctified by your wishes. The day after you left we had an elegant dinner at Mrs. Gilpin's—many, many were the regrets that you were not present. Mr.—— treated me with marked attention—drank wine with me first at table—talked a great deal of you, and thinks you treated him shabbily last summer by passing so near without stopping to see him. I tell you these things, as I think they show a desire on his part to meet you.... How I longed for you to eclipse them all, and be, as you always are, the life and soul of the dinner.[7]

It is evident that Harriet in her turn worshiped her uncle and to his admonitions and advice responded docilely, accepted his admonitions and advice on their face value, and attempted to model her behavior and her life according to his conception of what it should be. Thus, Harriet Lane was profoundly influenced by her uncle and she was carried along by his political success into important positions that would never have come to her otherwise. She, in her turn, made a great contribution to her uncle's success because she measured up to the demands of the situations in which she was placed in most remarkable ways. The uncle and niece formed a remarkable combination of interdependence and mutual success that would be hard to duplicate.

When Buchanan was appointed ambassador to England in 1852, he was apparently in a state of conflict as to whether or not he should take Harriet with him to England. He wrote to Harriet on March 19, 1853, "I think that a visit to Europe, with me as Minister, would spoil you outright. Besides, it would consume your little independence. One grave objection to my acceptance of the mission, for which I have no personal inclination, would be your situation. I should dislike to leave you behind, in the care of any person I know."

Buchanan took up his duties in London in the summer of 1853. Harriet was intensely desirous to go to London and wrote to her uncle in a letter dated October 14, 1853 that going with him to England would be "the future realization of a beautiful dream." To which her uncle replied, "Like all other dreams, you will be disappointed in the reality."[8]

Charming the Court of St. James

Apparently Buchanan's conflict lay between an intense desire to have Harriet with him and the fear that the social life in England would not be to her interest. But his devotion to Harriet had developed to such extent that she had now become essential to him. In February 1854, five months after his arrival in England, he invited Harriet to join him. She sailed in April 1854 and remained with him, acting as the mistress of his house, and returned to the United States in October 1855.

Prior to going to England, Harriet had continued to live in Wheatland. There she had met and entertained leaders of the government, and from time to time on visits to Washington had encountered official Washington society. One gathers from Buchanan's letters to his niece that she visited people a great deal in Washington, Philadelphia, and elsewhere and obviously moved among nice and important people. She attended balls and evidently had a wide range of social experience, probably beyond that of the ordinary on account of the prominent position of her uncle. All this was a preparation for the social requirements to which she was exposed on her arrival in England.

In England Harriet found herself a public figure in English society in the fullest sense of the word. Unfortunately there is no direct account of Harriet Lane's career in England and one is forced to rely on information derived from Ambassador Buchanan's letters to her and

HARRIET LANE AS A YOUNG WOMAN. Lane was one of the most celebrated young American women in the mid-nineteenth century. Orphaned as a girl, she was nurtured by her bachelor uncle, James Buchanan, who became president of the United States in 1857. She served in the White House as his first lady and gained fame as a hostess and social trendsetter. In 1866 she married Baltimore banker Henry E. Johnston. Photograph courtesy of the Library of Congress.

from her letters to her sister, Mary. From these sources, however, one gains an adequate picture of her.

Only twenty-four years old when she arrived, Harriet must have possessed remarkable poise. She evidently took her place in high English society at once, as if she had belonged there always. Almost immediately, through her uncle, she met the distinguished men and women of her time: Prime Ministers Henry John Palmerston, John Russell, and Benjamin Disraeli; the Emperor Napoleon III and the Princess Eugenia; and the various titled men and women who thronged the court and formed the social seat of England at that time. Buchanan entertained considerably and Harriet presided at the dinners and receptions as hostess. She dined with Queen Victoria and the Prince Consort, talking with the latter the entire evening and finding him "most cordial and pleasant." There is no indication in Buchanan's letters to her and in her letters to her sister that there was ever the slightest indication of any feeling of inadequacy.

Several Englishmen wanted to marry Harriet Lane and others paid her marked attention. But her attitude toward them was collected, if not cool. The feelings excited in her were those of cordial liking in one or two instances and respect, but nothing more than that. Either she did not have powerful emotions or they were so completely under control that they never appeared on the surface. She was never carried away in her love affairs, but always seemed able to view them in a judicial way. Her mind may have been very like that of her uncle, who was the soul of honor and integrity, full of great kindness but always reserved, never giving way to emotion that appeared on the surface, and free from introspective analysis. She had feminine qualities, as was shown by a lively interest in clothes. There is abundant evidence that she greatly enjoyed social events and her successes.

Some of the passages from her uncle's letters to her and hers to her sister are very delightful as well as revealing. The letters show, under a reserved exterior, a very human sort of woman. At this time Buchanan wrote: "England is now in a state of mourning for the loss of so many of her brave sons in the Crimea. The approaching 'season' will, in consequence, be dull, and this I shall bear with Christian fortitude. The duller the better for me; but not so for Harriet. She has enjoyed herself very much, and made many friends; but I do not see any bright prospect of her marriage. This may probably be her own fault. I confess that nothing would please me better than to see her married, with her own hearty goodwill, to a worthy man."[9]

In a letter to her sister, Mary, dated April 20, 1855, Harriet wrote that "Mr.—— has lost his favorite sister, and is in great distress, so I have not seen him for a time. I have made another conquest, who comes in a true American style *every day*. He is rich and keeps a yacht which costs him 2,000 pounds a year. Beaux are pleasant but dreadfully troublesome."[10] In still another, dated May 3, 1855, Harriet wrote:

> I have seen ——, and he ordered his gardener to send me from the country all the roses he had in bloom for the drawing-room. Preceding the

box came a sweet little note, which I of course answered in a *tender* way. Mr.——, the man of the yacht is getting quite desperate, as he is ordered to join his regiment for a month. He is constantly sending me flowers, and after his visit today, dispatched a magnificent bouquet. He is a very nice fellow and I really am sorry … Uncle of course knows and sees everyone who comes to the house and places such *confidence in me* that he gives himself no uneasiness. I have as many beautiful flowers now, as my drawing-room can well hold.[11]

In another letter to Mary dated July 13, 1855, Harriet wrote: "I have now … a man of high position, clever and talented, very rich and the only fault to find is his age which is certainly great, as he will be sixty next year. He has a daughter who is a widow, and I might pass for her daughter. But I really like him very much, and know how devoted he would be. I should have everything to my heart's best satisfaction, and go home as often as I liked. But I will write no more about it."[12] When Buchanan received an honorary degree from Oxford, the students greeted Lane's appearance with loud cheers.[13] It is remarkable that this country girl from Lancaster, Pennsylvania was able to go to the Court of St. James and be such an overwhelming social success.

Harriet returned to the United States in the fall of 1855; her uncle had intended to return with her but was detained in London for several months. Characteristically, Buchanan wrote to her after her departure, "Take good care not to display any foreign airs and graces in society at home, nor descant upon your intercourse with titled people;—but your own good sense will teach you this lesson. I shall be happy on my return to learn that it has been truly said of you, 'She has not been a bit spoiled by her visit to England.'" The admonition did not prevent him from adding, "I forgot to tell you that I had seen the good Duchess, who said many extravagant things about you."[14] In another letter: "Lord Clarendon told me yesterday that the queen had expressed her regret not to have seen you before your departure. He said she had heard you were to marry Sir —— and expressed how much she would have been gratified had you been detained in England. We had some talk about the disparity of your ages which I have not time to repeat, even if it were worth repeating. I said it was supposed Sir —— was very rich. 'Yes,' he said, 'enormously.'"[15]

In another letter to Harriet from Buchanan: "The queen at my audience of leave on Saturday, desired to be kindly remembered to you.

The Marquis of Lansdowne at parting from me said, 'If Miss Lane should have the kindness to remember me, do me the honor to lay me at her feet.'"[16]

What was the source of Harriet's appeal? It was felt by both sexes, old as well as young. To the old, she had the charm of verdant youth and verdant spirits, unsophisticated in an environment in which sophistication was universal. She moved in it, one must suppose, with a naturalness and spontaneity quite disarming and with an ease and poise that must have engendered respect beyond her years. But to men there must have been a sex appeal in addition as indicated by the many who wished to marry her. She had many suitors after she became hostess for her uncle in the White House, but there she was in an exalted position and capturing her would have been a public feat. Unfortunately, we have no knowledge of her courtships at the White House, only facts and names and know nothing of her inward feelings. She evidently enjoyed being courted and admired and had the ability, so notable in the case of Queen Elizabeth I, to keep her lovers dangling hopeful, not pulling them up, not letting them down or cutting the rope altogether.

First Lady of the Land

On her return from England in October, Harriet returned to Wheatland. Buchanan was nominated to the presidency in June 1856, and inaugurated on March 4, 1857. Thus, there was a hiatus in Harriet's public career of almost one year spent in Wheatland and about which we know nothing.

If Buchanan had hesitated to take his niece with him to England, there was no hesitation, now that he was President, about making her his official hostess. The complete confidence in Harriet as her uncle was about to embark on the presidency is illustrated by his entrusting to her the expenditure of the balance of the appropriation by Congress of $8,369.02 for the purpose of furnishing the White House. He wrote, "I wish you to consider that this sum must answer our purpose until the end of my term. I wish you, therefore, not to expend the whole of it but to leave enough to meet all contingencies up till 4th March, 1861."[17]

For her duties in the White House, what a wonderful preparation Harriet's experience in her time in England had been! The English court in the reign of Queen Victoria was the greatest school in social organization and behavior on the grand scale to be found anywhere and Harriet had not only seen it, but participated as an accepted actress on its stage. And at the embassy she had a little kingdom of her own to practice in. She returned from England with a training and knowledge such as none of her predecessors in the White House or contemporaries in Washington society possessed. On the assumption of her duties at the White House, she was granted a position as social leader and authority by general consent.[18]

For our information concerning Harriet during her White House period, we are dependent largely on newspaper reports and the literature of the time, and of the succeeding years when she began to become a legendary figure, pictured in an artificial and largely imaginary life. Obviously correspondence between her and her uncle had ceased and her sister, Mary, to whom she revealed the intimate details of her life and of her heart, had died in November 1855. Doubtless other letters from Harriet to her various friends are still in existence but they are not available.[19]

President Buchanan's secretary was his nephew, J. Buchanan Henry. In a letter to biographer George T. Curtis, Henry wrote:

> During the winter, or properly during the session of Congress, there was what might be called a State dinner, once a week, an entertainment of a much more formal and formidable character, in the large dining room, capable of seating about forty persons. The first of these dinners was, I think, given to the Justices of the Supreme Court, the next to the Diplomatic Corps, then to the members of the Senate, and the House of Representatives, including each member in his turn, according to official seniority, except in a very few cases where individuals had by discourtesy or offence rendered such an invitation improper. Miss Lane and I attended to the details of these social matters, including dinner and party attending, making visits, etc., for the President. Among the most troublesome of these duties was the proper assigning of precedence to guests at these so-called State dinners; a delicate task in these Washington entertainments, as any neglect would pretty surely give offence. Miss Lane, from natural aptitude and tact and the experience she had had in London whilst her uncle was minister there, managed these details very cleverly.[20]

What happened when Harriet arrived at the White House is exactly what might have been anticipated. Socially, a reign of youth began with Harriet as queen and the receptions and other social functions at the White House lost their perfunctory character and assumed an unprecedented grandeur. Harriet surrounded herself with a group of young women of her own age who were distinguished for their charm. The receptions and social gatherings that in previous administrations had been formal, stodgy affairs took on an unprecedented gaiety. Jefferson Davis was recorded as having remarked to Craven during his confinement at Fortress Monroe that Buchanan's administration approached more nearly "a republican court than the President's house had ever done before since the days of Washington"[21] because of Buchanan's wide acquaintance both at home and abroad that grew out of his ambassadorship in England. It must also have been the youth and charm of Harriet Lane herself. Colonel John W. Forney, although he had broken his friendship with President Buchanan, said that Lane was "the most accomplished young Mistress of the presidential mansion in modern times. She was a valuable auxiliary to her uncle, the bachelor President, and did much to assuage the asperities of his unfortunate administration."[22]

Harriet Lane had been in the public eye in London, and at the White House she became a public figure in the fullest sense of the word. It was there that she reached the height of her career and was the object of much comment in the daily papers. In 1857, when she entered upon her new duties, she was twenty-seven years old. Certainly she was the youngest mistress the White House ever had and she became almost a legendary figure during that period of her life. The year she became the first lady of the land, in 1857, a steamship for the United States Revenue Service was named for her. Secretary of the Treasury Howell Cobb suggested that the vessel be named for her.

Harriet herself evidently set fashions for feminine society. Mrs. Clement Clay, the author of *A Belle of the Fifties*, wrote, "Low necks and lace berthas made fashionable because of their adoption by Miss Lane were worn almost universally, either with open sleeves revealing inner ones of filmy lace, or sleeves of the shortest possible form, allowing the rounded length of a pretty arm to be seen in its perfection."[23]

Unfounded Romantic Rumors

At the White House Harriet continued to have her suitors. In Mrs. Clay's memoirs, which describe the social and political life in Washington and the South before and during the Harriet Lane period, we find

"Mr. Keitt of South Carolina and his colleague from North Carolina, Mr. Clingman, were looked upon as rival suitors for the hand of Miss Lane."[24] According to Mrs. Robert Saltzstein,[25] Harriet's uncle was thought to be hopeful that Harriet might marry Lord Lyons, the British Ambassador both during her uncle's administration and Lincoln's. An event of which the papers made much was the visit of the Prince of Wales to this country in 1859. The newspapers at the time implied that the prince was attracted to Harriet. Perhaps this is true but he was eighteen years old and she was twenty-nine.

One of the famous social events was a farewell reception at the White House on the final night of President Buchanan's administration. The article in the *Ladies Home Journal* recalled: "All Washington had come to say farewell. The band played alternately "Yankee Doodle" and "Away Down South in Dixie." Hour after hour the crowd passed through the doors until it numbered more than four thousand. Dressed in pure white, the mistress of the Mansion was greeted with effusive admiration by many. By many, too, it was believed that in looking upon her they saw the last woman who would grace the White House and upon her uncle as its last President."[26] This was a few months before the beginning of the Civil War; South Carolina and some of the sister southern states had already seceded.

President Buchanan lacked the magnetism and warmth to be a great leader. Indeed, he was not a leader at all. He thought as a lawyer thinks and tried to patch the breach between the North and South by legal means. Probably no other man as President could have succeeded in averting the Civil War since the issues on the two sides had become so antagonistic and the feelings so bitter. In any event, with the expiration of his term as President on March 3, 1861, he returned to his home in Lancaster, a defeated and unhappy man, living in the hope that history would vindicate him. Harriet, who was then thirty, accompanied her uncle. With retirement of President Buchanan from public office, Harriet's heyday ended and the period of her simple domestic life began. However, from a letter written by John D. Blake to Buchanan, we know that Harriet had attended one of Mrs. Lincoln's afternoon receptions where she was "the observed of all observers" and, "where she was constantly surrounded by crowds of acquaintances desirous of being introduced to her."[27]

We know nothing about Harriet's life at Wheatland during the succeeding six years. She is said to have read to her uncle, helped him in his correspondence and made him comfortable and would stay up with him at night when he would exchange anecdotes and talk over old times with his friends in Lancaster County.

Why did not Harriet marry any of her many suitors in England and the United States? One can only conjecture, but the conjecture was that like an opera singer in the fullness of her voice, she was too much absorbed in her career and her career was so entwined with that of her uncle that an abandonment of it would have been also an abandonment of him. It was not until this was over that her mind was free to consider a separate domestic life.

Embarking on the Sea of Matrimony

In October 1865 Harriet announced to her uncle her engagement to Henry E. Johnston. Johnston belonged to a much-respected Baltimore family. He, together with his brother, Josiah, carried on a prosperous banking business that their father had handed down to the two sons; and he was also a director of the Northern Pacific Railroad. He was probably extremely well-to-do but not rich. It was said that Harriet first met him at Bedford Springs when he was freshly graduated from Princeton. We know nothing about his courtship of Harriet or how the marriage came about.

The portrait of Johnston that now hangs in the Children's Medical and Surgical Center of the Johns Hopkins Hospital must have been made when he was a young man, years before his marriage to Harriet. It is that of a very handsome man, clean-shaven and with rather light brown hair, the face animated and kindly. The marble bust of Johnston made some ten years before his death shows him as having a beard and slightly bald and from it one would gain the impression that he had aged prematurely. He was at the time about forty-three years old. He must have been a lovely character, intensely proud of his wife and extremely generous, which is evidenced by the fact that the endowment that resulted in the founding of the Harriet Lane Home for Invalid Children, provided by Johnston in his will, stipulated that the home was to carry his wife's maiden name only. There is no doubt that Johnston was an exceptional man in every sense and that he fulfilled all the postulates laid down by her uncle for Harriet's husband-to-be.

On January 11, 1866, Harriet was quietly married. At the time she was thirty-six years old, and Johnston was one year younger. It is quite amusing that in the first letter that her uncle wrote to her a week after her marriage, he addressed her as "My dear Mrs. Johnston." He wrote, "I am much gratified with *the tone of your letter,* and think you have embarked on the sea of matrimony with a fair prospect that the voyage may be happy."[28] After a wedding journey that included a trip to Cuba, the Johnstons settled in Baltimore, taking a house on Monument Street near Mount Vernon Place.

In Ibsen's play, Peer Gynt is made symbolically to wander from his mountain home far away into the outer sophisticated world where he had incredible experiences and when they were over, to return to where he had begun. It is interesting that after a glamorous career was over—in which she was sought after by one man after another—and a distinguished public life, Harriet returned home, so to speak, and made the kind of unromantic marriage she might have made if she had remained a Lancaster girl. Harriet's married life was apparently quite happy. Two children were born, both sons. The older was James Buchanan Johnston, nicknamed Buck, born November 26, 1866, who early showed exceptional promise; the younger son was named Henry, born in 1870. Buck died in Baltimore on March 25, 1881, of rheumatic heart disease, as per the death certificate. Henry probably contracted the same illness and in the autumn of 1881 was taken to Nice, France, in the hope that the change in climate would restore him to health. He died while in France on October 30, 1882. At the time of their deaths, the older son was fifteen years old and the younger, twelve.

So sorrow entered Harriet's life. Following the death of their younger son, the Johnstons lived in Europe for another year and then returned to live quietly in Baltimore. In 1883, a year later, two years after the death of her two children, her husband died at the age of fifty-three, and Harriet was left desolate.

A Living Monument

The death of the two sons of Henry and Harriet resulted in the posthumous birth of the Harriet Lane Home, which became their living monument. The protracted illnesses of the two boys from the slow encroachments of rheumatic fever were without doubt responsible for the wish that the institution they proposed should be for "Invalid Children," that is, children suffering from chronic, as distinguished from acute, diseases. The Johnstons must have been made conscious by their personal experience, like countless others before and since, for the need of just such a provision.[29]

It seems unfair in the history of the Harriet Lane Home to give so much space to Harriet and so little to her husband, particularly because the endowment that resulted in the founding of the Harriet Lane Home for Invalid Children came entirely from the estate of Johnston. Early in his married life, Johnston apparently had at least toyed with the idea of establishing a hospital for boys with a training school attached, and his brother, Josiah, had considered establishing a corresponding hospital for girls, as indicated by records of acts of incorporation passed by the Maryland legislature. However, these plans were abandoned and the Harriet Lane Home for Invalid Children was incorporated on December 24, 1883, one year before Johnston's death and twenty years before Harriet's death. The will of Johnston reads as follows:

> Henry E. Johnston by his Will and Testament bequeaths all the rest and residue of his estate to his trustees for the said testator's wife for her life with the powers to her to dispose of the same by her will, and in default of such disposition in trust to hold the same to the use of the Harriet Lane Home for Invalid Children of Baltimore, but provided that if said corporation should become entitled to said residue after the death of his wife and Josiah Lee Johnston [Henry's elder brother] should express a desire to receive income of the whole or any part thereof, the enjoyment thereof by said corporation should be postponed until after the death of said Josiah Lee Johnston and the income paid to him until his own death.

Thus, by the terms of Johnston's will, Harriet was allowed the right to dispose of the residue of his estate in her will in any way chosen by her. However, she allowed the residue to stand for the purpose designated by her husband.

After her husband's death in 1884, Harriet gave up her Baltimore house to live in Washington in a house not far from the White House. She lived in Washington till the time of her death July 3, 1903, at the age of seventy-three years. Although she lived quietly, she appeared in society from time to time on special occasions. She is said to have retained her charm and dignity and was well known for her kindness. There is, however, no indication that during these last twenty-two years in Washington she re-entered public life in any way. She died at Narragansett Pier, Rhode Island, and was buried from her brother-in-law's house on Franklin Street in Baltimore, in Greenmount Cemetery.

Thus, the Harriet Lane Home for Invalid Children was conceived by Johnston. His bequest lay dormant until Harriet Lane, herself, died twenty years later and by her will activated it. Indeed, it remained dormant for another few years after her death since Josiah laid claim to the provision that he be the recipient of the income during his life. He, however, died a few years after Harriet, in 1906. Harriet Lane not only wished her husband's bequest to become a reality but she also designated the trustees of the Home before her death. They consisted of relatives and close friends, vested with the power to carry out the bequest. The total sum available amounted to four hundred thousand dollars. This sum by itself was insufficient to build and maintain more than a token institution. The trustees were thrown into a quandary as to how to make good use of the money with which they were entrusted.

Pediatrics, in the meantime, had come to be recognized as a sub-department of clinical medicine, but it was virtually unrepresented at the Johns Hopkins School of Medicine. The Johns Hopkins Hospital had no facilities for the care of children apart from the wards used for adults, and the medical school had none for teaching pediatrics.[30] Yet the study of childhood diseases was a subject looming in importance in medical investigation and in study. Consequently, the situation was ripe for a companionate marriage, or marriage a la mode, in which the partners would find assets in each other. The Harriet Lane Home had the money but only enough for a token building if it had to purchase land. The Johns Hopkins Medical Institutions had the land and also had the opportunity to develop pediatrics but lacked the building. The difficulties from the point of view of the Harriet Lane trustees lay in the expressed designation in Johnston's will that the institution be for the benefit of invalid children. However, in view of the advantages offered by the union with the hospital and the medical school, the term invalid children could be given a wide interpretation, based on the spirit of the gift rather than on the original interpretation of the words.

William H. Buckler, who had been a boyhood friend of James, the older son of Henry and Harriet, was one of the original trustees appointed by Harriet; he was also a member of the Johns Hopkins University board of trustees. His report and proposal to the Harriet Lane trustees in regard to the course that they should adopt is so important and far-reaching—actually prophetic in its vistas of the distant future—that I quote it in detail:

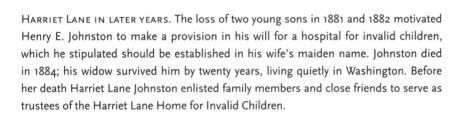

HARRIET LANE IN LATER YEARS. The loss of two young sons in 1881 and 1882 motivated Henry E. Johnston to make a provision in his will for a hospital for invalid children, which he stipulated should be established in his wife's maiden name. Johnston died in 1884; his widow survived him by twenty years, living quietly in Washington. Before her death Harriet Lane Johnston enlisted family members and close friends to serve as trustees of the Harriet Lane Home for Invalid Children.

Since the funds bequeathed to this Corporation by Mr. and Mrs. Johnston are soon to become available, I have been asked by your president to lay before you some suggestions as to what would seem to be the proper method of carrying out with the best possible results, the purposes for which the Corporation was founded. To begin with I assume that the institution contemplated by your founders was a hospital for children, not a home for crippled or incurable cases. This appears from the terms of the charter of 1883 in which the object is to provide for the care and cure of invalid children, and incidentally for the training of nurses. There is no doubt that a hospital can cure more cases and do a larger amount of good than can be done by a mere home.

Then Buckler went on to point out that "the administrative expenses of conducting a small hospital are proportionately greater than those of a large hospital." He recommended a working alliance with some well-equipped Baltimore hospital so as to minimize the heavy expense of administration, so that as much as possible of the income from the Johnston Fund could be devoted to the care and cure of disease. Indeed, he said, "If your hospital should be conducted on an entirely independent footing, its capacity could not be more than twenty-five to thirty beds since, when the cost of the land and building had been deducted, your income would not exceed twelve to fifteen thousand dollars per year. However, by making some such alliance as I have suggested, this income might be economized, and the capacity of the children's hospital could then be increased." He then went on to say, "The Johns Hopkins Hospital can offer a splendid site free of cost, and can reduce to a minimum the expense of running the hospital." Finally, he said, "That the proposed agreement would be in accord with the wishes of Mrs. Johnston herself may be inferred from the fact of her well known interest in The Johns Hopkins University to which she made a bequest of ninety thousand dollars, for a foundation of the Johnston Scholarships."

"There are several further advantages which the Harriet Lane Hospital would derive from such an arrangement," Buckler added:

> First, you could be assured that the medical care in the hospital would always be of first quality; and second, publication of scientific specialists on the diseases of children, carried out by the staff of your hospital, would place the institution among the foremost of its kind in the country, and would make the name of its founder, Mrs. Johnston, (Harriet Lane) well known in many parts of the world. Whereas, if your hospital operated independently with its own staff, its own separate plant, and a capacity of thirty beds, it would be difficult to see results comparable with those which could reasonably be expected from the union with the Johns Hopkins Hospital.

A resolution was then made and duly seconded that the president should appoint a committee to confer with the trustees of the Johns Hopkins Hospital. The president appointed Mary C. Speer, William

H. Buckler, and Blanchard Randall as members of this committee with an object of making an agreement between the institutions. The report of Buckler's recommendation was offered at the fourth meeting of the Harriet Lane trustees, held on April 3, 1905, a little less than two years after Harriet's death.[31]

In medical language, the conception had occurred and all that remained was the consummation of the subject. This occurred without delay. The contract between The Johns Hopkins Hospital and the Harriet Lane Home trustees was duly signed September 1, 1906. The Johns Hopkins Hospital agreed to furnish the building site, selected by them on their property, and retain the ownership of the land. The Harriet Lane trustees agreed to erect the building, at an estimated cost of $195,000 and the remainder of their funds was to be used for the care and cure of the patients. Thus was born the Harriet Lane Home for Invalid Children.

Notes

1. The Harriet Lane Home no longer exists. It was demolished in the spring of 1974 to make way for Johns Hopkins' new oncology center. At the time of demolition, a "wake" was held for the Home in the unheated and poorly lit amphitheater. For more information see Helen B. Taussig, Hugh Josephs, Alexander J. Schaffer, Leo Kanner, and Barton Childs, "Final Meeting in the Harriet Lane Home Amphitheater," *Johns Hopkins Medical Journal*, 137 (1975) 22–23.

2. This section of the Commonwealth of Virginia refused to secede from the Union during the Civil War, and Charleston became the capital of the new state of West Virginia.

3. George Ticknor Curtis, *Life of James Buchanan.* (New York: Harper & Brothers, 1883), Volume 1, 532.

4. Ibid., 536.   5. Ibid., 540.
6. Ibid., 100–101.   7. Ibid., 95.
8. Ibid., 103.   9. Ibid., 125.
10. Ibid., 146.   11. Ibid., 146.

12. Ibid., 147. Edwards Park adds that "Betsy Jäger Saltzstein, who is preparing a biography of Harriet Lane, permits me to say that the rich man in question was Sir Fitzroy Kelly (1797–1880) who served as King's Counsel for a while; was solicitor-general under Lord Derby's administration in 1852; from 1858 to 1859, was attorney general in Lord Derby's second administration. He was raised to the Bench in July 1866 as Chief Baron of the Exchequer."

13. William Perrine, "The Brilliant Social Reign of Harriet Lane," *The Ladies Home Journal* 18 no. 6 (1901): 12.

14. George Ticknor Curtis, *Life of James Buchanan,* (New York: Harper & Brothers, 1883), Volume II, 151.

15. Ibid., 157.

16. Ibid., 168.

17. Ibid., 240.

18. An anecdote published by the Lancaster County Historical Society (Autumn 1962) suggests that Harriet Lane and President Buchanan did not always perceive her position in the same light. "Surgeon General [Jonathan M.] Foltz shows us the self-assertiveness of Harriet Lane when he tells us 'there had been a tiff between Miss Lane and her uncle, who had intimated that she was there as his housekeeper. "Oh, no," she insisted, "I am here as the lady of the White House," and when he did not instantly assent to that she added that if that was not to be her position she would leave at once. She ordered her trunks brought down and that was being done when the President, with apologies, told her that it should be as she wished, but he had to beg her to remain "as the lady of the White House," a position which she filled most graciously.'"

19. As Park has already stated, at Harriet Lane's request the correspondence in her possession was destroyed following her death.

20. *Life of James Buchanan*, II, 235.

21. Ibid., 42.

22. Ibid.

23. Virginia Clay-Clopton, *A Belle of the Fifties: Memoirs of Mrs. Clay of Alabama.* (Tuscaloosa: The University of Alabama Press, 1999), 89. Put into narrative form by Ada Sterling and originally published by Doubleday, Page and Company in 1905.

24. Ibid., 95.

25. Betsy Jäger Saltzstein was writing a biography of Harriet Lane at the same time Edwards Park was writing this essay and they exchanged information freely.

26. Ibid., 42.

27. No source for these quotations could be located among Park's papers.

28. Curtis, op. cit., 645.

29. With the advent of antibiotics this, fortunately, is no longer true.

30. Yet in 1896 William D. Booker was appointed the "Clinical Professor of Diseases of Children" at John Hopkins' newly established School of Medicine. Like William Osler and others, Booker was a general physician who was also interested in children's diseases. He participated in the formation of the American Pediatric Society in 1887 and served as its secretary. Later, he served as its president in 1900–1901. His particular interest was in the "summer diarrhea" of infants, a common, severe, and often lethal disorder. For more information about Booker, see A. McGehee Harvey, "The First Full-Time Department of Pediatrics: The Story of the Harriet Lane Home" *Johns Hopkins Medical Journal* 137 (1975) 21–47.

31. Harriet Lane Home Board of Managers, Minutes from December 14, 1903, to November 8, 1950, 33–35, HLH-AMC. Buckler made both a thoughtful and practical decision in selecting Johns Hopkins:

"If, in order to find an institution with which such an alliance would be possible we look over the hospitals of this City, we shall find only one, namely, the Johns Hopkins Hospital, which is adequately endowed, ideally located and equipped with the best staff, nursing, etc. There are doubtless many other such institutions in this City which are doing excellent work, but they are all insufficiently endowed. They have to depend largely for their maintenance on support derived from pay patients, or from voluntary subscriptions, or from annual grants from the legislature, or from funds raised through the energy of their managers by fairs, sales, lectures, theatrical performances, etc. Their continued existence and their future operation are consequently more or less precarious, and in allying itself with such a body as yours any one of those institutions would have far more to gain than to give. Such an alliance would be unequal and therefore of doubtful advantage to your Board.

"On the other hand, The Johns Hopkins Hospital and your corporation could form a connection on terms not only equal but mutually advantageous. The Johns Hopkins Hospital can offer a splendid site, free of cost, and can furnish at a minimum expense the best of medical care, heating, lighting, nursing and superintendence, while your corporation can supply to the Johns Hopkins Hospital what that institution has long needed—a really good building for the treatment of children's diseases and an income sufficient to operate it with a capacity of seventy-five beds. The Harriet Lane Hospital could therefore do a far greater amount of good in alliance with the Johns Hopkins Hospital than it could possibly do as an independent institution."

The One Man We Desire above All Others

*Clemens von Pirquet, 1908–1911**

By Edwards A. Park and
edited by John W. Littlefield

According to the terms of the contract signed on September 1, 1906, The Johns Hopkins Hospital was to furnish the site of the Harriet Lane Home on its grounds and the managers of the Home were to erect and equip the building to be known as "The Harriet Lane Home for Invalid Children of Baltimore City."[1] The hospital was to supply "to the inmates [patients] of said building as good food and attendance as the inmates [patients] of the Hospital's own buildings." The general administration was to be conducted by the superintendent of the hospital. The medical care of the children was to be the charge of a

---

*Soon after completing the foreword concerning "Harriet Lane Johnston," which he labeled as his final manuscript concerning her and dated April 24, 1967, Edwards Park finished another manuscript describing the Austrian pediatrician-scientist Baron Clemens Freiherr von Pirquet, who was the first chairman of the department of pediatrics at Johns Hopkins and first director of the Harriet Lane Home. As with all his writings on the home, a copy of this manuscript is stored in the Alan Mason Chesney Medical Archives, The Johns Hopkins Medical Institutions, Baltimore, MD. It is labeled "von Pirquet (manuscript—complete)" and dated July 17, 1967. [Harriet Lane Home Archive, Record Group 4, series B, box 7, folder 20.] This manuscript seems less polished than that on Harriet Lane Johnston but it had reached the point at which Park had solicited and included corrections by Richard Wagner, who had studied under and then collaborated with von Pirquet for ten years, and who subsequently wrote his biography: *Clemens von Pirquet, His Life and Work* (Baltimore: The Johns Hopkins University Press, 1968).

For this chapter, as in the previous chapter, Park's own words have been used throughout, although occasionally abbreviated or edited for clarity. Also, the first two paragraphs were originally at the end of Park's previous chapter, entitled "Harriet Lane Johnston," but were deleted by Helen Taussig. It seems likely that Taussig felt that they would be better placed in the next chapter, as has been done here. In addition, the manuscript has been edited for style and length for this book. [JWL]

CHILDREN IN THE JOHNS HOPKINS HOSPITAL, CHRISTMAS, 1900. Before pediatrics became a separate specialty, children were treated at Johns Hopkins in the department of medicine. The patients who gathered with their nurses for this Christmas Day portrait in 1900 were all white, but many young patients then—and throughout the life of the Harriet Lane Home—were black children from the neighborhood.

physician-in-chief, nominated by the Medical Board of the hospital, subject to approval by the managers.[2] The subordinate medical staff was to be chosen by the physician-in-chief. The nursing head was to be appointed by the hospital, with approval by the managers.[3]

Splendid Auspices

With the agreement consummated, the site of the plot on the hospital grounds where the children's hospital was to be erected was agreed upon. The time had arrived to construct the stage and summon the actors. In the summer of 1905 the managers went into action. On the recommendation of the Advisory Board of the medical school, they sent Dr. Charles Emerson, who was at that time a resident physician in medicine, to tour the pediatric centers of North America and Europe to help generate ideas for the construction and operation of a children's hospital. "Hospitals were studied in this country, Canada, England, Scotland, France, Belgium, Austria, Hungary, and Italy," Emerson explained. "Those cities were visited where resided men prominent in pediatrics, since hospitals built under their supervision would be most likely to be of the best description, or if not, these men could tell how their present clinic could be improved." Emerson drew the conclusion that "It was very evident that the idea is now generally accepted that children need hospitals of their own, built with special reference to the needs of these patients." Dr. Emerson conducted his investigations with great energy and thoroughness, and on his return in 1906 the results were published in a monograph entitled "A Preliminary Report Concerning Construction of Hospitals for Children."[4] His report showed a remarkable grasp of the special problems relating to child care in institutions and is interesting since it shows existing thought on that subject in the early 1900s.

With the Harriet Lane Home now a definite member of the Johns Hopkins Hospital group, all was in readiness. The first steps were to appoint the medical director of the Harriet Lane Home, who was also to occupy the chair of pediatrics in the medical school and to develop plans for the Home's building.

The Sixth International Congress on Tuberculosis was held in Washington, D.C. in the autumn of 1908 under the presidency of Dr. William H. Welch.[5] At the conference, Clemens von Pirquet presented a paper on the cutaneous tuberculin reaction in children. It appears likely that the impression he made on Welch resulted in Welch's conviction that von Pirquet was the future professor of pediatrics Johns Hopkins sought, for Welch wrote to his colleague Franklin P. Mall, professor of anatomy at Johns Hopkins and perhaps the guiding spirit in the medical school.[6] The letter reveals Welch's behind-the-scenes diplomacy:

October 8, 1908

Dear Mall:

It is desirable that you should dine with me tomorrow, Tuesday night, at the Maryland Club at 7:30 to inspect Dr. von Pirquet with your falcon eye and celebrated "Raumsinn."[7]

Von Pirquet knows that he is under consideration for the directorship of our new children's hospital. He is Escherich's assistant in Vienna, who recommends him highly.

We must be non-committal at present, and keep the matter close within the bosom of the faculty, which, however, seems to have many excretory ducts.

Yours sincerely,

(signed) William H. Welch[8]

Dr. Alan M. Chesney, dean of Johns Hopkins' School of Medicine from 1929 to 1953 and author of the comprehensive history of the School of Medicine's early years, concluded that von Pirquet must have made a favorable impression at the dinner on the members of the Advisory Board, for a formal call soon followed. At about the same time von Pirquet received an invitation from Emile Roux, the head of the Pasteur Institute in Paris, to become a member of that Institute. It is remarkable that von Pirquet should have accepted the chair of pediatrics in Baltimore in preference, for it carried with it almost no facilities for clinical study, teaching, laboratory investigation, or any other activity. The only physical resources offered were one to two rooms in the general outpatient department of the hospital and three or four beds in one of the adult wards, in case they were desired. However the offer was a full professorship, the ultimate goal in Austro-German university life; von Pirquet was only thirty-three years old, young for that honor. He may have realized that the leaders of the medical school with whom he would be associated—Welch, Kelly, Mall, Howell, Halsted, Abel, Barker, and Thayer[9]—were an extraordinary group. And he may have sensed that they entertained revolutionary ideas in medical education. Four members (Welch, Halsted, Abel, and Mall) were themselves German-educated and fully cognizant of Germany's superiority in the medical sciences at the time. Their presence as colleagues might have given von Pirquet a sense of security. Finally, von Pirquet was a romantic and must have been lured by the spirit of adventure, i.e., to take part in a creative development in a strange land with such splendid colleagues.

A Particular Luster

Von Pirquet's appointment occurred in December of 1908 and in February of 1909 he arrived with his wife to take up his new duties. The von Pirquets established themselves in a large house on West Franklin Street.

When von Pirquet accepted the chair it was anticipated that he would make Baltimore his home and the future Harriet Lane Home the seat of his activities for years to come. However, he remained in Baltimore less than two academic years. Of all the remarkable people who have graced the Johns Hopkins School of Medicine and Hospital, von Pirquet was undoubtedly one of the most remarkable. That it was he who laid down the beginnings of the Harriet Lane Home adds a particular luster to its name.

Clemens von Pirquet was born in 1874 in Hirschstetten near Vienna, Austria. He came from a distinguished and aristocratic Austrian family and bore the title of baron. He first undertook a theological education at the University of Louvain, Belgium with the expectation of becoming a priest, but soon abandoned the church for medicine. After his medical student days were over he joined the pediatric clinic of Hermann Widerhofer in Vienna in 1910. Widerhofer died soon thereafter and was succeeded by Theodor Escherich. Escherich was the foremost pediatrician in the world at the time and was one of the most distinguished in pediatric history. His clinic was famous for its laboratory investigations of disease in children, in particular those of the intestinal tract, as well as for the coterie of clinicians and investigators whom he had gathered about him. Von Pirquet, aged twenty-seven, was the youngest of this group, and had the freshman title of assistant.

At the time Paul Moser, who was Escherich's first assistant, was working in the Serotherapeutisches Institut in Vienna on the development of an antiserum for scarlet fever based on the hypothesis that the streptococcus was the cause of the disease. Attracted by Moser's research, von Pirquet elected to work under him. Moser must have been impressed by the young von Pirquet's abilities since he soon accepted him as a collaborator.[10]

It was while working under Moser that von Pirquet's attention was caught by two episodes in one of Moser's studies that had escaped the notice of others. A child suffering from scarlet fever had received 100 cc of scarlet fever antiserum derived from an immunized horse. After an incubation period of seven days in which nothing unusual happened, serum sickness started. This is a syndrome characterized by the gradual development of fever, hives, swollen painful joints, swollen lymph nodes, etc. It lasts for several weeks, gradually trails off and then subsides completely, so that the subject seems to be in exactly the same state of perfect health as before the serum sickness had occurred. This was exactly the course in Moser's patient after the injection of the scarlet fever antiserum. Then, fifty days later, this same child was injected with 2 cc of diphtheria antitoxin because diphtheria had been discovered in the wards and immunization of the exposed children became necessary. The diphtheria antitoxin, like the scarlet fever antiserum, was obtained from an immunized horse. Fifteen minutes after the injection of the diphtheria antitoxin the child vomited, developed edema of the lips which later spread rapidly over the face, followed within a few hours by an eruption of hives that became general. Why was it that the injection of the diphtheria antitoxin—the second injection—was followed by a sudden violent reaction, which subsided almost as rapidly as it had developed, whereas the first injection—that of the scarlet fever antiserum—had been followed by a gradually developing and prolonged reaction with gradual trail-off?

Von Pirquet realized that both reactions were related and caused by the factor common to both, the horse serum. His theory was that the union of molecules of an antigen (horse serum) with the molecules of antibodies formed by the child against this antigen had created combined molecules that were toxic and that these toxic products were responsible for both reactions. Von Pirquet concluded that the differences in character and timing between the two reactions depended on whether the child's body was caught unprepared or prepared at the time of injection. When the scarlet fever antiserum was injected, the body was totally unprepared; when later the diphtheria antitoxin was injected, the body had been rendered fully prepared and ready to defend itself. Prior to von Pirquet's elucidations the symptoms comprising serum sickness had been an enigma and anaphylactic shock (the immediate severe reaction, as described above after the second injection) had been a mystery. No one had yet conceived that they were different expressions of the same internal process.

Escherich placed von Pirquet in charge of the scarlet fever ward at the St. Anna Hospital in Vienna.[11] It was there that von Pirquet's

PORTRAIT OF CLEMENS VON PIRQUET. Von Pirquet was only thirty-three years old when he arrived from Europe in 1909 to direct and design the Harriet Lane Home. Renowned for his scientific achievements, von Pirquet's appointment brought international prestige to Johns Hopkins. His time in Baltimore was brief, however. While the building was under construction, von Pirquet returned to Europe, where he soon was offered and accepted what William Welch termed "the leading chair of Pediatrics in the world," in Vienna.

partnership with Bela Schick started.[12] This association became a vital factor in the scientific careers of both men. Schick had graduated from the Karl Franz University in Graz in 1900. His interest turned to pediatrics and he became acquainted with the work of Theodor Escherich. When Escherich was called in 1901 from Graz to the chair of pediatrics in Vienna, he invited Schick to join his clinic and assigned him to the scarlet fever ward under von Pirquet.

At the St. Anna Hospital von Pirquet quickly took Schick on as a full collaborator. Although these two men were totally different physically, culturally, and in other ways they possessed much in common. Both were primarily thinkers and idealists, placing the pursuit of knowledge above everything and both were splendid observers. In character they were generous, not only toward each other but to others as well, as their different after-careers showed. Neither was a trained investigator in bacteriology, biochemistry, pathology, or any other scientific field. Neither commanded any special method, unless von Pirquet's grasp of statistics and mathematics are to be regarded as such. Neither was a scientist in the accepted meaning of the term nor did either ever become such. It seems astonishing that this was an asset, but it was the secret of their success. As a result of being able to approach problems uninhibited by the impediments of fixed scientific ideas, they interpreted observations in a simple and direct way. They were a pair of Parsifals,[13] whose strength lay in intellectual purity.

A Revolutionary Theory

From the time of von Pirquet's and Schick's collaboration it is impossible to separate their respective contributions. One gains the impression that von Pirquet was the one who was responsible for the grand strategy, while Schick was more gifted practically in an applied area. However, Schick was also the source of fertile ideas. Each must have furnished something that the other lacked and, without being able to say exactly what, they together provided a wonderful example of synergism. Schick gave von Pirquet complete credit for the revolutionary concept that resulted in the elucidation of serum sickness and anaphylactic shock. He also gave von Pirquet credit for perceiving that this concept was a fundamental principle in immunity, and that this could be extended to infectious diseases in general.[14]

Pursuing the idea that von Pirquet's explanation of serum sickness and anaphylactic shock could be applied elsewhere, he and Schick next studied vaccination against smallpox and again met with success. Following the first vaccination, there appeared a period of "nothingness" for ten days or so. Then a spot of inflammation appeared at the site, which in two or three days matured to a typical pustule. This pustule lingered for two or three days, then began to dry, and soon disappeared, leaving only a scar as a record. In a subject whose first vaccination was a "take," the second vaccination had a totally different sequel. After a very short period of nothingness, occupying only hours or a day or two, a spot of inflammation, accompanied by severe itching, rapidly developed. This was evanescent, rapidly disappearing without leaving any sign of injury. This accelerated reaction told the subject that he was immune and did not require further attempts at vaccination.

Von Pirquet's theory, in which Schick became a full collaborator, explained both phenomena. The first vaccination rehearsed serum sickness in all its details. The latent period following the inoculation was while the cells were in the process of manufacturing antibodies to the protein of the vaccine virus but had not yet discharged them into the blood. The gradual development of the pustule corresponded to the gradual buildup of the toxic molecules from the union of the antibody molecules with the foreign molecules of the vaccine virus. The gradual subsidence and final complete disappearance of the pustule corresponded to the gradual trailing off and ending of the formation of the toxic molecules. The first inoculation followed in miniature, therefore, the course of serum sickness in all its details. The von Pirquet theory explained equally well the quite different reaction that took place when the successfully vaccinated subject was re-inoculated. At the time of the first vaccination the cells of the body were completely unprepared; at the time of the second, however, they were completely prepared. The virus of the second inoculation had no chance, so to speak; the battle was immediate and the virus was quickly disposed of. The accelerated reaction following the second inoculation corresponded to anaphylactic shock in the horse serum studies. However, the shock in this instance was in miniature, confined to the inert skin.

The studies of vaccination obviously explained smallpox itself, i.e., the incubation period of two weeks or so while the body cells were engaged manufacturing antibodies but had not as yet discharged them into the blood, the slow development of the disease to a height as the discharge of antibodies got underway, the maintenance of the height for a short time, and then the slow decline of symptoms and complete recovery with the acquisition of immunity.

Von Pirquet envisioned that his hypothesis would apply to all infectious diseases characterized by a definite incubation period after exposure, gradual progressive development of symptoms to a stationary maximum, followed by a progressive decline with the development of subsequent immunity, including chicken pox, mumps, typhoid fever, etc. Prior to von Pirquet, the incubation period between exposure and development of symptoms had been explained by the necessity for the invaders to build to a critical point; the onset of disease occurred when this critical point had been exceeded and the onslaught had commenced. The development of resistance first began with this onslaught. Von Pirquet's conception was the converse of this: the body begins to develop resistance from the moment the invaders enter, and this resistance has to build up to a critical point before it challenges the invaders. The onset of symptoms is due to the meeting of offense with defense, with a result of recovery (immunity) or death.

In looking back at the work of these two young men, it should be noted how one step forward led without deviation to another. The studies on vaccination demonstrated that the skin could be used as a harmless test area for immunity of the body as a whole. Just stop to think of the practical importance that the use of the skin has had as an index of sensitivity of the body as a whole, to certain foods and to airborne elements such as the pollens causing hay fever and asthma.

Von Pirquet carried on his studies of serum sickness and developed his theory in 1902. In 1905, the classic monograph of von Pirquet and Schick was published, revealing their combined studies on serum sickness. It was in 1906 that von Pirquet coined the term allergy, derived from the Greek meaning altered work or altered activity. Now allergy is a household word.

The two investigators next turned to diphtheria and tuberculosis, two diseases in which the patterns were obscure, in order to see what the skin would tell. They began jointly on diphtheria but when injections of toxin gave no reaction, von Pirquet turned to tuberculosis. However, Schick's persistence succeeded. He was for a time bewildered, because he was looking for reaction patterns in some way resembling previous experience. He soon realized that he was dealing with a *primary* toxin (unlike horse serum or smallpox for which the body needs time to manufacture antibodies). If the test produced no reaction, it showed that antibodies to the toxin were present to neutralize it before it could damage the cells of the skin; if, however, the test was positive, as shown by a spot of inflammation at the injection site, it meant that no antibodies to the toxin were present and the damaging effect on the skin cells was uninhibited.

Schick's work was preceded by two great discoveries, namely the identification of the diphtheria bacillus by Edwin Klebs and Friedrich Loffler, followed by the recognition of its toxin and development of an antitoxin by Emil von Behring. Schick's test was the practical application of these prior discoveries and became known as the "Schick test." The Schick test and the later discovery of how to attenuate the toxin rank with the first two great diphtheria discoveries as equally important. In addition, Schick was also responsible for the principle underlying the "booster" treatment in diphtheria, tetanus, and kindred diseases.

Schick told Park that in the case of tuberculosis von Pirquet was for a considerable time perplexed to explain the skin reactions in accord with his theory. In retrospect his perplexity is easy to understand, for the defense against the tubercle bacillus is through the agency of cells. Lymphocytes, monocytes, plasma cells and leukocytes all move in, and neighboring connective tissue cells proliferate, resulting in the formation of barriers that imprison the bacilli. The cellular reactions in tuberculosis constitute just as much a defense mechanism as does antibody formation to the toxin in diphtheria.

Von Pirquet realized that the skin test in tuberculosis was in full accord with this theory of allergy.[15] A negative test means one of two things: either the tubercle bacilli have never entered the body or they have entered too recently for the resistance reaction, as shown by inflammation at the site of injection, to develop sufficiently to show. A positive test means that the bacilli have found entrance into the body, but it fails to show whether the infection is slight or widespread, for a small focus will produce as positive a reaction as widely disseminated tuberculosis. The physician is then forced to rely on accessory measures, such as x-ray, sputum tests, etc., to make certain that tuberculosis is the cause of the illness.

The Schick test for diphtheria and the von Pirquet test for tuberculosis were equally important, since to the pediatrician both were indispensable.[16, 17]

A Bombshell from Breslau

Well known for his accomplishments, von Pirquet arrived in Baltimore in July 1908 to take up his duties at the Johns Hopkins School of Medicine. He was received at the medical school with open arms. In appearance he was tall and solidly built. He spoke English fluently with a scarcely detectable accent. Moreover he had the gift of youth. In his relationships with people he was simple and outgoing and appeared at ease on formal or informal occasions.

Park wished he knew more details of von Pirquet's life in Baltimore. He knew that he lectured to students and presumed he taught from patients in the rooms accorded him in the general outpatient department of the hospital and the wards. He was extremely popular with the students and was often invited to the Pithotomy Club[18] and other student societies. He was also extremely popular with his colleagues, both the younger members of the faculty and the heads of departments. Dr. Welch made a particular effort to look after him and assure his satisfaction. Baltimore society welcomed and lionized him as well. Park recalled hearing him once remark that the elite were to be found in the South,[19] and that it was necessary to go there to find the cream.

In Park's opinion, von Pirquet was fascinated by the novelty of his new experience and greatly impressed by the cordiality and sincerity of his welcome. And Park believed that he was thrilled to be on equal footing with the great leaders of the medical school at that time. Also he regarded the system of education at Johns Hopkins—which was so different from that on the Continent—as greatly superior, and he sensed that a great new movement in medical education was developing at Hopkins. Of course, one of his most important occupations was designing the future Harriet Lane Home. Park did not doubt that von Pirquet found great satisfaction in being able to plan it exactly in accordance with his ideas.

Von Pirquet's year in Baltimore was a hiatus in his scientific activities. Although Park believed that he continued his work on skin tests, von Pirquet's year in Baltimore must be regarded as a scientific holiday. Schick told Park that in retrospect, von Pirquet regarded it as perhaps the happiest period in his life.

Toward the end of his second year at Hopkins, von Pirquet was offered the post of professor of pediatrics at the University of Breslau, and he wrote the following letter to President Ira Remsen, head of the Johns Hopkins University:

March 6th, 1910

Dear Professor Remsen,

Upon nomination by the Medical Faculty of the University of Breslau, the Prussian ministry of education has offered me the position of professor of Pediatrics at that University.

I have accepted this call.

Mr. Blanchard Randall[20] has suggested that I should not offer my resignation here but that I should ask for a leave of absence and have a chance to consider the question again after having tried the position in Breslau.

Mr. Randall's suggestion was very agreeable to me, as it gives me the possibility of coming back and continuing and developing the work here under more favorable conditions for both of us.

It would be gratifying to me if some such arrangement could be made by which my relations with the Johns Hopkins University and the Hospital were not completely severed at this time, so that I might assume the position in Breslau and still might have the opportunity, if on trial of this position it seemed to me best to return here, to be able to do so. Of course my salary would cease during my absence from the first of May, and I should agree to communicate at least before the first of next January to you my final decision, it being understood that the University is at the same time free to fill my chair if it so desires. If I return to this University I shall on January the first 1911 request an additional leave of absence until the Harriet Lane Home is completed.

Very respectfully yours,

Clemens Freiherr von Pirquet[21]

Although von Pirquet's letter to President Remsen came as a bombshell its request was entirely reasonable, in as much as the Harriet Lane Home building was not complete and until then von Pirquet would be marking time. The Advisory Board of the School of Medicine and the managers of the Harriet Lane Home had no choice but to acquiesce.

In the above letter von Pirquet had promised his decision by January 1, 1911 but he did not meet his deadline. Not having received any official word from him by the end of January, President Remsen wrote to von Pirquet, making an entirely new offer.[22]

January 31, 1911

My dear Doctor:

On behalf of the Trustees of the Johns Hopkins University, I take pleasure in making you the following offer in connection with the professorship of Paediatrics:

A yearly salary of $7500 on condition that you devote yourself entirely to the care of hospital patients (both free and pay), teaching and investigation, and do not engage in private practice. You will have as complete control of the clinic as is possible under existing conditions. That is, you will have absolute control of the admission of a specified number of free patients, the power of veto in the choice of head nurses, a specified budget for laboratory and teaching purposes, a small petty cash amount, and, through the Medical Board of the hospital and the Faculty of the University, practically free choice of all your upper assistants. The general financial and economic administration of the department will, however, remain in the hands of the hospital Trustees.

Such a position will make you eligible for a Carnegie pension, which would provide for you and your wife after retirement.

In order to make possible the payment of so large a salary, which will be the largest thus far paid to any professor in the University, you and your assistants will be expected to supervise the treatment of all private patients admitted to the Children's Hospital with the understanding that whatever fees are paid for such services will go into the Treasury of the Hospital and not to you.

Naturally, the pecuniary returns from such an arrangement may be much less than if you engaged in private or consulting practice; but, on the other hand, there will be certain compensations, such as uninterrupted time for work, greater facility for investigation, a regular income, and finally a retiring pension.

We hope that arrangements may ultimately be made, which will enable us to put the heads of the other main departments of the Hospital upon a similar basis. If this is done, the maximum salary will probably be $10,000 a year, in which you would naturally share. Even if such an arrangement does not prove feasible, we should look forward to advancing your salary to that figure, whenever the fees from pay patients in your department become sufficiently large to justify the expenditure.

Hoping that the proposition will be acceptable to you, and looking forward to having you with us next year, we are

Yours very truly,

(signed) Ira Remsen
President

This letter from President Remsen is of extraordinary interest. The three great clinical departments of the Johns Hopkins medical school were placed on a full-time academic basis in 1913.[23] In his history of the early years of the School of Medicine, Dr. Chesney pointed out that the possibility of making the clinical departments academic was already under discussion in 1909. From President Remsen's letter one would infer that the idea had matured to general acceptance, for the letter offers von Pirquet complete academic status, free from dependence on private practice for his income, with all the other privileges. Had von Pirquet accepted President Remsen's offer, pediatrics at Hopkins would have been the first department to become a full-time academic department, not only in this country but in the world.

When no reply from von Pirquet was received, President Remsen mailed him a copy of the letter on March 2. Von Pirquet's delay in replying was likely due to a new factor that had been injected into the situation. On February 15, 1911, two weeks after Remsen's first letter, Professor Escherich died, thus leaving the post of the Vienna clinic open. Von Pirquet must have realized that he would be considered to succeed Escherich.

Manifest Esteem

While the leaders of the medical school at Johns Hopkins and the managers of the Harriet Lane Home were in a state of suspense, word filtered through to some of the younger members of the faculty that von Pirquet had accepted Escherich's chair. Hoping the situation was redeemable, Samuel Amberg, acting head of pediatrics in von Pirquet's absence,[24] undertook to raise money, solely from junior colleagues on the medical faculty, to supplement any sum that might be needed for von Pirquet's return. Forty-eight members of the junior staff subscribed and an additional twenty-one indicated by telephone their willingness to add. The total amount raised was twenty-five hundred dollars. Chesney wrote that "The Trustees of the University could not see their way clear to accept this offer, however, but they could not have failed to appreciate its spirit, or the manifest esteem in which von Pirquet was held."[25] President Remsen sent an appropriate acknowledgment declining their offer, and then wrote to von Pirquet a third letter under date of May 18, 1911, asking for a definitive reply by cablegram to the letter that had been sent to him in January.

Von Pirquet did not reply until June 27. It is not known exactly what occurred in this interval. Correspondence between von Pirquet and Randall, which might have thrown light, is lost. We do know that Welch attempted to interest the Rockefeller Foundation in giving a grant of two hundred thousand dollars to the medical school with a view to placing the department of pediatrics under the leadership of von Pirquet on a full-time basis, and that his efforts failed.[26] In retrospect it seems astonishing that the Rockefeller Foundation did not leap at the opportunity, for it was only two years later, in 1913, that they established the four clinical departments of the Johns Hopkins medical school, including pediatrics, on a full-time academic basis. Von Pirquet was aware of this failure and also of the refusal of the university trustees to accept the proffered gift of the junior members of the faculty, as the following letter from von Pirquet indicates:

Breslau, June 27th, 1911

Dear President Remsen,

I am in receipt of your letters of January the 31st, and a copy of it sent on March 2nd, and finally a letter of May 18th. I cabled twice in reply (sic) of the last one.

The reason I did not answer your first letters was that I wanted to communicate with Mr. Randall and some of the professors about several points of the offer, before giving you an official and definite reply. The main point was that, although I was very much in favor of devoting myself entirely to the care of hospital patients, teaching and investigation, I did not consider a yearly salary of $7500 an adequate remuneration under these circumstances. I stated that for a salary of $10,000, I would be willing to accept your offer.

Meanwhile I have learned from Mr. Randall that you were not able to pay this sum and that you did not consider favorably the idea of the Johns Hopkins Alumni (sic) to contribute toward the amount asked for. Under the circumstances, to my great regret, I must decline your invitation, as I cabled you in my second telegram.

I have accepted the offer of the Imperial University of Vienna to be the successor of my teacher Prof. Escherich.

Let me thank you on this occasion once more for the many kindnesses, which you showed me during my stay in Baltimore. I may assure you that I shall always keep in memory the pleasure of having worked with the Johns Hopkins faculty and having been in association with such a fine body of students.

Please remember me to the trustees and the faculty.

Respectfully yours

(signed) Clemens Freiherr von Pirquet[27]

This was the first announcement that von Pirquet had accepted the professorship of pediatrics at the University of Vienna. However, the advisory board was willing to pursue von Pirquet and at the instigation of Welch, J. Whitredge Williams (the dean of the School of Medicine and a member of the Medical Board of the hospital) wrote to von Pirquet on October 13, 1911, requesting that he set forth the conditions under which he would return to Johns Hopkins. To his letter von Pirquet replied:

Vienna October 28, 1911
Strictly confidential

Dear Dr. Williams,

I am in receipt of your letter of October 13th which you wrote in behalf of the faculty and of the Harriet Lane Home, and which I appreciate as an honor and as great sign of confidence.

My answer to your main questions is that I am willing to go back to Baltimore, if favorable conditions are offered to me.

As to these I follow the order indicated in your letter:

a. A yearly salary of ten thousand dollars, which is understood to pay me as a university professor, and as the medical director of the Harriet Lane Home.

b. I would like to have no private practice at all and therefore be eligible to a Carnegie pension.

c. Fees from private patients for my attendance in the hospital or for consultations in the hospital would be paid to the Harriet Lane Home.

d. In order to run a good and scientific paediatric [sic] clinic at least three full time paid assistants will be necessary; for the scientific budget for assistants and apparatus etc., a yearly endowment of at least $5000 should be available.

e. My position could not be subordinate in any way to the Superintendent of the J. H. Hospital or some other medical supervisor. In scientific matters, in the use of the clinical budget, in the medical care and the acceptance of patients in the Harriet Lane Home, I should be absolutely free. As to business matters and the general running of the Home, things would have to be carried out on a basis of mutual understanding.

As to the time of my coming back, I would like to come as early as possible. But there is one serious trouble now, which makes it impossible for me to give any final answer. My mother is seriously ill, we do not know whether it is an osteomalacia or a myotoma or a sarcoma. In her actual state I could not leave her. In case her illness should lead to a bad ending this winter, or on the other hand, in case of her complete recovery, I could come next fall.

If you cannot meet my conditions or if you cannot wait on account of the uncertainty of my time of arrival, I would full appreciate your feelings....

Please remember me kindly to the Trustees of both Institutions.

Yours very truly,

Clemens v. Pirquet[28]

Von Pirquet's confidential letter was read to the Medical Board of the hospital on November 13, 1911, whereupon the body voted to refer the entire correspondence to the trustees of the hospital and the board of managers of the Harriet Lane Home and recommended "that von Pirquet be invited to return if the conditions set forth by him can be fulfilled."[29]

The One Man We Desire above All Others

The end of the drama can be described in few words. Dr. Welch again undertook to obtain a grant from the Rockefeller Foundation. Welch wrote to Frederick T. Gates of the Rockefeller Foundation on March 30, 1912,

Von Pirquet in the one man we desire above all others. He stands at the front, as his present position indicates, and you will probably recall the opinions as to his exceptional qualifications of Dr. [Simon] Flexner and his brother as well as what I said to you about him. He would surely be a great stimulus to the much needed development of Pediatrics in this country. It is something of a surprise that he is willing to relinquish the leading chair of Pediatrics in the world to come to Hopkins, but he was most favorably impressed with the general spirit and environment here and especially with the high class of our students, whom he regarded as superior to those whom he has to teach in Vienna. At any rate, he is willing to return and we are most eager to secure him. . . .

If we could secure v. Pirquet on these terms we could at least demonstrate in a conspicuous instance the merits of the much discussed plan of "Whole-Time Professors," and I know that this point will make an especial appeal to you as it does to me.

Chesney concluded his account by reporting that the "letter failed to bring the hoped for result."[30] Since no other source for the necessary funds could be found, all hope of securing von Pirquet vanished. Dean Williams notified von Pirquet of the impossibility of meeting his requirements and the phoenix died, not to rise again.

The negotiations between von Pirquet and the leaders of the School of Medicine were extraordinary. It is Park's opinion that von Pirquet's acceptance of the Vienna professorship was all the time final in his mind but that he had a romantic attachment to the Johns Hopkins position. The conflict was between reason and emotion; he could not resist flirtation.

If von Pirquet was open to criticism for double-dealing and reprehensible on that account, so were the leaders of the medical school equally reprehensible for their part. It was completely unethical to conspire to entice von Pirquet from his newly accepted post. Such underground treatment of one university by another is, to say the least, dishonorable; it is simply never considered.[31] Indeed, in retrospect is seems as if the leaders of the medical school must have been out of their minds when, in their eagerness to obtain von Pirquet, they turned their blind spot to his condition, "my position could not be subordinate in any way to the Superintendent of the Johns Hopkins Hospital or some other medical supervisor." There would be chaos if a single head of a clinical department was singled out to be given an authority over that of the superintendent of the hospital. The negotiations show the strength of the impression that von Pirquet had made on the minds and hearts of his colleagues at the medical school and, reciprocally, the excitement that von Pirquet's time in Baltimore had created in him.

We cannot allow this remarkable man to drop from the page without a brief sequel. The period at Breslau had been as unproductive of investigative work as at Baltimore. It was only on his return to Vienna that von Pirquet's intellectual interests again found expression.

Although Schick was still in the clinic and remained there until 1923, their collaboration never resumed. At this point in his scientific career, von Pirquet turned completely away from the investigation of immunity to nutrition. Schick wrote to Park that after the onset of the First World War, von Pirquet had a prophetic realization that the problem of nutrition would become paramount. In his approach to its study, his aim concentrated on the development of some new system for the estimation of the food requirement of the individual that was practical and at the same time sound.[32] His system had an enormous success in the mass feeding of undernourished Austrian children after the end of the First World War. When the economy of Austria was thrown into chaos and semi-starvation prevailed, the United States government entered on behalf of the starving children. The American Children's Relief Administration was placed under the direction of President Herbert Hoover. One of Hoover's first acts was to appoint von Pirquet as its director. Four hundred thousand children were fed according to his system, which had been perfected just in time to meet the crisis. Its success was an abundant reward for von Pirquet's years of labor. His biographer Richard Wagner has stated that this period, in which von Pirquet stood witness to his triumph, was one of his happiest. The system was subsequently used for similar problems in Russia.

As a result of inflation, the situation for members of the faculty of the University of Vienna was also critical and they were reduced almost to starvation. The Rockefeller Foundation came to their rescue.

As a result of his efficiency as an administrator and his towering personality, von Pirquet's reputation rose to such an extent that he became a nominee for the presidency of the Austrian republic. He fell into acute depression, however, at the very height of his career. When he was about to journey to Berlin to receive a prize and deliver a lecture on allergy, he and his wife committed suicide. He was then fifty-five years old.

Von Pirquet's former student and colleague Richard Wagner remembered his mentor:

As a remarkable teacher, von Pirquet attracted students from all over the world. Many great honors, national and international as well, were bestowed upon him. He was a Harvey and a Silliman lecturer in the United States after World War I;[33] the President of the Union Internationale de Secours aux Enfants; the Chairman of the Committee for Infants' Care at the League of Nations in Geneva; and the President of the Austrian Society of Public Health. He was buried in an honorary grave of the city of Vienna; a housing project of the city was named for him; [and] in a village near Vienna, Perchtoldsdorf, there is a Clemens von Pirquetgasse.[34]

It is Park's opinion that von Pirquet would not have been successful in Baltimore had he returned. The situation at the Johns Hopkins School of Medicine demanded a pioneer who was content with little and willing to improvise and adapt. The clinical departments of the medical school were established on an academic basis (full time) in 1913. The salary of the professor of pediatrics was then ten thousand dollars a year, the same that von Pirquet had stipulated in his negotiations. The operating budget allowed by the university to the department of pediatrics was barely enough to provide salaries for an instructor, resident, and biochemist, all young and inexperienced. As regards the Harriet Lane Home support, funds were sufficient to operate only one floor of the general hospital and the pavilions von Pirquet designated for scarlet fever and diphtheria remained vacant except on one or two occasions when there were epidemics. The von Pirquet plan for the pavilions was financially unsound, since it required a full nursing staff in residence even for a single patient. Park believed that von Pirquet totally misjudged the situation; he assumed that in rich America, support would be unlimited. Moreover in actual practice he never could have been granted the autonomy that he demanded.

Von Pirquet was fashioned for grand projects and grand ideas. He was totally unsuited for the task of building a hamlet in an Iberia completely foreign to him. His place was in an established Rome, and Vienna was his Rome. His department of pediatrics and his pediatric hospital were both splendidly supported by the state, equipped with a corps of experienced assistants, and von Pirquet, according to Teutonic heritage, was the absolute monarch.

Notes

1. In her will, Harriet Lane Johnston stated "I direct that its benefits not be confined to children residing in the City of Baltimore only, but that they be given to white children without respect to creed, nationality, or residence, and with preference in favor of boys if the income shall not suffice for all children without respect to sex." [HLH-AMC, RG 1, box 1, folder 1] This preference for boys perhaps reflects the tragic loss of Johnston's two sons as well as the sexist attitudes of the era, while the exclusion of black children likely reflects the prevailing prejudice in Baltimore at the time of her will. The managers

of the home were easily (and appropriately) persuaded to interpret "invalid children" broadly to include all sick children. Ever since the Home opened in 1912 under John Howland's leadership, it has treated all sick children regardless of color or gender. The words "invalid children" have been used less and less often, and the words "of Baltimore City" almost never.

2. This physician-in-chief would also be appointed professor of pediatrics by the Advisory Board of the School of Medicine.

3. The Home was to pay the hospital at the rate of $1.40 per day per patient. If, however, the number of patients fell below twenty-five, the minimum monthly payment by the Home to the hospital was to be not less than nine hundred dollars. The agreement was to remain in force for twenty years, subject to reconsideration and renewal at ten-year periods after that time. In the event of cancellation, the hospital was to take possession of the building and its equipment, and reimburse the managers of the Home for their value.

4. HLH-AMC, box 1, folder 2.

5. William H. Welch was dean of the Johns Hopkins medical school from 1893 to 1898 and continued thereafter to be the major player in the evolution of this new school, as well as in medicine nationally. See his biography by Simon and James Thomas Flexner entitled *William Henry Welch and the Heroic Age of American Medicine* (New York: Viking Press, 1941).

6. Park also might have given this accolade to Welch.

7. Welch is probably using the term "Raumsinn" in a colloquial style to refer to Mall's awareness of the overall situation at the hospital and medical school.

8. Alan M. Chesney, *The Johns Hopkins Hospital and The Johns Hopkins University School of Medicine, A Chronicle, Volume III, 1905–1914*, 78 (Baltimore: The Johns Hopkins Press, 1963). All subsequent references to Chesney in this chapter refer to volume III.

9. William Welch, Howard A. Kelly, Franklin P. Mall, William Henry Howell, William S. Halsted, John Jacob Abel, Lewellys F. Barker, and William Sidney Thayer.

10. Park here added a note that "It is not generally appreciated in this country that Moser preceded [Alphonse R.] Dochez and [George Frederick Dick and Gladys Henry] Dick in the production of a successful antiserum for scarlet fever."

11. Sanct Anna Kinderspital was one of the oldest children's hospitals in Europe.

12. See Bëla Schick, "Pediatrics in Vienna at the Beginning of the Century," in *Pediatric Profiles* edited by Bordon S. Veeder (St. Louis: C. V. Mosby Company, 1957), 247–57, which reviews Moser's work, Schick's collaboration with von Pirquet and great admiration of him, and Schick's own important studies on diphtheria.

13. Parsifal is a figure of Arthurian legend and the hero of an opera by composer Richard Wagner. Parsifal rose from an innocent orphan youth to lead the Knights of the Holy Grail.

14. This sentiment is from a letter from Schick to Edwards Park written from New York probably many years after Schick moved to the United States in 1923. In this letter Schick reaffirms his great admiration for von Pirquet,

mentioning "his fine personality, his democratic philosophy, his sensitive understanding, his tolerance, etc." He also states that von Pirquet "was a man not belonging to one nation but to the whole world. He was a born leader in international affairs." This presumably refers to von Pirquet's leadership of efforts under the Hoover Commission to diminish undernutrition in children after World War I, first in Austria and then in Russia, and subsequently the consideration of him for the presidency of Austria. Bela Schick to Edwards Park, probably after 1930, HLH-AMC, RG 4, series b, box 7, folder 21.

15. Edwards Park adds a note: "It would be easier to understand von Pirquet's conception if 'resistance' were substituted for 'immunity.' In vaccination against smallpox, measles, typhoid fever, etc., resistance becomes so highly developed as to confer immunity. However there are exceptions even there. In tuberculosis resistance rarely, if ever, rises to complete immunity. Resistance may be little or great, but it is as clearly a defense mechanism as are antibodies to the diphtheria toxin in the blood."

16. Since Park wrote these words in 1967, the vast majority of young children have been immunized against the diphtheria bacillus as part of the DPT shot given routinely in infancy. Consequently the frequency of diphtheria has dropped markedly and so has the use of the Schick test.

17. For a modern appreciation of von Pirquet's achievements, see A. M. Silverstein, "Clemens Freiherr von Pirquet: A pediatrician explains immune complex disease in 1906," *Nature Immunology* (2000): 1, no. 6, 453–455. Silverstein mentions that in 1903, when von Pirquet was a twenty-nine-year-old pediatric resident, he sent a sealed letter that outlined his theory to the Academy of Sciences in Vienna. (This was a rarely employed method to claim scientific priority for his concept.) The letter was only to be opened at the request of the author and this was done in 1908, when the letter was read at a session of the academy.

18. A notorious social club established by Johns Hopkins medical students in 1897, best known for its bawdy annual shows that lampooned fellow students and the medical faculty. See Janet F. Worthington, "The Anals of Hopkins," *Hopkins Medical News* 27, (2003): 18–21.

19. Baltimore and Maryland were then generally regarded as belonging more to the South than to the North.

20. Randall was president of the board of managers of the Harriet Lane Home.

21. Chesney, *The Johns Hopkins Hospital and The Johns Hopkins University School of Medicine, A Chronicle, Volume III, 1905–1914,* 106.

22. Ibid., 123–24.

23. Johns Hopkins was the first medical school in the country to make such a major move. It was made possible at Johns Hopkins and subsequently elsewhere by large endowments from the Rockefeller Foundation.

24. For several years Amberg had been assisting William D. Booker with pediatric patients in the dispensary.

25. Chesney, *The Johns Hopkins Hospital and The Johns Hopkins University School of Medicine, A Chronicle, Volume III, 1905–1914,* 126.

26. Ibid., 123. At the same time Welch continued to try to interest the Rockefeller Foundation in making a much larger grant in the future so that

the other major clinical departments might become full-time academic departments also, but the foundation was not ready to do so.

27. Ibid., 127.

28. Ibid., 195–96. Chesney noted that he omitted "only the portion in which von Pirquet mentioned other pediatricians who might be considered for the Hopkins chair."

29. Ibid., 197, which in turn refers to the minutes of the Medical Board of the hospital, in Chesney's *The Johns Hopkins Hospital and The Johns Hopkins University School of Medicine, A Chronicle, Volume III, 1893–1905*, 75.

30. Chesney, *The Johns Hopkins Hospital and The Johns Hopkins University School of Medicine, A Chronicle, Volume III, 1905–1914*, 201–02.

31. For better or worse, times have changed since Park wrote this. Likewise "double-dealing" with the purpose of improving one's situation at home is hardly uncommon nowadays.

32. See Richard Wagner, *Clemens von Pirquet, His Life and Work* (Baltimore: The Johns Hopkins University Press, 1968), 121–51, for a detailed description of the derivation of this method.

33. Clemens von Pirquet, "Nutritional Treatment of Tuberculosis," Harvey Lectures of 1921–1922, series 17, 89–94. Harvey Society of New York. The Silliman lecture took place at Yale University.

34. Richard Wagner, "Clemens von Pirquet, Discoverer of the Concept of Allergy," *Bulletin of the New York Academy of Medicine*, 40 (1964): 235.

A Model and a Gem

The John Howland Era Begins *

By Edwards A. Park,
EDITED AND EXPANDED BY John W. Littlefield   47

WILLIAM S. THAYER, a long-time and respected senior faculty member in the department of medicine at Johns Hopkins, spoke the following words on the occasion of the unveiling of a plaque in memory of John Howland.[1]

> "There are certain comrades of whom we like to say, 'Here was a man'—a simple and rather obvious comment that carries with it a deep meaning. Such a one was John Howland. As we speak his name there comes to us a mental picture of strength, courage, vigor, energy; a physical frame that was a finely adjusted machine, sure, accurate, graceful, unfailing in

---

*Edwards Park's memoranda concerning John Howland's career differ in length and degree of organization. They consist of discrete, generally unrelated memories, anecdotes, and opinions. Some are early drafts while others are closer to a final version. On the last page of one of his last drafts, probably written in 1968, Park noted, "No biography of Howland has ever been written. The activities of the Harriet Lane Home so center around him or emanate from him that what I now proceed to write will amount to a biographical sketch during the most important creative period of his professional life." Only one draft has a date (July 25, 1957), and it gives some of Park's memories of the Harriet Lane Home forty-five years after its opening, beginning with von Pirquet's plan for the building, continuing with Park's criticisms of it in practice, and concluding with reminiscences of the opening ceremonies in 1912. The date of this draft suggests that Park, having left the chairmanship a decade earlier, had begun to organize in detail his history of the Howland era, which then occupied him until his death in 1969. In the draft probably written in 1968 he added some further anecdotes about the opening ceremony in 1912.

An undated five-page outline of the matters concerning Howland that Park planned to cover (Harriet Lane Home Archive, RG 4, series B, box 8, folder 7, Alan Mason Chesney Medical

its movements; a clear, bright, frank, alert, penetrating eye; a mind as keen and agile, as accurate and well adjusted as the frame in which it was housed; and with it all, a character simple, clean, pure, wholesome, strong."

Howland came to Hopkins in 1912 as the successor to Clemens von Pirquet. Howland was the obvious choice to succeed von Pirquet; his own successor Edwards Park wrote that Howland's "qualifications towered so above those of all others that no alternative existed."[2] Wilburt C. Davison, a Howland trainee and resident, interim director of the Harriet Lane Home after Howland's death, and later dean of Duke University School of Medicine, agreed: "By 1910 no other man in pediatrics in this country had shown such progressiveness and promise."[3] Unfortunately Howland died unexpectedly and prematurely in 1926.

In an obituary in the journal *Science*, Edwards Park wrote that Howland was "one of the four or five great figures in medicine at the present time, and in the history of the Johns Hopkins Medical School he should be numbered among its distinguished creators."[4] In his John Howland Award address in 1952, twenty-six years after Howland died, Park reaffirmed that "At the time of his death Howland was by far the most distinguished figure in American pediatrics and, had he lived, he would have received every honor which could have been bestowed on one of the most outstanding figures in medicine in this country."[5] Likewise, Davison wrote in 1950, "Dr. Howland was the leading pediatrician of this country, if not in the world.... His life ended in 1926

Archives, The Johns Hopkins Medical Institutions, Baltimore, MD) has guided the editing of this and the two following chapters. I have relied greatly on Park's draft memoranda for these chapters, especially a long one (pages 1–69) concerning Howland's life, education, and career prior to coming to Baltimore in 1912 (RG 4, series B, box 8, folder 11), and very frequently I quote him verbatim. Had Park lived more than one more year, he might have continued to polish and join together his drafts concerning the era of his predecessor and so create a most readable and fascinating story. He got close to his goal. And he would have done all this better than anyone coming later could ever do. However, to create these chapters it was often necessary to add my own words to his. Readers who are interested solely in Park's words can read his memoranda in the Chesney Medical Archives.

but in those fourteen years he accomplished his ambition of placing pediatrics in this country on a firm university basis."[6]

The Lure of the Game

John Howland was born in New York City on February 3, 1873, one of six children, only three of whom survived to adulthood. His father, Judge Henry Elias Howland, was a man of great personal charm and a prominent citizen. Judge Howland was also a well-known figure in the social life of New York City, well-to-do if not rich, and he moved in fashionable circles. But he retained a freshness and simplicity that also characterized his son.[7] Dr. Howland once told Park that his father loved to sit behind his family home in Walpole, New Hampshire, whittling while talking with his old cronies. Howland's mother was Sarah Louise Miller Howland, of a well-known New York family, and she was an unusually accomplished pianist. She must have been composed of the metal of which her son, John, was made, for once she was called, without warning, from the audience at a symphony concert to take the place of the solo pianist who had failed to appear, and she is said to have done this without hesitation and with resounding success. John Howland must have taken much after his mother, for this was just the kind of feat of which he was capable, for the more critical the situations, the more efficient his abilities—whether of mind or body—became. Charles Howland, John's older and equally illustrious brother, once told Park that it was from his mother that the "cutting edge" of John Howland's mind was inherited.

John Howland enjoyed a privileged upbringing. He spent his boyhood in New York City, at a summer home on Long Island, and at the Howland family home in Walpole, New Hampshire. He studied at the Cutler School in New York, King's School in Stamford, Connecticut, and was finally prepared for Yale at Phillips Exeter Academy, where he was a member of the football team and graduated in 1890. He entered Yale in the class of 1894 at the age of seventeen. His brother, Charles, said that he was "a hearty, wholesome boy, better than average, developing slowly, and each year a little better than the year previous."

At Yale Howland made no effort to distinguish himself as a student, though he graduated in the upper fourth of his class. He did win great distinction as an athlete and in the social life of the college. He was a member of the tennis team each of his four years, became intercollegiate tennis champion, and was elected president of the Intercollegiate Tennis Association. He was also substitute stroke of the university crew and an editor of the *Yale News*, which in itself assured social prominence. In the senior year he was elected to Skull and Bones, the famous senior society. In short, he was one of the most popular and influential men in his class. On graduation from Yale Howland was but twenty-one years old. He was a member of the United States doubles tennis team and was ranked by experts sixth in the United States. Once, Park asked him how he had escaped a tennis career. He replied that he realized success in tennis and in medicine were incompatible. He went on to say that he preferred to give up the game rather than not play in championship form. He told Park that as a match progressed he was never conscious of the slightest fatigue and in tournament play rather expected to lose the first two sets, relying on his superior endurance in the concluding three. On entering medical school Howland deliberately gave up tennis except for occasional diversion, and later turned to golf.

Although Charles Howland thought his brother had long considered medicine as a career, Dr. Graham Lusk, who knew Howland well at Bellevue Hospital a few years later, felt the decision was made during his sophomore year at Yale. In any case, Howland next had to choose a medical school, specifically one of the three in New York City, since he lived there. In 1895 the College of Physicians and Surgeons (later to affiliate with Columbia University) and the Cornell Medical College extended their curriculums from three to four years, due to beginning recognition in New York and elsewhere that medical education in this country was outdated and inadequate.[8] However the New York Medical College (later to affiliate with New York University) still required only three years of study.[9] The primary focus was on anatomy through extensive memorization of *Gray's Anatomy* text, dissections of two cadavers, back-to-back lectures on other subjects, and quite limited exposure to actual patients. For example, the demonstrations of patients held in amphitheaters or dispensaries provided little opportunity for students themselves to take histories and examine patients. Consequently students who were eager to obtain good hospital internship appointments made extensive use of private tutorials in the theory and practice of medicine in order to score highly on the subsequent internship examinations.

In this situation Howland decided upon a daring plan, despite the advice of friends and physicians whom he consulted. Since all three

PORTRAIT OF JOHN HOWLAND. Howland was the first director to practice in the Harriet Lane Home. Already an esteemed specialist in pediatric medicine when he was called to Baltimore in 1912, Howland recognized that Johns Hopkins offered a superior approach to medical education. He seized the opportunity to create a program to study childhood diseases according to his own ideas.

schools gave the same MD degree, and since it was evident that the most important medical education occurred after graduation from medical school during hospital internships and residencies, he chose New York Medical College, then generally regarded as the "worst" of the three. He depended upon private tutorials to prepare him to win an internship at the more prestigious College of Physicians and Surgeons and thus saved a year in comparison with his contemporaries. For this strategy to succeed the tutorials were crucial. The most famous tutorial was conducted by Dr. Ellsworth Eliot and known as the Eliot Quiz. Eliot possessed a most extraordinary memory for every detail in *Gray's Anatomy*. What he succeeded in doing, coupled with the students' practical experience in dissection, was to enable the student to recite the descriptions in *Gray's Anatomy* virtually by heart. The sole object that Eliot had in mind in his teaching was to enable the student to obtain a hospital appointment. The tutoring in Eliot's Quiz was so effective that almost every one of his pupils obtained an internship in one of the coveted hospitals.

Six internships were available at the Presbyterian Hospital and Howland obtained one of these appointments. He elected a service in internal medicine and began in July 1897 when he was twenty-four years old. While an intern, Howland managed to obtain a medical degree from Cornell University Medical School in addition to his degree from the New York Medical School.[10]

On completion of his two years at the Presbyterian Hospital, Howland secured without a break an internship at the New York Foundling Asylum which furnished the best preparation for pediatrics. This internship was for a single year and was awarded by selection, not by competitive examinations. Howland began there in July 1899. It's uncertain why he chose to devote a year to pediatrics at the asylum but the most probable reason was to broaden his experience to include children. He liked children and had a charming way with them, able to speak to them at their level. It chanced that there he came in contact with the most progressive, stimulating, and all-powerful personality in pediatrics at the time, Dr. L. Emmett Holt. Park believed that this unexpected association was responsible for his choice of pediatrics as a career.

The New York Foundling Asylum was a most unusual institution* and a year there was an indelible experience. Life among the Sisters of St. Vincent de Paul was unique and the medical experience was magnificent. Pediatrics at the time consisted of two main fields: infant feeding and contagious diseases. The young children presented every kind of problem in nutrition and since they were all housed together and had no acquired immunity, infections constantly sprang up and reached epidemic proportions at times.[11] The wonderful opportunity afforded by the service at the asylum was to see disease at the very beginning of its development as well as to be able to follow its course. Autopsies were possible in practically all fatal cases. The opportunity to compare the conditions after death with those thought present in the living had great educational value. This year at the asylum undoubtedly furnished the foundation of Howland's knowledge of disease in children.[12]

*See Appendix C.

Learning from the Masters

Meanwhile, war between the United States and Spain had broken out. After graduating from his year at the asylum, Howland served for a short period on a government hospital ship as a surgeon in charge of soldiers returning from Cuba who had typhoid.[13] With the cessation of hostilities he left to spend a year (1900) visiting and studying in the great German and Austrian clinics of that time. He studied at the University of Vienna clinic, then regarded as the "Mecca for Medicine."[14] There the opportunities were manifold for exposure through observation and coursework to the most advanced medicine, pathology, bacteriology, immunology, etc., in the world at the time. Howland's trip to Europe before the plunge into medical practice, like his decision to spend a year at the asylum, was undoubtedly to broaden his knowledge, and not with any idea of an academic career. For Howland this year was an eye-opener. Howland told Holt many times that "it was this first trip to Germany [and Austria] which gave him the inspiration to be an investigator of disease rather than merely a successful practitioner.[15]

It must have been on his return from Europe in 1901 that Holt asked Howland to be his office assistant—an offer Howland immediately embraced. If Howland had elected to make his start as a general practitioner in internal medicine, advancement would have been slow and tedious. Through association with Holt, his career's success was assured. Holt dominated pediatrics as no other physician had done before. In pediatric circles in New York City his word was law and he dictated almost every pediatric appointment there. The reason Howland accepted the offer was not just Holt's powerful influence but also the chance to drink in pediatrics at the very source. And he may have perceived that children's diseases were almost a terra incognita and offered extraordinary opportunities for investigation. The two years of apprenticeship to Holt exerted a profound influence on Howland. One could detect it in a whole variety of ways: his methods of infant feeding, the Socratic method of teaching in his informal clinics, his methods of dealing with private patients, etc. It can be said that Howland largely shaped his career in imitation of Holt but, of course, Howland broke through the imitation into his own phenomenal creative development.

After Howland's period of service as Holt's assistant ended, they remained close until Holt's death in 1924. This was evidenced by Holt's choice of Howland for the coveted directorship of the pediatric service at Bellevue Hospital, his early selection as an attending physician at the Babies Hospital (later part of the Columbia University College of Physicians and Surgeons), and finally his invitation to co-author Holt's textbook *The Diseases of Infancy and Childhood* are sufficient isolated evidences. In summary, Howland was hand-picked by Holt for the important posts in pediatrics in New York, and "so far as [Holt] was able he threw on Howland his mantle."[16]

Prodigy of a New Era

In 1903, when he was thirty years old, and while working in Holt's office, John Howland married Susan Morris Sanford, the daughter of Dr. Leonard James Sanford, the leading practitioner of New Haven, Connecticut. Sanford had been a classmate of Judge Howland's at Yale and had remained a great friend. While a student at Yale, Howland had developed typhoid fever and jaundice and Sanford took him into his own house where he was nursed until he recovered. We do not know when Howland's affection for Susan Sanford began, but it may have begun during this time. They had four children: Katherine, John Jr., Louise, and Elihu.

When Howland's role as office assistant to Holt ended, there was little opportunity to carry out the investigation of disease that Howland wanted to do. Research at the Rockefeller Institute, which had just opened in 1903, was restricted to the basic sciences; in the clinical departments at the College of Physicians and Surgeons and at Cornell University Medical School investigation was practically unknown. To earn a living, Howland entered the private practice of pediatrics. He rose rapidly in reputation, and according to the fashion then in vogue in New York he accepted multiple professional positions: he became visiting physician at St. Vincent's Hospital; attending physician at Willard Parker Hospital; pathologist and attending physician to the New York Foundling Hospital; and instructor and associate in pediatrics at the College of Physicians and Surgeons. The greatest success possible in New York lay before him. However, he wanted a small hospital and laboratory service such as at the Yale Medical School, one that would furnish support and opportunity for study and investigation.[17]

From 1903 to 1910, Howland's bibliography revealed an investigative energy nothing short of phenomenal for the time, with at least thirty papers published in these seven years. Some were reports of cases that he regarded as so unusual as to demand record while others were extensive reviews of the literature, accompanied by his original contributions founded on autopsy studies. The topics he chose had their origin in problems encountered in his private or hospital practice. Howland's magnum opus during this period—and it ranks as one of his most important contributions to science—was in calorimetry. It seems most probable that his interest in energy metabolism developed after his return to New York when he committed himself to pediatrics and became aware of the importance of energy metabolism in the growing child. In his own John Howland Award address, L. Emmett Holt Jr., himself an expert in this field, noted that Howland's metabolic studies "brought him prompt recognition. Before they were completed, he had been appointed the head of the Children's Medical Service at Bellevue. He was elected to the American Pediatric Society, one of the youngest members ever elected, being only ten years out of medical school, and he was invited to give a Harvey lecture on the 'Scientific Basis of Infant Feeding.'"[18] Holt observed that "the early 1900s saw the formation of the Rockefeller Institute, the Society of Experimental Biology and Medicine, and the 'Young Turks' (the American Society of Clinical Investigation). [Of this last] Dr. Howland was a charter member and a moving spirit. The ferment was going on all over the country. But it was difficult for a clinician who had to make a living by practice to devote the necessary time to do first-class scientific work, and there began to be talk of the need for full-time posts."[19] There were others of the same ilk as Howland in the great clinics in Germany and Austria, but in American pediatrics he stood alone. He was the first of the present-day academic clinicians and the youthful prodigy of the new era.

St. Louis Sojourn

The nascence of academic medicine in this country had its beginning in the founding of the Johns Hopkins School of Medicine in 1893. The next milestone was the creation of the Rockefeller Institute in 1901. The next marker was the publication in 1910 of the study of medical education in North America by Abraham Flexner, who examined all 155 medical schools in the United States and Canada for the Carnegie Foundation for the Advancement of Teaching. His report disclosed that many of these schools were privately owned makeshift

NURSES IN MILK ROOM. The feeding of sick children was of particular interest to John Howland and his colleagues. Each day student nurses worked diligently in two rooms in the basement of the Harriet Lane Home used exclusively for the preparation of Howland's protein milk formula. Photo by the A. Jackson Company.

schools where it was possible for an aspirant to an MD degree to purchase it, so to speak, through a formality of education. Flexner's report touched off a revolutionary reform in medical education in this country. Diploma mills were eliminated and medical schools were forced to greatly expand and improve their teaching.[20]

When the Flexner Report was submitted by the president of the Rockefeller Foundation to Robert Brookings, the major supporter of the Washington University medical school, he was horrified. Brookings asked Flexner, "What shall we do?" Flexner replied, "Abolish the school. Form a new faculty, reorganize your clinical facilities from top to bottom, and raise an endowment which will enable you to repeat in St. Louis what President [Daniel Coit] Gilman [the first president of the Johns Hopkins University] accomplished in Baltimore." Flexner's advice was then submitted to the trustees of the medical school and received their unanimous approval. Steps were immediately taken to secure a new faculty in St. Louis."[21] Emmett Holt Jr. recounted that "In 1910, three full-time clinical chairs were created, in medicine, surgery and pediatrics. And Howland was an obvious choice for this last one."[22]

Howland immediately accepted the invitation to go to St. Louis. In preparation for his professorship, he went to Germany at the medical school's expense. He chose Adalbert Czerny's clinic in Strasbourg as his place of study.[23] In Germany, Czerny was a youthful prodigy, comparable to Howland in America. Czerny reached full professorship in Breslau at the age of thirty-one and as the most distinguished pediatrician of the time. Howland took a house in Strasburg for the year with his wife and children. The year at Czerny's clinic had an enormous impact on Howland, since it inspired his ideas concerning the nutritional disorders of childhood and showed him the possibilities of chemistry as a tool of research. Also, it gave him the opportunity to see with his own eyes a great German clinic under a great German leader in which the advancement of knowledge was the prevailing motif. It was Park's belief that when Howland assumed his duties at the Johns Hopkins School of Medicine, he took Czerny's clinic as his model.

In the summer of 1911 John returned to take up his duties at the Washington University School of Medicine. From the very beginning he was most unhappy and clashed with colleagues and staff on personal and professional issues. Emmett Holt Jr. noted that this time in St. Louis "was a period of continuous disappointments and frustrations. Promised research facilities did not materialize."[24]

The prospect of a new hospital for children was in the making at Washington University but for its planning and construction two more years of waiting would be required. Probably for a combination of reasons, Howland and David Edsall, who held the chair of preventive medicine, resigned after a stay of only six months. According to Davison, Howland "did not like the city and felt that the medical profession there did not appreciate him. As one of his earlier associates put it, 'Howland wanted life served up to him on a silver platter.'"[25] Howland was not a missionary or an idealist. He had returned from Germany with a definite research program and his energy and his nature demanded the opportunity to put it immediately into effect. He chose to return to New York City in his dual role there, supporting himself by medical practice but carrying on his research studies in his free periods, instead of enduring a prolonged and inactive wait in St. Louis.[26]

The Harriet Lane Opens for Business

John Howland must have had an inkling that Johns Hopkins would open its doors to him. It is likely that he knew he was second on Hopkins' list when they hired Clemens von Pirquet in 1908 and that von Pirquet might not return to the position after his leave of absence. In any event, when von Pirquet definitely eliminated himself in the spring of 1912 and the chair of pediatrics was quickly offered to Howland, he accepted without a moment's hesitation.

The opportunity at Johns Hopkins went beyond even Howland's most ambitious dreams. The Harriet Lane Home for Invalid Children had been completed and was generally regarded as the model of a children's hospital. He was free to create a fresh department *de novo* according to his ideals. The medical school was far ahead of the competition and the leader in medical education in the country, with a primary aim of scholarship. To be sure, the salary offered was only four thousand dollars. But a certain amount of consultation practice that would inevitably come to him could be dealt with at the hospital with all its various facilities with little expenditure of time and would be a considerable supplement to this salary. Moreover, he had independent financial resources. He would be free to pursue his interests as teacher, investigator, and clinician, under conditions that were well-suited to him. Howland arrived in Baltimore to take up his new duties in the summer of 1912. The Howlands took a house on Eager Street, just east of Charles Street.

In 1913, a year after the Howlands came to Baltimore and only two years after the Rockefeller Foundation and its General Education Board had declined to provide William Welch with a salary of ten thousand dollars to meet von Pirquet's request, the foundation changed direction. It offered endowment funds to Johns Hopkins' medical school in order to support full-time salaried appointments in all the major clinical departments. Full professors were given a salary of ten thousand dollars a year. Under this arrangement the faculties of medicine, surgery, and pediatrics would terminate all traditional private practice, giving all the fees earned from consultations on patients to the School of Medicine. The intention was to encourage faculty to devote themselves primarily to teaching and research, while continuing to care for outpatients and inpatients.[27] John Howland was delighted with this arrangement, since he regarded private practice as an

FRONT VIEW OF THE HARRIET LANE HOME. When the Harriet Lane Home for Invalid Children opened in 1912, it was one of only a few hospitals designated for the treatment of pediatric patients. Howland quickly modified some of Clemens von Pirquet's original ideas for the building to suit his own requirements. The Harriet Lane was situated just west of the Phipps Psychiatric Clinic, which still stands.

encumbrance, and his would be the first pediatric department in the country to embrace the full-time system.

The Harriet Lane Home for Invalid Children opened its doors for business in the fall of 1912. The formal opening was on November 21, but the Harriet Lane began to function in late September. In the first week of October the dispensary portion was put to use. Its open door for the admission of patients had been advertised in the local newspapers. In the middle of November the first patients were admitted into the wards. Admissions slowly increased and before long the hospital was in full operation, although on a small scale.

Only enough funds were available to open twenty-four beds on one floor of the main building. Racial segregation was in effect throughout

THE FIRST HARRIET LANE STAFF. John Howland attracted extraordinary young physicians to serve on his staff. Kenneth Blackfan (seated on Howland's left), eventually left to lead departments of pediatrics in Cincinnati and then Harvard. Edwards A. Park (seated on Howland's right) succeeded Howland as director of the Harriet Lane Home. Interns Arthur L. Walters, Eleanor B. Wolfe, and William B. McClure (seen standing behind Howland) served as junior members of the first resident staff.

the Johns Hopkins Hospital and was accepted by Howland as well. The ward on the east side was reserved for white children and the ward on the west side for African American children without respect for age or disease.[28] The observation ward was used as von Pirquet had designed, a "purgatory" in which children who might be carriers of the classical group of infectious diseases could be kept until safely admitted to the main building. The east and west pavilions, slated for patients with diphtheria and scarlet fever respectively, were not used at this time. Thus the total capacity for patients of the Harriet Lane Home for several years was fifty-seven beds.[29]

A ceremony to mark the formal opening of the HLH was held on

November 20. This date was chosen by Howland in consultation with a subcommittee of the board of managers, who were given the power to arrange the event in such manner that the opening would have a religious and churchly character. Blanchard Randall, president of the Harriet Lane Home board of managers, gave the Home to the Johns Hopkins Hospital and Winford Smith, the superintendent of the hospital, during a rather characteristically ponderous speech, accepted it as a member of the Hopkins family. L. Emmett Holt, Howland's mentor, gave the keynote address.[30]

Holt's address was full of the calories of forward-looking wisdom, but was not in the least thrilling. He began by pointing out the great importance to the city of Baltimore of a hospital devoted to children. He then dwelt on the greatly increased advantage of a hospital when it is an integral part of a medical school. The association assured that the clinical work—the care of patients—be at the firing line of medical progress. He went on to elaborate how research and clinical work interdigitated. Contact with sick children reveals the need for research and research, in its turn, answers the need. Finally, he pointed out how academic medicine elevated the standards of physicians in the community. In closing he said, "I do not believe the best work is possible in hospitals ... with three or four hundred beds. Small ones would accomplish more. The one hundred beds provided in this institution I do not think should be increased." He added that while the ward service should be small, the size of the outpatient department might well increase. Howland read a very short speech, simple and to the point, despite his abhorrence of public speaking. All the time that the addresses were being made the audience was obliged to stand; Park suspected there was a general sigh of relief, which was not in each instance of a "religious and churchly character," when all was over.[31]

A Model and a Gem

From Howland's description of the Home a reader might think that he approved the von Pirquet design completely and intended to use the building exactly as von Pirquet envisioned. But Howland's vision was different from von Pirquet's and demanded the creation of new facilities. Moreover, many of von Pirquet's arrangements were found to be inadequate as soon as they were put to the test, and were either abandoned or converted to other uses. It was von Pirquet's intention to use the fifth floor of the Harriet Lane as a sanitarium for

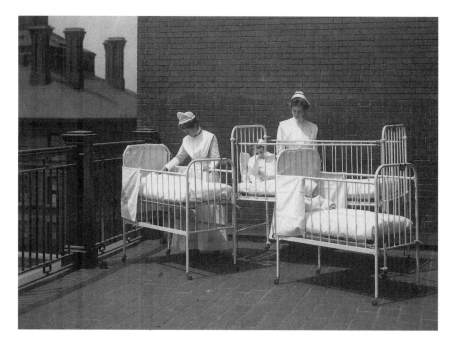

NURSES AND PATIENT ON PORCH. Sunshine and fresh air were part of the course of therapy for many patients. There were roof gardens on the second floor of each of the three rear pavilions and, when this photograph was taken in 1912, on either end of the fifth floor of the main building. All beds were on casters so that they could move easily. Ten years later, this open top floor was transformed into interior space for laboratories.

children with tuberculosis. But Howland abandoned this idea at once. The fifth floor was not used for any purpose until 1922-23 when it was entirely reconstructed in order to furnish a suite of laboratories.[32] During Howland's tenure two laboratories in the basement on the east side and later the laboratories on the fifth floor were constructed. Howland reserved the basement laboratory on the north side for himself and W. McKim Marriott (and later for Benjamin Kramer, James L. Gamble, and Alfred T. Shohl) while the chemical investigators of the Home used the other laboratory on the south side."[33]

Howland abandoned without trial von Pirquet's intention to use two rooms opening off the hallway connecting the east and west wards for the housing of wet nurses and von Pirquet's plans for the scarlet fever and diphtheria pavilions were never put into operation. However, the two pavilions were most useful when other disease emergencies arose, such as the poliomyelitis outbreak in 1916. The teaching of contagious diseases in the Harriet Lane Home remained neglected until the municipal hospital for contagious disease, Sydenham, became available in 1930 and its staffing and teaching facilities fell under the jurisdiction of the pediatric department of the Johns Hopkins Hospi-

REAR VIEW OF THE HARRIET LANE HOME. The Harriet Lane Home was comprised of four buildings in an attempt to control epidemics. Patients with noninfectious diseases obtained treatment in the main building. Von Pirquet planned the layout so that the east pavilion would house patients with diphtheria and the west pavilion would house those with scarlet fever. Patients suspected of having an infectious disease went to the center pavilion for diagnosis. The Phipps Psychiatric Clinic can be seen behind the pavilions.

tal.[34] To some extent the observation ward (the middle pavilion) was used during Howland's time as von Pirquet had intended: for the observation of possibly contagious children. In actual practice the observation ward retained its purgatorial usefulness but with a much more liberal interpretation than von Pirquet had planned. The plans of construction of the Harriet Lane were lost.[35] The plumbing arrangements were, therefore, never known. In order to find out where the pipes lay it was necessary to explore. The walls were massive and the floors made of concrete, and the tasks of locating a leak or installing new pipes were rendered exceedingly difficult. When Howland attempted to use the flue system, it was found that they all ended blindly in the walls. When he established the chemical laboratories in the basement, it was necessary to put in new flues and a fan system. There was a basement that extended under the entire structure, including the amphitheater and the pavilions. It was continuous and constituted a veritable labyrinth. Through no fault of von Pirquet, it was constructed in such a way that in heavy rains the cement floors under the pavilions were inundated with water as much as eight inches deep and were useless for storage purposes for which the basement was designed.

Perhaps the most shortsighted planning of all was the dispensary. The main criticism was its small size. The waiting room was large enough, but only four examining rooms were provided for the use of three interns, three or more teachers, and groups of eight students. And one of the four rooms had to be subtracted in order to serve as a treatment room for general diagnostic procedures. A most annoying omission was a pre-entrance examining room. The entrance from the street, so to speak, opened directly into the waiting room. As soon as the Phipps Building was completed in 1913, the hallway leading from the Harriet Lane dispensary into it was utilized as a pre-examining room, with a view to the exclusion of contagious diseases. However, this elaborate arrangement for the isolation of contagious children upon entrance proved a perfect farce. The special passageway arranged around the waiting room, so as to avoid contaminating the latter, issued into a temporary holding room with three cubicles, defended by curtains. Often five or six cubicles would have been necessary. Because of a shortage of nurses the isolation room could not be policed; when one would go out into it for some reason, one might find parents and children, say, with measles, diphtheria, or scarlet fever, pleasantly assembled in conversation outside the cubicles. Another problem was the lack of a clinical laboratory in the dispensary. For urine and blood examinations, the dispensary depended on improvised arrangements elsewhere. The dispensary remained most inadequate throughout Howland's tenure. An omission that was nothing short of astounding was the failure to provide research laboratories. Von Pirquet was not a laboratory man; he had accomplished his momentous work as a clinical observer. Had von Pirquet remained at Hopkins, it is possible that research would have continued to be of a clinical nature.

The amphitheater did not differ from medical school amphitheaters in general—it had a pit with blackboards behind and accommodations for the audience in front. The distinguishing feature of the Harriet Lane amphitheater was that the audience was expected to stand, facing the pit and occupying the posterior (southern) half of the

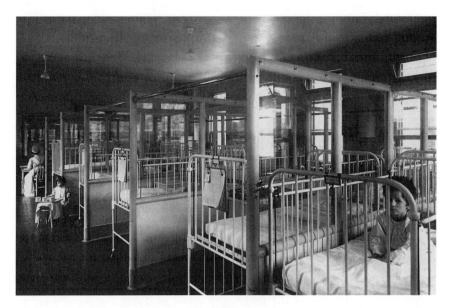

WARD VIEW, C. 1915. The need for surveillance of patients meant there was little privacy, but large exterior windows provided natural light and ventilation. Each ward accommodated about fourteen children, all in beds with high protective railings. When this picture was taken, probably in the observation pavilion, the only two patients there were under the care of one nurse.

auditorium space. It was semicircular in shape, halfway surrounding the pit and consisted of six giant steps, twenty-four inches wide and nineteen inches high. In order to maintain standing equilibrium in the hourlong lectures or clinics, support was provided by a wooden rail running around the front of each step, elbow high, on which to lean. However the rail by itself was not enough. To prevent the accident of falling underneath in a lapse of consciousness, or to prevent members in back from kicking those in front, steel sheeting extended from the rail to the front of each step. This superstructure was broken on either side of the middle third by two aisles in the concrete for ingress and egress.

After several months, Howland had the entire superstructure removed, leaving the bare concrete. The students were then required to sit on the concrete. This was not only hard but on occasion cold and damp. A bright student, very likely the bottom-most in the class, brought with him one day a wooden seat, a practical invention, under the circumstances comparable to that of the first match. The use of wooden seats spread until the idea reached Howland. This caused him to have wooden seats, loose on the concrete, generally provided. This simple arrangement solved the problem. The seats could be shifted at will so that the legs of the student behind could be inserted between the bodies of the students in front. Thus the advantage of bringing the students as close as possible to the demonstration table was preserved. As a result of these changes, the little amphitheater with its concrete structure resembled a Roman arena cut in half. But it proved most satisfactory and became one of the special, rather loved, features of the Home.

This list of shortcomings of the Harriet Lane Home building must not be interpreted as a condemnation. When one considers von Pirquet's plans in detail, one cannot but be impressed by the meticulous care with which each possibility was thought out. There were many splendid features and the external architecture, while not beautiful, was pleasing. As one of the interns pointed out, the diamond-shaped stone inserts in the brick were symbolic of diapers and indicated the nature of the building.[36] The wards and private floor were excellently planned and porches for outdoor treatment were furnished. With its fresh paint, glittering metal, and glass partitions, it seemed a model and a gem.

Notes

1. W. S. Thayer, "Remarks at the Unveiling of the Plaque by Manship in Memory of John Howland, "*Bulletin of the Johns Hopkins Hospital* 46, no.1 (1930), 155–158. The plaque is now on the second floor of the Children's Medical and Surgical Center at the entrance to the neonatal intensive care unit. The inscription on the plaque, "Lux Extincta Lucet" (the light extinguished still shines), was suggested to Mrs. Howland by Thayer, who had previously noted it in the newspaper *Le Temps* when he was in Paris.

2. Edwards A. Park, chapter draft, page 1, RG 4, series B, box 8, folder 11, HLH-AMC. This polished draft is labeled "The Howland Period from 1912 to 1926." In fact it actually covers his life from 1873 to 1912.

3. W. C. Davison, "John Howland (1873–1926)," *Journal of Pediatrics*, 46 (1955): 473–486. [This was also published in *Pediatric Profiles*, ed. Borden S. Veeder (St. Louis: C. V. Mosby Co., 1957), 161–74.] Park quoted extensively from this publication by Davison in his writings about the Howland era, as well as from Davison's obituary of Howland in 1926 and his essay entitled "John Howland: The Seventy-Fifth Anniversary of His Birth," in *Journal of the History of Medicine and Allied Sciences* 5 (1950).

4. Edwards A. Park, "John Howland," *Science* 64 (1926): 80–83. Similar laudatory remarks appeared in other journals, such as W. C. Davison, "John Howland, M.D., 1873–1926," *American Journal of Diseases of Children* 32 (1926): 117–18; the *Journal of the American Medical Association* 86 (1926): 1991–1993; and David L. Edsall, "John Howland, February 3, 1873–June 20, 1926," *Medicine* 5, (1926): 194–96.

5. Edwards A. Park, "John Howland Award Address," *Pediatrics* 10 (1952): 106. The John Howland Medal is the highest award of the American Pediatric Society. Since 1952, the medal has honored those who have made significant contributions to pediatrics. This lengthy address covering Howland's career is a major source for chapters II, III, and IV.

6. Wilburt Davison, "John Howland: The Seventy-Fifth Anniversary of His Birth," 197. This article also contains Howland's complete bibliography.

7. That an aspect of Howland's boyhood personality persisted into his adult life is suggested by the oft-repeated comment by those who knew him that he was always "boyish" or a "boy at heart." Several of these comments may simply represent repetition by subsequent authors, but in any case it became part of Howland's public persona.

8. The Flexner Report of 1910 (issued by the Carnegie Foundation) suggested many improvements for the curriculums of medical schools, including lengthening studies from three to four years.

9. According to Park, who followed Howland by six years, the curriculum in all three schools was still much the same when he attended medical school.

10. Park marveled at this accomplishment: "How in the world in the hectic life as staff officer at Presbyterian Hospital he managed to do the additional work that must have been required to qualify—or indeed why he should have cared to obtain the degree—I have no direct knowledge. Possibly he feared that the Regents of New York State might demand four years of study. Perhaps he got some special satisfaction from this tour de force."

11. Infectious diseases commonly encountered at the asylum included croup, pneumonia, otitis, mastoiditis, as well as the various infections due to the streptococcus and staphylococcus, not then recognized etiologically. Diphtheria was endemic.

12. L. Emmett Holt Jr., "John Howland: Turning Point of American Pediatrics," [John Howland Award Address], *Journal of Pediatrics* 69 (1966): 867.

13. Ibid.

14. Bela Schick, "Pediatrics in Vienna at the Beginning of the Century," in *Pediatric Profiles*, ed. Borden S. Veeder (St. Louis: C.V. Mosby Co., 1957), 247–57.

15. Park, "John Howland Award Address," 87.

16. Edwards A. Park and Howard Mason, "Luther Emmett Holt," *Journal of Pediatrics* 49 (1956): 342–69.

17. Park, "John Howland Award Address," 88.

18. Holt Jr., "John Howland: Turning Point of American Pediatrics," 870. The Harvey Lectures, given once a year under the auspices of the Harvey Society of New York, were prestigious and quite an honor, and have remained so to the present time. According to Edwards Park, Howland spent "hours of reading and preparation.... It was received with the greatest applause as a great feat of scholarship and sane conclusion.... The lecture was John's formal debut as the great leader of the new movement in Pediatrics, if not Medicine at large, to go to the laboratory in search of new knowledge and of certitude." RG 4, series C, box 13, folder 2, HLH-AMC.

A decade later, on March 31, 1923, Howland gave a second Harvey Lecture in New York entitled "The Etiology and Pathogenesis of Rickets," which was equally well received.

19. Holt Jr., "John Howland: Turning Point of American Pediatrics," 870.

20. Abraham Flexner, *Medical Education in the United States and Canada, a Report to the Carnegie Foundation for the Advancement of Teaching*, Bulletin Number 4 (Boston: Merrymount Press, 1910), 346—this volume is commonly referred to as *The Flexner Report*. See also Abraham Flexner, *I Remember* (New York: Simon and Schuster, 1940), 124–25, as well as an updated version of this autobiography (Simon and Schuster, 1960, 81–82) for the complete story.

21. Within a few years the Washington University School of Medicine received similar endowment support from the Rockefeller Foundation in order to shift its faculty to the full-time system. It gained excellence, and for many years has been in the top rank of medical schools. Other medical schools soon followed in this path.

22. Holt Jr., "John Howland: Turning Point of American Pediatrics," 870.

23. The great rival clinic to be considered was that of Escherich in Vienna. However Escherich's interests were oriented toward bacteriology, whereas Howland had already committed himself to investigation by biochemical methods.

24. Holt Jr., "John Howland: Turning Point of American Pediatrics," 870.

25. Davison, "John Howland (1873–1926)," 183.

26. Indicative of the difference between the personalities of Clemens von Pirquet and John Howland, the former, at least prior to his receiving the offer to return to Austria, appears to have been willing to wait two years or more for his plans for a children's hospital to become a reality in Baltimore, while the latter could not wait for his plans to be realized in St. Louis.

27. For extensive coverage of the introduction of the full-time system into the Johns Hopkins School of Medicine, see Alan M. Chesney, *The Johns Hopkins Hospital and the Johns Hopkins University School of Medicine: A Chronicle*, volume III 1905–1914, (Baltimore: The Johns Hopkins Press, 1963), 128–87; and for a short summary of this transition see Thomas B. Turner, *Heritage of Excellence, The Johns Hopkins Medical Institutions, 1914–1947*, (Baltimore: The Johns Hopkins University Press, 1974), 20–22. Also see Flexner, *I Remember*, 176–84, and Flexner and Flexner, *William Henry Welch and the Heroic Age of American Medicine* 297–328.

28. In 1925 or 1926 Howland was asked by the Rockefeller Foundation to review the status of the department and he asked Ashley Weech to do this. Ashley Weech to Edwards Park October 21, 1968, RG 4, series B, box 8, folder 22, HLH-AMC. In "The Johns Hopkins University School of Medicine: Department of Pediatrics" in *Methods and Problems of Medical Education*, Weech confirmed that the separation of white and black patients continued until the end of Howland's career at Hopkins, at least on the fourth floor, which by then was used for sick infants. This separation was terminated by Howland's successor, Edwards Park.

29. Alan Chesney acknowledged that "the principal defect in the Har-

riet Lane Home at the time it was opened and for a long time thereafter was the lack of an endowment sufficient to maintain it at full operating capacity. Built to care for 100 inpatients, its funds were sufficient to care for only one fourth of that number and its potential from the point of service to the school and to the community was correspondingly diminished. At the time it was estimated by [Superintendent of the Hospital] Dr. [Winford H.] Smith that the sum of $25,000 a year as additional income would have sufficed to put the new enterprise on a satisfactory financial basis and to permit it to operate at full occupancy, but that sum was unhappily not then forthcoming." Chesney, *The Johns Hopkins Hospital and the Johns Hopkins University School of Medicine: A Chronicle*, volume III (1905–1914), 219–20.

30. Luther Emmett Holt, "The Children's Hospital, the Medical School, and the Public," *Johns Hopkins Hospital Bulletin* 24 (1913): 89–92.

31. Edwards Park, who had arrived at Hopkins a few weeks before this event, wrote his comments about the opening ceremony fifty-six years later (1968), when he was ninety-one years old. He admitted that his recollections were "decidedly dim."

32. In 1913 or 1914 John Howland was called to the professorship at Harvard by his friend and admirer, David Edsall, who had become the Jackson Professor of Medicine at the Massachusetts General Hospital [Aub and Hapgood, *Pioneer in Medicine, David Linn Edsall of Harvard*, 122]. Park suggested that one of the conditions under which Howland consented to remain in Baltimore was that the fifth story of the Harriet Lane be completed to correspond to the rest of the building and be converted into research laboratories. However, it seems likely that this renovation of the fifth floor was done in 1922 or 1923 (after a second unsuccessful call to Harvard) and that Park refers here to the renovation of the basement laboratories soon after Howland took charge of the Home.

33. It should be remembered that Edwards Park was eighty years old when he wrote this, before he received the plans of the original building to refresh his memory. Park clearly struggled to remember other changes made in the structure of the building.

34. Thomas B. Turner confirmed and clarified this story: "Since 1909, visits had been made to Sydenham Hospital by Hopkins medical students for instructional purposes, but such visits were few in number and did not represent a serious educational effort." In 1930 a small committee was appointed by the then president of the university to conduct a survey of the status of the medical school, as had been done profitably ten years earlier. Among its recommendations a year later—doubtless prodded by Park—was to improve "the instruction of medical students in the diagnosis and treatment of communicable diseases." Several possible ways to do this were considered, and eventually a coordinated effort at Sydenham by Hopkins, the University of Maryland School of Medicine, and the City of Baltimore was decided upon. "Park was much interested in the move and was prepared to rotate Harriet Lane interns through the Sydenham service, sharing the extra cost with the city," Turner explained. "The plan came into full operation in 1935, when Francis F. Schwentker [later Park's successor as director of the Harriet Lane] became the chief of the service at Sydenham and a member of the pediatric

staff at Hopkins.... In 1960 ... the Baltimore City Hospitals assumed responsibility for patients with communicable diseases." Turner, *Heritage of Excellence*, 306–7.

35. The plans were found sometime after Park wrote this.

36. Later on the front of the building became completely covered with ivy, extending to the very roof. In the ivy hundreds of starlings nested and Dr. David Edward Davis, an associate professor in comparative behavior at the School of Hygiene and Public Health and assistant dean who investigated the starling colony reported that each starling had an individual perch that it occupied every night.

A Lush Meadow of Opportunity

Howland's Colleagues and Staff

By Edwards A. Park,
edited and expanded by John W. Littlefield   71

JOHN HOWLAND'S FIRST order of business at Johns Hopkins was
to assemble the resident staff for the new Harriet Lane Home. He
brought with him from St. Louis as his first resident pediatrician Kenneth Daniel Blackfan, who had worked as a pathologist and a bacteri-
ologist in Albany, New York, and then trained in pediatrics in Philadelphia before going to St. Louis with Howland when Howland accepted
the chair of pediatrics at Washington University. He also recruited
three interns from the class that had graduated from the Johns Hopkins School of Medicine in 1912: William B. McClure, Arthur L. Wa-
ters, and Eleanor B. Wolfe. All three of them worked together in the
outpatient department.[1]

Blackfan was a remarkable man. He was born in 1883 in Cambridge, New York. His grandfather was a doctor and his father was
a doctor and a farmer, interchanging both activities as circumstances
determined. Kenneth Blackfan never had a college education; We are
not sure that he even completed high school, for the medical schools
of that day demanded only two years of high school education. He
once said that he had moved with a fast group of medical students but
realized the fatuity such a life led to, abandoned his friends, and settled
down to serious work. Blackfan came under the instruction of an in-
spiring young professor of pathology and bacteriology only nine years
his senior while at the Albany Medical College. This was Richard Mills
Pearce, then professor of experimental medicine at the college, who
later occupied at the University of Pennsylvania the first chair of research medicine in the United States. Dr. Pearce recognized Blackfan's
abilities and developed a special interest in him.

After graduating in 1905, Blackfan spent the next four years with his father in general practice in Cambridge. But according to James L. Gamble, "Richard Pearce spent his summers in Dorset, just over the line in Vermont. There, Blackfan found friendly interest and encouragement, which gradually produced the determination to find out what might lie over the horizon in medicine."[2] A nascent attraction to pediatrics was nurtured by several months in the pediatric department at an Albany hospital. In 1910 he went to Philadelphia armed with letters of introduction from Pearce to David Edsall, then an associate professor of medicine at the University of Pennsylvania, who had just been made president of the American Pediatric Society,[3] and to Samuel Hamill, a well-known Philadelphia pediatrician. Initially Blackfan was resident-in-charge under Hamill at the St. Vincent de Paul Foundling Hospital (1909–1910)[4] and then instructor in pediatrics at the Polyclinic Hospital under Edsall (1910–1911). Edsall and Pearce encouraged Howland to take Blackfan with him to St. Louis for additional training in pediatrics. Howland did so and a few months later he brought Blackfan to the Harriet Lane Home. According to Clement Smith, historian of the Children's Hospital of Boston, "Blackfan thus found himself centrally established in what was to be the birthplace of modern American pediatrics."[5]

Gamble, who came to work in Howland's laboratory in 1915, described this experience as "a lush meadow of opportunity."[6] For Blackfan as a young clinician, the adjoining wards must have been no less fertile; for a number of years he was to know them with the intimate personal knowledge of the resident. Much later, Blackfan told at least one impatient young Boston house officer how he knew after each of those Hopkins years whether he had learned more than he knew the year before. If he decided he had, he stayed another year. When for the first time the answer was negative, he left Baltimore in 1920 and went directly to Cincinnati as professor of pediatrics. In 1923 he was called to be head of pediatrics at Harvard as physician-in-chief of the Children's Hospital.

When Howland was away, particularly during his summer vacations, Blackfan had entire charge of the wards. This was in accordance with the Johns Hopkins residency system, which Howland adopted in full. But it was also well deserved, for Blackfan was by far the best physician in the department and he was medically fashioned in Howland's own image.

At the end of Blackfan's lengthy residency he had risen to the rank

JAMES GAMBLE AND KENNETH BLACKFAN IN BOSTON. Before Blackfan, right, accompanied John Howland to Baltimore, they had worked together at Washington University in St. Louis. Blackfan was the first chief resident at the Harriet Lane Home, a position he held for seven years. Gamble arrived in 1915 to work in Howland's laboratory. By 1923 both were at Children's Hospital in Boston, where each enjoyed a cigarette as this photograph was taken.

of associate professor and had accumulated extensive pediatric and nursing experience. Howland planned for Blackfan to go into private pediatric practice in Baltimore and retain some connection with the department. Although Howland had great admiration for Blackfan and was extremely fond and proud of him he always regarded him as a subordinate. He never regarded Blackfan as having university caliber. He recognized Blackfan's worth as a clinician, but could never get past the idea that Blackfan had risen from the ranks, so to speak, and had never had a college education. Blackfan's adoption of a subservient attitude toward his chief did not help his case. Blackfan, however, made an outstanding success of his professorship in Cincinnati.

As a physician, Blackfan brought to bear his immense clinical experience, which was combined with rare wisdom and judgment. He was a born teacher and his rounds were intensely didactic, extending beyond the directions for the care of the child to the reasons therefore, punctuated with instructions to his junior staff about what not to do as well as what to do. His clinics were splendid demonstrations of practical pediatrics at their very best. Though he did not work actively in the laboratory himself, Blackfan had an intense interest in research and constantly made suggestions that bore fruit in the work of others. Although Blackfan was intensely interested in the investigation of disease, Howland did not allow him to go into the laboratory. Howland was insistent that his resident have no other duties than those imposed by the care of children in the wards and to be always on hand at his post if needed. However, Blackfan was anxious to go into the chemical laboratories and learn there biochemical methods. As it was, he always kept abreast of the research in the department and slipped into the chemical laboratories in the evenings.[7] He was later offered the deanship at Harvard Medical School because of the general confidence in his fairness and wisdom, but he declined and remained the professor of pediatrics at Harvard for the rest of his career.

In 1909 Edwards Park became the office assistant to Dr. Theodore Janeway, who was then professor of medicine at the College of Physicians and Surgeons in New York. With Janeway's consent Park spent six months in Germany in 1912, studying the pathology of rickets under Professor M. B. Schmidt in Marburg. While there he received a cablegram from Howland, whom he met at the New York Foundling Hospital in 1907–1908, offering him the position of instructor in pediatrics at a salary of eight hundred dollars a year. On receiving a cablegram from Janeway releasing him and advising him to accept the offer, he did so. On Park's arrival in Baltimore in the fall of 1912 he was met at the station by Howland. Howland explained to Park that his duties would be to take care of the Harriet Lane Home dispensary, which had not yet opened. He then took Park to the Harriet Lane Home and introduced him to Blackfan and Amy MacMahon, the supervisor of the Harriet Lane, and showed him over the building, which was completely unoccupied at that time.

EDWARDS A. PARK AND JOHN HOWLAND. Park, left, first met Howland when they were both at the New York Foundling Hospital in 1907–08. Four years later, Howland "called" Park to be the first director of the outpatient department of the Harriet Lane Home, a position he occupied until 1917. In 1921 Park left the Harriet Lane to start a new department of pediatrics at his alma mater, Yale University, but he returned to Hopkins in 1927 to lead the department of pediatrics after Howland's death.

The pattern of organization that Howland set at the very beginning of his tenure held until the time of his death in 1926 with only slight modification. Howland arrived at his office about half past nine or ten o'clock in the morning and he attended to mail or other duties of an administrative nature. At eleven o'clock he conducted rounds with Blackfan and later on with the interns as well. His teaching occurred daily from twelve to one. At one o'clock he had lunch, returning at two. In the afternoon he saw ambulatory private patients in his office by appointment and took care of any administrative work that came up or had not been completed in the morning. But a certain part of the afternoon, usually the latter part from half past three until half past five, he reserved for work in the laboratory. He left for home usually at about six o'clock.

Blackfan started his rounds on the wards at nine o'clock each morning (after completing the necessary visits to private patients) accompanied by the interns, and finished between half past ten and eleven, with all in readiness for Howland's rounds at eleven o'clock. In the afternoon Blackfan carried out or supervised difficult treatments. He also taught small groups of students in the wards. He personally admitted all new patients, coming down to the dispensary to examine them. Blackfan performed these examinations in the afternoon or in the evening as circumstances determined, and then wrote them up himself. He was on hand for emergencies and in the evening he made rounds again before going to bed. Since he lived in the Harriet Lane Home he was frequently called to the wards or the dispensary for emergency situations at night.

The Personal Touch

Howland's organization of his interns was interesting. They were assigned to the children admitted to the wards in rotation, and they also worked in the dispensary. The important part of the arrangement was that when a child was discharged, his doctor on the wards took care of him in the dispensary. Thus each intern had his own group of patients, bed and ambulatory, just like a practicing physician, but without the home visits. Each intern also did all the laboratory work required, including bacteriology. The arrangement was ideal, for it gave the intern an understanding of his patient as an integrated whole. The interns became interested in their patients as individuals and many patients in their turn returned with enthusiasm to their doctors in the Harriet Lane. The plan was only possible because the Harriet Lane was so small. It was a contrast to the present system in which the division of labor makes it necessary to piece together the perspective of the child from charts and sheets of data. In Howland's clinic the personal touch was kept in all its purity.

In 1912 Howland placed the dispensary in Park's charge and it opened at nine o'clock. One of the three interns in rotation, the dispensary admitting officer, arrived at eight o'clock at the dispensary

John Howland's program for the education of interns promoted personal relationships between doctors and their patients. The intern who cared for a child admitted to the hospital later cared for that same patient after discharge, when he or she returned to the dispensary for follow-up visits. Many patients formed warm bonds with their doctors and enjoyed coming back to the Harriet Lane.

entrance and screened the children as they arrived; he then segregated those having or suspected of having diphtheria or one of the exanthemata. Admissions to the dispensary were supposed to stop at nine but did not. Park had three assistants, all pediatricians from the town: Lyman Whittle, Richard A. Urquardt, and J. H. Mason Knox Jr. Knox, one year older than Howland, was already quite well known in pediatric circles in this country.[8] He and Park shared the teaching.

At nine o'clock eight students would arrive, all of the fourth-year class. The dispensary course occupied a quarter of the school year and it was an elective course. Each student was assigned one patient after another, and was expected to take a complete history and perform a complete physical examination, recording both in writing. On completion, students would report to Knox or Park to review the case. When the treatment was agreed upon, students were expected to enter it in the charts. When a patient returned to the dispensary, care was taken

to ensure reassignment to the student to whom he or she had been assigned in the first place. Thus the student was made to feel that the patient was his responsibility. This unique experience made the course in
the pediatric dispensary extremely popular and one of the most sought
after.

The interns arrived at eleven o'clock at the conclusion of Blackfan's
rounds, often earlier. The same system applied to them as to the students, except that as they became more experienced, they were trusted.
From the educational viewpoint, the cultivation of the bond between a
patient and an intern or a student throughout the medical process was
nothing short of ideal. The sense of personal responsibility felt by care-
givers stimulated interests, thoughts, and efforts that no other method
could have inspired. Another feature of Howland's organization related
specifically to the all-around education of the intern. The necessity to
choose what laboratory work was required and to then perform it provided a well-rounded experience. Later, when the intern issued forth
into private practice and was obliged to dictate laboratory work done
by others, he was especially able to judge what was required and to es-
timate its value.

This system at HLH was strained during the First World War.
Hugh Josephs (1892–1980) was a medical student in the Harriet Lane
at the time and remembered that period: "In 1918 ... the Harriet Lane
wards and dispensary were run by an assistant resident, Margaret Handy, and three third-year students, [Horton] Casparis [later professor
at Vanderbilt], [Harold L.] Higgins [later chief pediatrician at Massachusetts General Hospital], and myself. How we got through [the
final] two-month period before the new staff arrived, I do not know.
We were on call day and night, and as far as I know, we never left the
hospital during that time." Josephs also provided a glimpse of the disorders encountered in those early days:

> [There was] diarrhea in the summer, with its dehydration and acidosis, the
> successful understanding and treatment of which were the first great con-
> tribution of the workers at the Harriet Lane. Intravenous infusions were
> beyond our skills at that time, but we used intraperitoneal infusions with
> complete freedom. Pneumonia in the winter; we had no drug for that. We
> would wrap the babies up and put them out in the cold where they gener-
> ally did well. Typhoid in the fall; the city water was safe but these children
> had been with their parents picking berries and fruit in the country and

drank country water. Congenital syphilis at any time; we could recognize that across a room in a crowd.... Rickets, the second great triumph of the Harriet Lane.... And anemia, more common and severe then than now, which we were beginning to find curable by iron, although transfusion remained the method of choice for some time to come.[9]

Wilburt Davison added, "Getting leave for Christmas dinner or to go to the movies was extremely difficult. Harold Stewart started his internship on July 1, 1918, arriving with a straw hat, and as he did not go out of the hospital until the following June he never needed a winter hat."[10]

Nurturing Influential Leaders

When Blackfan relinquished his residency position in 1918 after six years, the next resident was Thomas Rivers, whose impressive career was chronicled in an oral history by Saul Benison.[11] Rivers, who had graduated at the top of his class at Johns Hopkins School of Medicine in 1915, recalled:

> If you took your interneship and residency at the Johns Hopkins Hospital, your medical career was assured.... The medical interneship was supposed to be the choice interneship, and I broke all the rules when I went over to Dr. John Howland and asked him to give me the interneship in pediatrics.[12] He looked at me as if I had lost my mind. It was the first time that the top man in the class had ever asked for that interneship. Pediatrics at that time was not the specialty that it is today. There was Luther Emmett Holt and there was John Howland, and most of the other fellows were laughingly referred to as baby feeders. Actually it was not a very attractive field.

Howland advised Rivers to take his internship in medicine with Theodore C. Janeway if he was serious about going into pediatrics. Rivers agreed and spent a year with Janeway, a superb clinician, and gained valuable experience.[13] When Rivers finished his year with Janeway [1915–1916] he returned to Howland who made him an assistant resident. After two years he appointed Rivers resident.[14]

Rivers recalled this role as quite challenging:

> During rounds Dr. Howland would frequently go up to a patient's bed, while I would pick up the history[15] and start to talk about the patient. Invariably Dr. Howland would take the history from me, look at it, and

PORTRAIT OF THOMAS RIVERS. Rivers was a resident at the Harriet Lane Home after graduating from the Johns Hopkins School of Medicine in 1915. He and John Howland greatly admired each other's abilities. Subsequently Rivers made significant contributions to the study of viruses at the Rockefeller Foundation and, later, at the National Foundation for Infantile Paralysis. After he retired, Rivers recorded an extensive oral history in which he shared his impressions of working with John Howland.

begin to quiz me on the detail in it. Sometimes there were one hundred babies on that service, and I had to know what every baby had, what he didn't have, and what we thought he had. I had to be able to tell Howland a pretty straight story. I don't know whether he got a big kick out of doing this, but I know that he held me responsible.

I got along well with Howland, but this doesn't mean that I agreed with him all the time. Actually, Howland did some things I didn't approve of. For example he wouldn't make rounds with his internes[16]…because he didn't want to be bothered with them.[17] Sometimes he was unfair in the matter of appointments. When I joined his service as assistant resident, an earlier classmate of mine, Grover Powers, was already there.… By rights Howland should have appointed him his second resident [following Blackfan], but he appointed me.

Davison remembered, "Thomas Rivers' memory made the life of the residents who followed him very rugged, because Rivers could recite the temperature, pulse, and weight of every patient whenever Howland called him. Howland never could understand why the rest of us could not do likewise. I even thought Rivers was bluffing, but whenever I checked him he had quoted the correct data. Howland regarded Rivers as the ablest resident he ever had, though he was a bit in awe of him."[18]

Rivers left pediatrics after two years as assistant resident and one as resident for Howland, perhaps because his fundamental interest was not in clinical pediatrics or adult medicine but in investigation.[19] Subsequently, Rivers became well known for his research on viruses while director of the Rockefeller Hospital, and then held a senior position in the National Foundation for Infantile Paralysis. In later years Rivers expressed his unbounded admiration for John Howland to Park on several occasions. He regarded Howland as a great man.

When Rivers left for military service in 1918, Blackfan continued as overall supervisor of care until 1919, when William M. Happ became resident. Happ was an investigator by nature and was interested in extending his studies of the blood groups to the newborn. Whenever he had the opportunity, he sneaked off to the obstetrical ward or the laboratory. Park remembered when Howland would arrive on the award exclaiming, "Where's Happ?" Howland never liked Happ as a resident because he would not be "the boy on the burning deck." Happ stayed only one year in this position, though Howland would have done well to retain him in a research capacity. Later Happ became the professor of pediatrics at the University of Southern California.

Horace G. Stewart (1920–22) followed Happ as resident, and he, in turn, was followed by Horton R. Casparis (1922–23), who eventually chaired the pediatric department at Vanderbilt University. A. Ashley Weech (1923–24) was the next resident and also an instructor in pediatrics, having been an assistant in pediatrics along with several others, including Katherine Dodd. Within a few years both Weech and Dodd went to Cincinnati, with Weech as chairperson. Subsequently, Dodd moved to the University of Arkansas as chairperson, and eventually to Emory University. Then came William J. Scott (1924–25) and, finally, Alexander J. Schaffer (1925–26).

The last of Howland's residents, Alexander "Buck" Schaffer, went into private practice in Baltimore but remained closely involved with the Harriet Lane Home. He became especially interested in the care of newborns and was one of the first pediatricians in this country to become expert in this new subspecialty, writing its first textbook in 1960[20] and coining the words "neonatology" and "neonatologist."

Another notable person in the Harriet Lane during Howland's time was Wilburt Davison. Davison graduated from Johns Hopkins' medical school in 1917 and then trained and worked in pediatrics under Howland. He contributed expertise in infectious diseases and rose to the rank of associate professor and from 1924 to 1927 he was assistant to the dean of the medical school, Lewis Weed. After Howland's death in 1926 Davison also served as interim head of the pediatric department. At that point he moved to Durham, North Carolina, to become dean of the newly organized Duke University School of Medicine as well as professor of pediatrics.[21]

Members of the research staff were allowed to work in the dispensary but were not given ward privileges (the ability to admit and care for patients on the wards). W. McKim Marriott was so essential to Howland in the laboratory that he had great difficulty obtaining consent even to work in the dispensary. The same situation developed later in Benjamin Kramer's case. Both had fairly to force their way. Park was in a somewhat different situation. He was free to work in the laboratory as soon as his dispensary job, which took only half a day, was over.[22]

Davison suggested why the number of children in the Harriet Lane Home stayed limited:

> The pediatric department remained small for the reason that Howland could not delegate any responsibility, or to put it another way, he could not share authority with anyone. The result was that other members of his department never had the chance to develop their own ideas. His department was pyramidal with him at the top; there were no independent peaks. He kept everyone and everything completely under his immediate control. He was thus able to spend every afternoon in the laboratory. He would not allow us to split the outpatient into specialties and gave no responsibility to any of us, except to Kenneth Blackfan during summers while [Howland] was on Cape Cod. He felt his responsibilities toward his patients perhaps more keenly than any other physician.[23]

Davison added, "As an administrator, and indeed in all aspects of his life, Howland showed a most amusing thrift, mixed with much generosity and large-mindedness. Dean Lewis H. Weed [1923–29] ... told me after Howland's death that each year he turned back a considerable unexpended budget—this although we were on skimpy salaries. He had many of the canny instincts of the Scots. For example, instead of paying some of the staff salaries from the departmental budget, he would persuade the Rockefeller Foundation to provide some of us with fellowships."[24]

A Master Clinician

As a clinician John Howland had few peers. His diagnoses usually were either correct or as close as possible. To arrive at a conclusion he brought to bear accurately remembered experience, a wide and exact knowledge of disease (which increased noticeably when he became joint author of *Diseases of Infancy and Childhood* with Holt), and shrewdness. He had the kind of memory, often possessed by great clinicians, which enabled him to recall the name of the child, the time when the child had been a patient, and the bed he or she occupied on the wards. He admitted it when he did not know something and he did not take risks in order to show brilliance or superiority. He was at his best under difficult circumstances. Therapeutically he was conservative and his sound judgment certainly helped him avoid numerous mistakes. He realized fully the value of waiting for time to clarify situations. Howland understood children and his relations with them were delightful to watch. He could meet a child on his or her own level and children trusted him at once.

Davison noted that Howland,

> ... was the life and inspiration of the clinic; arriving at nine in the morning and leaving after six in the evening to go home and study and write—a constant example of the fact that success is founded on hard work. His great drive was motivated and powered by his faith in the investigative approach, both clinical and experimental. All visitors to the Harriet Lane Home were impressed by its beehive-like activity, which included everyone from professor to intern. He believed in punctuality and was sarcastic about anyone being late.... he usually was exceedingly cautious about committing himself. He had something of the feeling that the professor should not be caught in error or without an encyclopedic knowledge of the condition in hand.... He did not like to be caught wrong.[25]

Howland's friends and biographers perpetuated a number of amusing clinical anecdotes about him. Weech remembered that,

Although Howland generally had the better of us, we did our level best to get even and trick him if we could. I remember a very young baby (about two months) who was admitted with a soft fluctuant swelling over the calvarium anterior to the fontanel and approximately, [but] not exactly, in the midline. To our great surprise the baby turned out to have a strongly positive reaction to the routine tuberculin test. When the baby was seen by Doctor Howland on morning rounds we went to a great deal of pain to lace up the sleeves of his gown so that it would be difficult for the professor to see the result of the test. We then told him that we residents had considered the possibility of the soft swelling being either [a] meningocele or dermoid cyst, but that after considerable discussion we had concluded that the former diagnosis was most probably correct. Howland took the bait and argued at once for a dermoid cyst. With great glee we then removed the gown so that the flaring tuberculin reaction was visible. The great man threw up his hands in the air and exclaimed, "Tuberculosis and syphilis, we have always with us!"[26]

Davison recalled an example of "Howland's clinical acumen" that took place one day during rounds when Howland "repeatedly avoided one bed. Finally the staff decided that they would insist on a diagnosis. Howland listened to their pleading and after some reflection said, 'Give me an opthalmoscope.' He looked at the child's eyegrounds and said 'Lead poisoning.' He was right."[27]

Seizing New Ideas

Howland's attitude toward new ideas deserves attention. When a suggestion was made to him Howland often rejected it or appeared to be uninterested. Then, after a month or two, he would present it back as his own idea. When this happened his staff believed that he had no recollection of the idea's source and it caused them great amusement. In regard to new ideas, particularly if they involved changes in policy, his conservatism showed itself strikingly. He demanded that proposed changes be tried elsewhere before they were accepted, especially in infant feeding. This extreme reluctance to depart from custom held the Harriet Lane Home back in later years. Howland was very receptive to suggestions in the research field, however. Davison confirmed that "Howland was a skeptic and usually was not inclined to accept an idea unless it was his own or he thought it was. Members of his staff became very clever at dropping hints for something they wanted done until Howland conceived it to be his own idea and executed it." Kenneth Blackfan realized that Howland loved to make the diagnosis himself. On rounds Blackfan, who knew as well as anyone what a particular diagnosis was, recited the symptoms and signs in such a way that Howland would suddenly exclaim, "Why, Blackfan, this child has meningococcal meningitis." Blackfan greatly enjoyed the success of his guile.

One of Howland's special delights in both his major and minor clinics was to open retropharyngeal abscesses with his forefinger, the nail of which had been pruned to a point. Children with this condition were always saved for his clinics, if possible. Indeed, except in extreme circumstances, no member of his staff ever opened a retropharyngeal abscess on the wards because of the known thrill Howland got out of doing it himself. Howland also loved to intubate and extubate, and children requiring this were held over for him and, in particular for his clinics, whenever it was safe.

In Howland's days the problem of infant feeding was still paramount in pediatrics. Howland's views were a mixture of those of his two great teachers, L. Emmett Holt and Adalbert Czerny. He used an exclusive protein milk diet for the treatment of diarrhea and also for celiac disease. Later, Howland added two and a half percent sugar to his protein milk but with some doubt in his mind. When a child vomited, he used to follow the teachings of Holt and first dilute, then take out the fat, and then, if necessary, the sugar. In this country it was Marriott who first perceived that the difficulties in infant feeding were largely created by the mistaken ideas and rigid attitudes of the pediatricians themselves.

The Unconscious Teacher

As a teacher Howland was exceptionally gifted. He loved teaching and was at his best when employing the Socratic method. He liked to lead the student near pitfalls and was greatly amused if he fell in, but he was also pleased to the same extent if the student was bright enough to escape. Some students regarded Howland as the best teacher in the medical school while others dreaded him even though he was a kind person. Students were assigned in pairs to patients whom they were expected to study the night before the clinic. The next day Howland developed the case by asking questions, teaching students how to think. Park thought Howland's clinics were the best of his experience. He told Park he thought it a great mistake to go into a case exhaustively, for what the student remembered were a few things they saw with their eyes or learned by feeling with their hands.

These clinics were informal. His formal clinics at noon on Saturdays, at which he presented patients in illustrated lecture fashion, were not as good according to Park. Strange as it may seem, Howland showed a certain insecurity at these formal clinics and quite regularly used to ask for feedback. Sometimes he thought they were terrible.[28] Howland was a remarkable example of the unconscious teacher, the sort for whom teaching was instinctive. Thomas B. Turner, in his *Heritage of Excellence*, noted that "In his tremendous appeal to students, Howland seems to have filled the gap left by Osler," who left Johns Hopkins in 1905 to become Regius Professor of Medicine at Oxford University.[29]

In his obituary of Howland, Davison's opinion differed:

> Though Howland was highly regarded as a teacher by the students, he was dreaded for his sarcasm. He liked to "ride" the students and house staff. I doubt whether one student, now professor of medicine, will ever again fail to undress a patient completely, including diapers, after Howland's caustic comments when the physical examination presented in his clinic failed to note that the patient had a four-inch tail. Another student will be more careful in oral examination after he missed a perforated palate and Howland quoted Mercutio's speech from *Romeo and Juliet*, "'Tis not so deep as a well, nor so wide as a church door; but 'tis enough, 'twill serve."[30]

In regard to teaching clinical pediatrics, Davison told the story that "Marriott once said, 'John, do you know what you are doing?' You are giving clinics on subjects that are rare and unusual because you are interested in them and nothing about the common diseases and ailments of childhood.' Howland took it as a blow below the belt and said, 'You are wrong.' Marriott replied, 'Give the students an examination and see what they know of practical pediatrics.' Much to Howland's amazement they made a very poor showing."[31]

There are a number of delightful stories that illustrate Howland's interactions with the medical students. For example, Hallie Clark Rigby, class of 1917, remembered that her classmate George Wilkinson was sleeping through one of Howland's clinics. Howland awakened him abruptly and asked him "What am I discussing, Mr. Wilkinson?"

"Protein milk," Wilkinson replied. "How do you know that, Mr. Wilkinson? You were sound asleep," Howland persisted. "That's all you ever talk about, sir," answered Wilkinson.[32]

William J. Orr, a junior faculty member from 1922 to 1924, remembered Howland's surprise at one of Howland's "bull sessions" with students (the informal clinics held every other day):

> As per usual two of the students were brought down to the center of the arena to be sacrificed in the name of pediatrics. The case they presented was one of tracheo-esophageal fistula. As one of the students progressed with the discussion of the case, he proceeded to draw on the blackboard and lecture in a well-informed way on the various types of fistulas that might occur. At first Dr. Howland was only slightly impressed but as the student progressed with his dissertation, Dr. Howland sat down and listened more attentively with an expression of amazement and surprise. When the student finished he had consumed a good portion of the hour. The class was dismissed. Dr. Howland on his way out of the amphitheater inquired of Dr. Horton Casparis as to the identity of the student who had taken over the fourth-year clinic and stolen Dr. Howland's thunder. Casparis's reply was, "Oh, he was just Professor of Embryology at Princeton before he studied medicine."[33]

Davison remembered his own awkward experiences when Howland found teaching less than a pleasure:

> Howland hated personal battles and was rather supine in doing his part in them. He turned them over to the rest of us. He avoided disagreeable tasks whenever possible. For example it was his custom to go on the wards about four o'clock in the afternoon on the day before his clinics in order to select patients. If he could not find an interesting one, he often said, to the great amusement of the junior staff, "Get Park to teach." After Park left, I was the victim. The worst instance of passing the buck was when the Boston surgeons invited him to a meeting of the New England Pediatric Society to defend his medical treatment of pyloric stenosis. He bravely accepted and then at the last moment sent me in his place to fight the losing battle, for he realized in going over the records that the surgical treatment was better. I reaped the abuse intended for him as the Boston surgeons demonstrated that although medical therapy was adequate for mild pylorospasm, surgery was necessary for true hypertrophic pyloric stenosis.[34]

Davison also noted that Howland was willing to tread on sacred territory:

> Howland loved to argue and whenever he could find something on which his juniors felt deeply or cherished ideals, he would make a provocative statement. He soon found that I would rise and writhe whenever he would say that Osler's reputation was due to his personality, and not to what he had done. Unfortunately, Howland never had the opportunity of knowing Osler and imbibing his spirit. Furthermore, as a pioneer in the full-time, white-coated, laboratory field, he had a little antipathy, jealousy and scorn, conscious or unconscious, for the frock-coated bedside physicians of the preceding generation. He would frequently and irritatingly say to me, "What did Osler do to merit his fame? Dr. Holt was a greater man than Osler." ...I marshaled the tangible evidence of Osler's greatness, and it was considerable, but he always claimed that he was unconvinced.[35]

Keen Perceptions, Superb Judgments

John Howland's scientific career began not long after his return from his first period of study in Europe. Following a publication in 1904 on the lesions of dysentery, many papers on a variety of subjects came from his pen. At first his interests seem to have been mainly clinical and pathological, but soon they turned to the chemical aspects of disease. Among his most noteworthy contributions were those on the effects of chloroform poisoning on the liver, the measurement of the chemical and energy metabolism of sleeping children, the acidosis accompanying "intestinal intoxication," and numerous studies on infantile tetany and rickets. His investigations into diarrhoeal acidosis, tetany, and rickets represent his most important scientific work. Howland and Marriott, applying the concepts of Lawrence Henderson,[36] proved the existence of an acidosis in intestinal intoxication and showed that it was not an acetone body acidosis. In infantile tetany, Howland and Marriott showed that the calcium of the blood was diminished and made the treatment with calcium chloride a routine procedure.[37]

The great contribution to rickets by Howland and Benjamin Kramer was the discovery that the disease was characterized by a diminution of the inorganic phosphorus of the blood.[38] Previous investigators had thought of the disease as dependent upon an abnormal metabolism of calcium. After Elmer V. McCollum and coworkers at the Johns Hopkins School of Hygiene and Public Health discovered that rickets could be produced in rats by varying the calcium and phosphorus in the diet, Howland and Kramer perceived the principle that the deposition of lime salts in the body is dependent upon a solubility product relationship between the calcium and phosphorus in the circulating fluids. Howland and Park proved the effectiveness of cod liver oil in rickets.[39] Howland's later papers represent a study of the principles governing lime salt deposition in bones."[40]

Howland was an opportunist, as almost all clinicians are obliged to be. In general he chose subjects for his studies in which from the beginning he could see the end. The subjects chosen for his earlier studies appeared to be as chance offered, but later, when he became interested in rickets, his subjects had continuity. In his studies with the calorimeter he worked alone, but otherwise, he almost always worked in collaboration with someone else. Often, the collaborator was chosen because he or she possessed some special knowledge or ability that Howland did not. Howland's later work was done chiefly with Marriott, and then Kramer. In Park's opinion, Howland's great asset was his almost unerring judgment in the choice of significant topics for investigation.

Early on, Howland perceived the importance of chemistry for the investigation of disease in children. He did not provide technicians in the chemical laboratory but insisted that the investigator gain his or her own experience in the use of the required methodology in the laboratory in order to have full faith in the results. Although he had little knowledge of theoretical chemistry, Howland was remarkably skilled in technical procedures. He admired their logic and enjoyed the challenge of attainable accuracy. Another reason he objected to the employment of technicians was that he thought that departmental money was more wisely spent on staff members than on technical assistants.

L. Emmett Holt Jr.,[41] in his address upon receiving the Howland Award in 1966, provided additional details and another perspective about the pioneering research of Howland's group from the point of view of a participant:

The last phase of Dr. Howland's career—I think it could be called the crowning phase—was the fourteen years he spent in Baltimore. It was marked by two major scientific achievements: the demonstration of acidosis in infantile diarrhea, and the joint study with McCollum's department of experimental rickets, which culminated in the discovery of vitamin D.

Acidosis had been suspected by German pediatricians as an accompaniment of diarrhea but had not been demonstrated. The Kussmal type of breathing was known to be associated with experimental acidosis in animals. But, as knowledge began to unfold about acid-base equilibrium, Dr. Howland became intrigued with the idea that acidosis was perhaps the underlying chemical basis for what the European pediatricians had called "alimentary intoxication." Perhaps this was the toxic factor and he was going to find it. The convenient tools of today were not at hand; there was no Van Slyke apparatus, no pH meter. But with the aid of Marriott ... acidosis was diligently searched for and in time was effectively demonstrated by four different techniques: (1) by the increased tolerance to alkali, as judged by the amount needed to make the urine alkaline, (2) by the decreased CO_2 tension of the alveolar air, (3) by the characteristic alteration of the hemoglobin dissociation curve, and (4) by a colorimetric procedure applied to blood serum. The proof was conclusive.

While the work was in progress in Baltimore, a distinguished investigator in New York was also at work on the problem. Oscar Schloss was in touch with [Donald Dexter] Van Slyke and the apparatus he was developing to measure the CO_2 content and capacity of the serum, and [with this new instrument] he had independently demonstrated the existence of acidosis in diarrhea. When he learned of the work of Howland and Marriott, he generously withheld his own paper until after the publication of their work, in order to give them the priority, which he felt they deserved.[42]
It was a disappointment that the correction of acidosis failed to correct the "alimentary intoxication," as had been hoped. The role of dehydration in bringing out the symptom complex remained to be clarified, and in that Marriott, Gamble, and Schloss played leading roles—the first two after they had left Baltimore.

The work on experimental rickets was a remarkable demonstration of what can be accomplished by a mass attack on a problem. It is hard for us today to realize how important a problem rickets was in those days. Clinical rickets was evident in at least one-third of all pediatric hospital admissions and autopsies showed the incidence in infants to be over 90 percent. From time to time severe chest deformities were encountered that threatened life. There were numerous bone deformities that we now see occasionally in the metabolic forms of rickets, and dystocia[43] resulting from early rickets was an important obstetrical problem. In magnitude, though not in mortality, rickets was certainly the number one pediatric problem.

The arrival of Dr. McCollum in Baltimore [in 1917] was a godsend to Dr. Howland, and they soon joined forces.[44] In Wisconsin McCollum had pioneered in studies of dietary diseases, using rats, and had discovered Vitamin A [the first fat-soluble vitamin]. An experimental approach to the study of bone disease, however, needed expert knowledge of bone pathology and microchemical methods for the study of the minerals concerned in bone metabolism. These last, the pediatric department was in a position to supply. Shipley[45] and Park supplied the pathological talent and Kramer the micromethods.... They must all have worked together in the planning of the studies, and no doubt McCollum's fertile brain was an important ingredient of their success, but an outstanding success they were. Rickets was produced in rats, the dietary conditions which gave rise to it were well defined, the potency of cod liver oil and of ultraviolet radiation were established beyond a doubt, and the findings were beginning to be applied clinically. The chemical diagnosis of rickets had been added to the roentgenological diagnosis, and therapy was being worked out quantitatively. I think that Dr. Kramer's contribution to this study is one that has not been generally appreciated; without the microchemical methods which he supplied, the work would not have been so fruitful.[46]

When I [L. Emmett Holt, Jr.] arrived in Baltimore, in the fall of 1922, the Harriet Lane Home was ten years old. The first crop of graduates had moved on.... The existing members of the permanent staff, besides Dr. Howland, were four: Kramer, Shipley, Davison, and Josephs;[47] to this group were added six neophytes, of which I was one. The investigative effort was still heavily oriented toward the problems of rickets and bone calcification.

Magic in the Laboratory

Howland's staff soon grew as it became known that a new kind of clinic—aiming at goals higher than merely preparation for medical practice—was being organized at Johns Hopkins. Marriott came in 1914 from St. Louis. Grover Powers was an intern in 1913 and remained, a bulwark of the department, until 1921 when he left to go with Park to Yale.[48] In 1915 Gamble and Warren Sisson joined Howland's staff, attracted by the new opportunities. Alfred Shohl also came that year. In 1917 Marriott left to become professor of pediatrics at Washington University, taking Sam Clausen, an intern of great promise, with him.[49] The following year Kramer took Marriott's place. Frederick Tisdall arrived in 1918, sent specifically to the Harriet Lane from Toronto in order to obtain a foundation in pediatrics.[50] Davison and Horton Casparis came in 1919 and Graham Ross[51] followed in 1920.

Marriott was a trained biochemist who came to Baltimore to specialize in clinical medicine and the opportunity at the Harriet Lane Home was the best gateway. Howland made an agreement with Marriott whereby Marriott would organize and take charge of the biological chemistry laboratory while Howland would teach him pediatrics. But Marriott was brilliant and so useful to Howland in the laboratory that Marriott had great difficulty convincing Howland to honor his part of the bargain. Marriott's grandfather had been an inventor, and he was one by nature too. He was extraordinarily interested in gadgets and able to contrive them on short notice. In addition to establishing that acidosis existed in the acute diarrheas of children, and that the acidosis was not due to organic acids, Howland and Marriott also found that the calcium in the blood in tetany of infants was reduced exactly as in parathyroid tetany.[52] Howland and many others had enormous admiration for him. It seemed that there was a good deal of the magician about him. In the chemistry laboratory Marriott was able in one way or another to meet Howland's requests, often by the following morning.

In their general outlook on life Howland and Marriott were in strong contrast. Marriott was what might be called a belligerent pacifist; Howland was vehemently pro-British and outspoken in the belief that our entrance into the war against Germany was not only necessary, but also right. Park remembered the acrimonious discussions across the broad soapstone top of the chemical laboratory table, interspersed between measurements. Howland tried to prevent Marriott from going to St. Louis. He believed that Marriott had insufficient clinical training to be a competent head of a clinical department. But Marriott eventually left the Harriet Lane for Washington University. In a way it is too bad than Marriott and Howland were ever separated. They made a wonderful combination; Marriott had the imagination and the ingenuity and Howland supplied the balance.

Gamble was Howland's beloved disciple. Gamble used to stop each morning at Howland's house in order to bring him to the hospital. Gamble would arrive at the appointed time, half past eight, and quite regularly Howland would appear at the door exclaiming, "Wait, Gamble, till I have had a cup of coffee." Gamble would go in and find that Howland had not yet sat down to breakfast. Park felt that Howland was devoted to Gamble as to very few, but never realized his potential until Gamble left for Children's Hospital in Boston in 1922, and his work on the metabolism of starvation in children, done in collaboration with Ross and Tisdall, was published.[53] Howland made a determined effort to get him to return to the Harriet Lane but Gamble was firmly established by then.

Gamble's intellectual mentor for his pioneering research in the applications of the principles of acid-base metabolism to clinical medicine was Lawrence Henderson of Harvard, under whom he had studied initially. In contrast, Howland probably exerted no intellectual influence on Gamble but Gamble admired Howland enormously. Gamble was the great artist of pediatrics, and his work, known everywhere, had great influence outside pediatrics.[54, 55]

Kramer followed Marriott as biochemist at the Harriet Lane. He came seeking an opportunity to enter clinical medicine, and not because of any particular interest in pediatrics. Shortly after he arrived at Hopkins he developed micromethods that opened up new fields in the metabolic studies of children. Gamble once stated that Ross, Tisdall, and he could never have performed their classic studies on the metabolism of starvation had it not been for the development of the necessary micromethods by Kramer. Indeed, one of the immediate results from Kramer's development was the discovery that rickets was characterized by a low plasma phosphorus. Kramer and Howland performed their original measurements on McCollum's, Shipley's, and Park's rachitic rats, in which the disease had been produced by diets low in phosphorus. Kramer then showed that the depression of the plasma phosphorus also held in the rickets of human beings. (Coincidentally, two Danish researchers, P. Iverson and E. Lentrup, made the same discovery.) This revelation of the secret of the changes in bones was of immense importance in the understanding of rickets. Howland did everything possible to keep Kramer in academic medicine but Kramer left the field.[56]

During the spring of 1921 Howland received from his old friend David Edsall, by then dean at Harvard's medical school, a second offer to come to Boston and head the Harvard department of pediatrics after the resignation of John Lovett Morse.[57] Edsall had tried in vain to achieve this in 1914 following the death of Thomas Morgan Rotch. Howland visited Harvard in April of 1921 and returned to Baltimore to think it over (and doubtless discuss it with the senior administration at Hopkins). By May he had decided not to accept. In the next year or so the fifth floor of the Harriet Lane was turned into additional laboratories.[58] In 1923 Harvard recruited Blackfan instead.

Davison thought that Howland "was greatly pleased when he was offered the professorship of pediatrics at Harvard. He took great delight in declining it, either because he was a Yale man or because the position was not full time and he would have had to cater to private patients whose demands he always disliked, though he could be very gracious if the private patient really was ill."[59] Graham Lusk, Howland's former colleague at Bellevue and then professor at Cornell, said that Howland "had one great temptation, the offer of the chair of pediatrics at Harvard. The appeal to his New England character was strong. He told me he could speak to everyone standing on a street corner in Boston and be understood by them. But he felt that acceptance would have meant the loss of three precious laboratory years from his life, and so he resolved to remain in Baltimore."[60]

Notes

1. Alan M. Chesney, *The Johns Hopkins Hospital and the Johns Hopkins University School of Medicine: A Chronicle*, volume III (1905–1914), 220–21. Edwards Park was director of the outpatient department. Cordial notes from Walters and Wolfe in response to inquiries from Park are preserved in the Alan Mason Chesney Medical Archives (hereafter referred to as AMC), The Johns Hopkins Medical Institutions, Baltimore, MD.

2. J. L. Gamble, "Story of an Education: Memorial Exercises at the Children's Hospital, February 27, 1942, for Kenneth D. Blackfan," *Harvard Medical Alumni Bulletin* 16, (April 1942), 3–5.

3. Edsall was interested and active in pediatrics as well as adult medicine, as William Osler had been earlier. Indeed Osler had helped to found the American Pediatric Society in 1888 and had occupied its presidency in 1891–1892. Benjamin H. Robins and A. Christie, "Sir William Osler, The Pediatrician," *Journal of the American Medical Association*, 106 (1963): 124–29. Pediatrics was usually a part of general medicine in those days, and in a few hospitals, e.g., at the Massachusetts General Hospital, remained so until the mid-twentieth century.

4. James L. Wilson, Blackfan's long-time resident at the Boston Children's Hospital, wrote a biographical profile of his chief. In regard to Blackfan's experience at the St. Vincent Foundling Hospital in Philadelphia, Wilson suggests that this "must have been a shocking place for him to work. It is said that there was an infant mortality of some 90% of those under one year," much as

at the New York Foundling Asylum. James L. Wilson, "Kenneth D. Blackfan (1883–1941)" *Pediatric Profiles* (St. Louis: C. V. Mosby Co., 1957), 212.

5. Clement A. Smith, *The Children's Hospital of Boston—Built Better than They Knew*, (Boston: Little, Brown and Company, 1983), 143–44.

6. James L. Gamble, "Acceptance of the John Howland Award," *American Journal of Diseases of Children* 90 (1955): 486.

7. In 1923, after David Edsall, then dean of Harvard Medical School, had failed in a second attempt to get Howland to Boston and had turned to Blackfan, Howland told Park on more than one occasion that Harvard was making a great mistake in pursuing Blackfan. By 1922–23 James Gamble had moved from Hopkins to Harvard. Gamble fully realized Blackfan's potential and was largely instrumental in his call to Harvard. Blackfan and Gamble together led Harvard's pediatric department to a height never before obtained, in the opinion of many.

8. Howland was expected to give Knox the privilege of admitting his private patients to the Harriet Lane Home in return for a favor he did the hospital and/or School of Medicine. This favor was probably Knox's influence with the Thomas Wilson Fund, which led to new funds allowing the opening of the west ward of the third floor of the HLH. But Howland procrastinated, providing Knox with neither the faculty appointment of clinical professor, which Knox wanted, nor admitting privileges. Knox did give some student clinics for Howland in his areas of interest and at times made inpatient rounds, but any orders he wrote were not carried out.

All this might have reflected Howland's awareness and concern that Knox had wanted the chair in pediatrics and was quite disappointed not to have won it. Perhaps more likely, according to Park, Knox's abilities did not fit into Howland's scheme for the department. Howland wanted the academic and research aspects of the department to consist primarily of the new scientific approach to pediatric diseases, whereas Knox's experience and interests lay in the social aspects of pediatrics, such as the welfare of children, safe milk, adequate nutrition, access to care, infant mortality, and other public health matters. While in active private practice, Knox became a national leader in these areas. Locally he supported the construction of the Thomas Wilson Sanitarium, which had been established "for the purpose of securing a summer retreat for sick children from the heat and unhealthfulness of the city" of Baltimore, as other cities were doing at that time, and he volunteered there for many years. Gradually he became completely occupied with public health matters, and in 1922 he became the head of the Bureau of Child Hygiene in the Maryland State Department of Health, staying there until his retirement in 1942. Edwards A. Park to Mrs. Margaret de L. Streb, March 10, 1969, RG 4, series B, box 9, folder 13, HLH-AMC.

9. Helen B. Taussig, Hugh Josephs, Alexander J. Schaffer, Leo Kanner, and Barton Childs, "Final Meeting in the Harriet Lane Home Amphitheater," *Johns Hopkins Medical Journal* 137 (1975): 21–22.

10. Wilburt C. Davison, "John Howland (1873–1926)," *Journal of Pediatrics* 46 (1955): 480.

11. Saul Benison, *Tom Rivers: Reflections on a Life in Medicine and Science*, an oral history memoir (Cambridge: M.I.T. Press, 1967), 38 et seq. Rivers

grew up in rural Georgia in the town of Jonesboro, which is now a suburb of Atlanta. He went to Emory College, but needed five years because his prior schooling was insufficient. At Emory he became interested in biology and chemistry, and decided upon a career practicing medicine. He graduated first in his class, summa cum laude, with the highest grades ever seen there, and was easily admitted to Johns Hopkins School of Medicine. However, after two years he was advised to drop out because he had developed atrophy of his left hand, diagnosed as "progressive central muscular atrophy of the Aral-Duchenne type, [which] usually ran a fairly rapid and fatal course." Back in Jonesboro, doubtless discouraged and bored, he obtained a job through a friend as a laboratory assistant in the San Tomas Hospital in Panama. There, because of shortages of staff, he saw and participated directly in a large amount of medical and surgical care, i.e., "At medical school, everyone is making damn sure you don't get too close to anything. In Panama . . . I was right in the middle of it." After eighteen months he decided to return to Hopkins and was easily readmitted.

12. At Hopkins and elsewhere in those days and even for many years thereafter, there were no competitive exams for these positions. Individuals were chosen by the chief.

13. Janeway came from New York City to head the department of medicine at Hopkins in 1914.

14. In the academic year 1917–18, Howland promoted Blackfan from instructor in pediatrics to associate in pediatrics, in 1918–1919 to associate, and in 1919–1920 to associate professor. But in that year Blackfan left for the University of Cincinnati. Park agreed that Blackfan served as resident for seven or eight years. Yet Rivers states here that he became resident in 1917–1918, and this is confirmed in the records of the medical school [Thomas B. Turner, *Heritage of Excellence: The Johns Hopkins Medical Institutions 1914–1947* (The Johns Hopkins University Press, 1974), 573]. Perhaps with Blackfan's promotion in 1917–1918 to a higher faculty status, he could no longer be called resident from the point of view of the medical school, although he continued to supervise the care of all the children admitted to the Harriet Lane. More likely, for 1917–1918 a new position between the faculty and the interns and assistant residents called "chief resident" was created, with Rivers the first incumbent.

15. The "history" meant the temperature, pulse, and respiration chart, which in those days—at the Harriet Lane and elsewhere as late as 1950—hung from the bottom of the bed.

16. Edwards Park recalled that Howland's eleven o'clock rounds, which should have been Grand Rounds ... consisted of Howland and Blackfan only, since the interns were obliged to leave for their dispensary duties. This was the time assigned for dispensary experience; also they were required there by the press of work. Park noted that this defect was corrected several years later by a shift of the dispensary to the afternoon. But this shift produced another defect that was worse. The interns were obliged to carry out their history taking and examinations of the sick children on the wards into the night.

17. According to Davison, "When a famous German pediatrician visited the Harriet Lane Home during ward rounds, Howland only introduced his

chief aides and the resident. The German professor, noting the horde of assistant residents and interns standing around, said 'And who are all these young gentlemen?' Said Howland with an impatient wave of his hand, 'Oh, just house officers, house officers,' and swept on into the ward rounds." Wilburt C. Davison, "John Howland (1873–1926)," *Journal of Pediatrics* 46 (1955): 479–80.

18. Ibid., 480–81.

19. Rivers joined the army in January 1918. In his oral history, Rivers recalled, "One day Dr. Howland was visiting the Surgeon General's Office in Washington, when he ran into Rufus Cole of the Rockefeller Institute. Dr. Cole was complaining 'We have just formed a commission to go down to the hospital at Fort Sam Houston in San Antonio, Texas, to investigate pneumonia following measles, and, while we have people who know about pneumonia, we haven't a single man on the commission who would know a case of measles if he saw it.' When Howland heard this, he said, 'Well, I have a pup over at my place, who has his commission and is waiting for orders, who would know measles,' and on Howland's say-so I was put on the Pneumonia Commission." Benison, *Tom Rivers: Reflections on a Life in Medicine and Science*, 54. This seems to have been the start of Rivers' research career.

20. Alexander J. Schaffer, *Diseases of the Newborn* (Philadelphia: W. B. Saunders Co., 1960).

21. In a 1950 memorial article on the occasion of what would have been Howland's seventy-fifth birthday, Davison provided a list of the subsequent careers of Howland's major trainees, and L. Emmett Holt Jr. updated this list a decade later. Wilburt C. Davison, "John Howland: The Seventy-Fifth Anniversary of His Death," *Journal of the History of Medicine and Allied Sciences* 5 (1950): 198. L. Emmett Holt Jr., "John Howland: Turning Point of American Pediatrics," *Journal of Pediatrics* 69 (1966): 874.

22. Park further explained that when he left for France, "In 1916 Howland replaced me in the dispensary with Grover Powers and I became a full-time research worker without any clinical outlet. I was eventually given some ward responsibility but the staff ignored my orders because they knew that Howland would appear later and write his own." RG 4, series B, box 9, folder 21, HLH-AMC.

23. Davison, "John Howland (1873–1926)," 480.

24. Ibid., 484. Possibly Dean Weed was unaware of the trips by Howland et al. to the annual meetings of the Young Turks in Atlantic City each spring, described by Allan Butler as he introduced James L. Gamble for the Howland Award in 1955: "These trips [were] made in Dr. Gamble's French grey 1915 Cadillac touring car that was loaded on the return trip through Philadelphia with such laboratory equipment as could be purchased with the yearly unexpended balance that otherwise would be returned on June 30 to the University." James L. Gamble, "Acceptance of the Howland Award," *American Journal of Diseases of Children* 90 (1955): 484.

25. Davison, "John Howland (1873–1926)," 476–78.

26. Ashley Weech to Edwards Park, March 5, 1964, RG 4, series B, box 8, folder 22, HLH-AMC. In 1927 Weech published a detailed review of the organization and operation of the department at the end of Howland's tenure. (A. Ashley Weech, "Johns Hopkins University School of Medicine: Depart-

ment of Pediatrics," *Methods and Problems of Medical Education*, eighth series, New York: The Rockefeller Foundation, 1927.)

27. Davison, "John Howland (1873–1926)," 476–77. Park remembered that Henry Thomas, the neurologist of the hospital, and Blackfan wrote a modest case report entitled "Recurrent Meningitis Due to Lead in a Child of Five Years," *American Journal of Diseases of Childhood* 8 (1914): 377–80, which provided an earlier example of a case involving lead poisoning. The importance of this case report was that it revealed ... the cause of a clinical syndrome so distinctive that, once the clue of lead poisoning had been suggested, it could be immediately recognized as such. Example after example accumulated in the Harriet Lane records and similar case reports appeared elsewhere. Perhaps because the original discovery had been made at the Harriet Lane Home, special interest in the condition persisted and led to further important studies here, for example, studies in recent years on therapy by Julian Chisholm. One of these was that chronic lead ingestion caused characteristic changes ... in growing bone. The changes could be recognized clinically in the form of a band of radio-opacity, due to an increased density of structure at the cartilage-shaft junction recognizable in the x-ray film and of more value in indicating lead poisoning than the line in the gum, since it was more regularly present.

28. In the obituary Park wrote for Howland, Park noted that "Unlike his [Howland's] father, who spoke in public with great fluency, [John Howland] spoke with great difficulty and usually wrote out what he intended to say and familiarized himself with it beforehand." Edwards A. Park, "John Howland 1873–1926," *Science*, 64 (1926): 83.

29. Thomas B. Turner, *Heritage of Excellence: The Johns Hopkins Medical Institutions 1914–1947* (Baltimore: The Johns Hopkins University Press, 1974), 122.

30. Davison, "John Howland (1873–1926)," 481.

31. Ibid., 477.

32. Turner, *Heritage of Excellence*, 122–23.

33. Memorandum from William J. Orr to Edwards Park, February 24, 1951, RG 4, series C, box 12, folder 31, HLH-AMC.

34. Davison, "John Howland (1873–1926)," 481.

35. Davison, "John Howland (1873–1926)," 482–83.

36. Lawrence Henderson, a renowned theoretical physiologist at Harvard, first described the principles underlying effective buffer systems and subsequently enlarged these concepts to the several buffers in whole blood. Henderson taught and inspired James Gamble. Henderson and his contemporary and close friend Walter Cannon were compared by N. K. Chambers and T. G. Buchman in "Shock at the Millenium II: Walter B. Cannon and Lawrence J. Henderson," *SHOCK* 16 (2001): 278–84. John Howland and W. McKim Marriott, "Acidosis Occurring with Diarrhea," *American Journal of Diseases of Children* 11 (1916): 309–25.

37. John Howland and W. McKim Marriott, "Observations upon the Calcium Content of the Blood in Infantile Tetany and upon the Effect of Treatment by Calcium," *Quarterly Journal of Medicine* 11 (1917–18): 289–319.

38. John Howland and Benjamin Kramer, "Calcium and Phosphorus in

the Serum in Relation to Rickets," *American Journal of Diseases of Children* 22 (1920): 105–19; also Benjamin Kramer and John Howland, "Factors Which Determine the Concentration of Calcium and of Inorganic Phosphorous in the Serum of Rats," *Johns Hopkins Hospital Bulletin* 33 (1922): 313–17.

39. John Howland and Edwards A. Park, "The Radiographic Evidence of the Influence of Cod Liver Oil in Rickets," *Johns Hopkins Hospital Bulletin* 32 (1921): 341–44.

40. John Howland, Paul G. Shipley, and Benjamin Kramer, "Studies upon calcification *in vitro*," *Biochemistry Journal* 20 (1926): 379–87. For those interested in more details of research during Howland's tenure, see A. McGehee Harvey, "The First Full-Time Academic Department of Pediatrics: The Story of the Harriet Lane Home," *Johns Hopkins Medical Journal* 137 (1975): 32–40; the second of Howland's two Harvey Lectures entitled "The Etiology and Pathogenesis of Rickets," delivered to the Harvey Society in New York City in 1923; and Edwards A. Park, "The Etiology of Rickets," *Physiological Reviews* 3 (1923): 106–62.

41. After obtaining his medical degree at Hopkins, L. Emmett Holt Jr. trained under Howland and joined his faculty to do research. Later he went to New York as chairman of the department of pediatrics at New York University.

42. Park called this "most gallant act" by Schloss "an act of courtesy and generosity from a younger to an older man which deserves unstinted praise." See Harry H. Gordon, "Oscar Menderson Schloss," in *Pediatric Profiles*, ed. B. S. Veeder (St. Louis: C. V. Mosby Co., 1957), 202–10.

43. A deformed and narrow pelvis making delivery difficult for mother and child.

44. E. V. McCollum, "Cooperative Research Experiences with Dr. Park," *Journal of Pediatrics* 41 (1952): 646–50.

45. Paul Shipley (1888–1934) came to Hopkins in 1913 with an MD from Yale. First an assistant in the department of anatomy, he shifted in 1917 to pediatrics in order to work on the calcification of bone with Park, who had just returned from working with the Red Cross in France, and later with Kramer. Shipley authored numerous publications concerning rickets and related topics and was made an associate professor in 1926, but died prematurely and suddenly in 1934. At that time he was also assistant chief physician at the Harriet Lane Home.

46. Holt Jr., "John Howland: Turning Point of American Pediatrics," 870–73.

47. Hugh Josephs authored an extensive and classic monograph on the "The Anemias of Infancy and Early Childhood," *Medicine* 15 (1936): 307–452, as well as "two dozen or more shorter publications" according to the personal history he wrote for the twenty-fifth class report for his Harvard class of 1914. He became a well-known pediatric hematologist and stayed at the Harriet Lane for his entire career.

48. Grover Powers later succeeded Park as chairman of pediatrics at Yale.

49. Later Clausen became professor and chairman at the University of Rochester.

50. Tisdall later returned to become professor at the University of Toronto. See the biographical essay about Tisdall by J. Harry Ebbs in *Pediatric Profiles*, 244–46.

51. Graham Ross was later professor at McGill University.

52. Marriott did his finest work at Washington University, where he proved that "intestinal intoxication" was, in reality, only the group of symptoms produced by dehydration. In later years Marriott's work was very influential and he did more than anyone else in the country at the time to break down the fetishism that enveloped infant feeding. Borden S. Veeder, "William McKim Marriott (1885–1936)" in *Pediatric Profiles*, 218–28.

53. J. L. Gamble, G. S. Ross, and F. F. Tisdall, "The Metabolism of Fixed Base During Fasting," *Journal of Biological Chemistry* 58 (1923): 633–95.

54. For more general information on the impressive achievements and career of James Gamble (1883–1959), see Clement A. Smith's comments in *The Children's Hospital of Boston–Built Better than They Knew* (Boston: Little, Brown and Company, 1983), 148–53. Also Malcolm A. Holliday's profile of Gamble in *Journal of Pediatrics* 122 (1993): 156–61.

55. When Gamble received the John Howland Medal and Award from the American Pediatric Society in 1955, his address included memories of Howland's laboratory. "This laboratory was ... the first one in this country for the study of disease in the clinic by quantitative methods of chemistry. It was the consummation of John Howland's clear vision of the value of such equipment in a university department of medicine. Dr. Howland had a boyish pride and joy in his laboratory. He often worked there himself, carrying out some measurements which Marriott had assigned him. Those of us of the laboratory group at the Harriet Lane never thought of [Howland] as 'The Chief.' His attitude was that of an approving elder companion in the entertaining pursuit of new information by the methods of chemistry. There was in his laboratory a happy lack of program and a delightful spirit of free adventure." A. M. Butler and James L. Gamble, "Presentation of the John Howland Medal and Award of the American Pediatric Society to Dr. James L. Gamble," *American Journal of the Diseases of Children* 90 (1955): 483–90.

56. Benjamin Kramer left the Harriet Lane in 1925 to become the chief pediatrician at the Brooklyn Jewish Hospital and the professor of pediatrics at the Long Island College of Medicine. Years later he described his difficulties and reasons for making the decision in a lengthy letter to Edwards Park, dated November 7, 1958. RG 4, series B, box 9, folder 14, HLH-AMC. In short, Howland discouraged Kramer's suggestion of a professorship of experimental pediatrics at Hopkins, and furthermore, Kramer was anxious to have his own department. Howland recommended him highly to the Universities of Minnesota, Iowa, and Rochester; he was considered by each but turned down. He attributed this to anti-Semitism in American medicine. On the other hand, the offer from the Brooklyn Jewish Hospital included a clinical professorship at the Long Island College of Medicine [later the Downstate Medical Center of the State University of New York] and provided the "opportunity to set up a university type of pediatric department in a community of about three million people." Benjamin Kramer to Edwards Park. On the subject of Kramer's departure, Park commented: "John [Howland]

felt that the bottom had dropped out of his investigative work when Kramer left, and I believe that such was the case." RG 4, series B, box 8, folder 23, HLH-AMC.

57. Smith, *The Children's Hospital of Boston—Built Better than They Knew*, 129–30.

58. L. Emmett Holt Jr., "John Howland: Turning Point of American Pediatrics," 872.

59. Davison, "John Howland (1873–1926)," 479.

60. "Memorial Meeting for Dr. John Howland," *Bulletin of The Johns Hopkins Hospital* 41 (1927): 321.

Meadow of Opportunity

A Most Companionable Man

John Howland's Persona

By Edwards A. Park,
edited and expanded by John W. Littlefield   103

John Howland's ever-youthful freshness and spontaneity, his sense of fun, his power of reminiscence, his intensity, and the wealth of his experience and knowledge gave him an ever shifting variety and charm. He loved being with people and probably could not have gotten along in life without good companionship. When with him, one could not help but be conscious of his warm nature.

Howland had a great sense of humor and an unusual gift at mimicry. He had known interesting people and had interesting experiences so his conversation was full of interesting and amusing anecdotes. He was a positive character, outspoken in his likes and dislikes, and entertained no halfway opinions of any subject. At the same time he remained extraordinarily boyish and simple. He was interested in all sorts of sports and contests and could give their histories. He was interested in battles, especially those of the American Revolution and the Civil War. Though not especially fond of music, he was devoted to Wagner's operas and could recite from the librettos. He was not contemplative, but loved outdoor activities. He was devoted to his family and was never happy when separated from them for any long period. He was a delightful host and had great numbers of friends.[1]

In 1950 Wilburt Davison noted: "Dr. Howland was a stern disciplinarian but had a lively sense of humor" and "students enjoyed and profited from his clinics, for he always made them think, and his spontaneous humor made the description of even the dullest details interesting."[2] In 1956, however, Davison painted a somewhat different portrait of John Howland:

[He] was such a paragon of the virtues of scientific medicine that sometimes to those who did not work with him he did not seem human. He was right too frequently.... However, in spite of or because of these virtues ... he had human foibles like the rest of us, and we, his disciples, enjoyed demonstrating them. He was most extraordinarily able, lovable, and irritating.... He had pride especially in his clinical acumen, he was frugal, he loved arguments, he had strong likes and dislikes, but a very weak sense of humor....

[He] was a stern disciplinarian famous for never expressing praise. He was very critical, not only of his own staff, but of everyone else. He ... could be friendly or aloof, usually the latter. He rarely invited the students or house staff to his home.[3] All of his associates greatly respected him, but there was always a certain formality when talking to him. In his absence we referred to him as "John," but always as "Dr. Howland" in his presence. Even now at the age of 62, I feel embarrassed in omitting "Dr." before his name.[4]

When L. Emmett Holt Jr. gave his own Howland Award address in 1966, he provided the last personal memories of Howland available to us. During his childhood Holt knew Howland as the senior office assistant in his father's office who was in the Holt house every day. When Howland, previously a star athlete at Yale, visited the Holt family's camp on Saranac Lake in the Adirondacks, he was

our most glamorous visitor.... On one of these visits [he] reached the conclusion that he would give up tennis [since] championship tennis and medicine were incompatible ... and he formally presented my teenage sister with the racquet that had won the intercollegiate championship. It was a specially built racquet, made from designs ... by the English champions of that day, and it was much too heavy for my sister, but would she ever play tennis with anything else?

When I went to medical school in Baltimore, I spent a great deal of time at his house; most of my Sunday evenings were spent there. They were wonderful evenings. Dr. Howland was a great raconteur, interested in everything under the sun, and full of interesting experiences. A young medical student sitting at his feet could not help but imbibe some of his philosophy—his enthusiasm for adding to medical knowledge [and] not just applying it.... I was just one of many who came under Howland's spell. One wanted to be like him, to do the kinds of things he was doing.[5]

Davison recalled that Howland "hated to waste time or money" and noted that during the spring meetings at Atlantic City, the pediatric group from Hopkins often ate at Child's restaurant where the menus printed both the prices and the caloric content of meals in parallel columns. Howland inevitably would pick the item that gave "the most calories for the least money. The result was always hot cakes, syrup and sausage."[6]

In his dress and in his habits Howland was simple to the point of puritanical plainness. He wore the same felt hat for several years until it was finally lost. Mrs. Howland used to object to it loudly and may have gotten as much pleasure from objecting to it as he did from wearing it. Davison reported that Howland "told Charles Harris that this [the hat] had been a constant worry to him because it cost a dollar a time to get it cleaned until he found that he could buy a gallon of gasoline for twenty-two cents and pour it into his hat and let it drain through, thereby saving seventy-eight cents."[7]

Howland was greatly interested in certain sports, particularly track events. Strangely enough, he did not seem interested in the national and Davis Cup tennis tournaments, not nearly so much as in the golf tournaments, according to James Gamble.[8]

He was the most ardent golfer I have ever known. He played not by the round but by the day. If after eighteen holes in the morning and another eighteen in the afternoon, there was daylight left, he would play some more. My only rigidly prescribed assignment in the department was to play with him on Sunday mornings as a tuning-up exercise for the afternoon foursome, which was the event of the week for him. I was not good enough to participate in the foursome.

In 1915 I [Gamble] got my first car and this greatly extended our golfing operations. Howland became a nonresident member in the newly developed Pine Valley course in New Jersey between Philadelphia and Atlantic City. It is a very beautiful and difficult course with a pleasant dormitory to spend the night in. We often went there for a few days, taking along, as a pretext, laboratory data for contemplation. We never looked at them.

Our most memorable visit to Pine Valley was en route to the meetings of the American Medical Association at Atlantic City. We set out on a Friday morning and, according to plan, played golf all day Saturday and Sunday. It was lovely June weather. We were to move on to Atlantic City

Monday morning. But it was another beautiful morning. Howland got out his program and, after careful study, announced that there was not a single paper in any of the sessions that he was the least bit interested in. So we played golf all day Monday. Tuesday morning was even lovelier and the same procedure produced the same result. There was not much debate Wednesday morning. It obviously did not make sense to go to Atlantic City for just one day. So we had five solid days of golf. On our return to Baltimore several of Howland's friends expressed surprise at not seeing him at Atlantic City. "Oh," he said, "thousands of doctors go to those meetings. It is quite easy to miss one's friends."

Social Issues

After Park joined Howland's clinic in Baltimore in 1912, he was a frequent guest at the Howland house and came to know Susan Howland well. Park described her as a beautiful, tall, gracious woman, possessed of great charm and an unusual dignity. She was mid-Victorian in her attitude regarding her place as being in her home and her duty the welfare and happiness of her husband and family. They seemed to adore each other and she gave him a beautiful home. And, as an ever willing and perfect hostess, she more than met all the social requirements of his position. Her husband, in turn, adored her. He protected her from contact with the world so effectually that she seemed completely unaware of the struggle of life and its iniquities. She was composed of sterling stuff, had strong convictions, and exerted a profound influence on her husband, being largely, if not chiefly, responsible for his social standards and behavior.

The Howlands' younger daughter, Louise Howland Drake, shared fond memories with her children (Susan Drake and John Howland Drake) about visiting her father's "wonderful study at [their home at] Oak Place[9] that looked out over the gardens. There he spent his time studying and reading." Louise also remembered that this study housed wounded animals the children had found … and Dr. Howland tended until their recovery. She mentioned to her children that Howland "treated various birds, including an owl, but her favorite was a bat he kept in a shoebox on the bookshelf."[10]

In 1920 the Howlands created a summer home on Cape Cod near Chatham.[11] A year earlier they had bought and moved to Mill Hill on Pleasant Bay two handsome older houses in succession, the first from its original location "across the cranberry bog," where it was called the Warren Jensen Nickerson House, and the second from the nearby town of West Brewster, where it was called the Eben Ryder House. These houses are now part of the well-known Wequasset Inn on Mill Hill. (The inn stated in its fiftieth anniversary brochure that the Ryder House, a "lovely Square Top," is now its centerpiece.) Before Howland had the Eben Ryder House "flaked down" (peeled or scraped off) and moved to Pleasant Bay in Chatham on large flatbed trucks, it had been a store and post office.

Once, Park said to Susan Howland that he had the impression John did not read a great deal. She emphatically contradicted him by saying that "He [Howland] read every evening and went to bed about eleven o'clock."[12] Davison agreed with her and wrote that Howland left "after six at night to go home to study and write."[13] It is likely that his evening reading was chiefly medical, in particular the manuscripts sent in for publication to the *American Journal of Diseases of Children*, of which he was an editor. Park believed Howland was a wide reader of great intelligence and thoughtfulness. His opinion was that Howland's wide knowledge was due in large part to the excellent quality of his reading, and to his remarkable memory, which held not only what he read but also what he learned from conversation.

In contrast to his older brother, Charles, Howland was a staunch conservative.[14] John, while admiring his brother immensely, possibly looked somewhat askance at the Charles's social attitudes. Howland's social interests were fairly sharply limited to what his environment happened to include. He was not especially interested in politics and certainly not affiliated with any political parties. The Howlands accepted conventional Baltimore society and moved in the so-called "upper circles" but never to the extent of interfering with his work, which always came first. Howland seemed to have had little understanding of, and little sympathy with, psychiatry, at least as taught by Adolf Meyer.[15] It appeared too indefinite and nebulous for Howland's immediately practical mind. And he did not tolerate dogma in any form. Speculation that seemed to him to lie outside the possibility of actual experience did not interest or trouble him.

Unlike his mentor Emmett Holt Sr., Howland had little interest in the child welfare movements in pediatrics. Park thought that Howland looked upon the pediatricians who made that side of pediatrics their life work as being, on the whole, inferior. He once said to Park that he was unwilling to have his department extend into child welfare because it could not deal adequately with that and with the pediatrics of disease successfully.

Emmett Holt Jr. pointed out that "Dr. Howland was inclined to take a dim view of women in medicine. He appreciated the talents of a number of outstanding women, such as Margaret Handy[16] and Katherine Dodd,[17] whom he had on his staff, but he has little sympathy for what he called 'aggressive feminism.'" Howland's opinion extended to nurses as well. "On one occasion the superintendent of nursing at the Johns Hopkins Hospital gave an impassioned plea for a BN degree"—a fine idea but ahead of its time—"and Howland vigorously opposed it."[18] Park agreed: "Howland never approved of women doctors. From time to time he was obliged to take women interns because the internships were awarded according to the standing of the students in the graduating class. He believed that women had no place in medicine and their education was economically unsound, because so large a proportion married and never made use of it. Margaret Handy once told me that as a condition of acceptance, he made her promise that she would not marry for forty years."

Around 1920 Howland had an attack of jaundice, as he had with typhoid fever while at Yale. The Hopkins internist he consulted found some enlargement of the liver and spleen, but felt that there was no cause for alarm. Howland decided to give up smoking and learned the habit of chewing gum. He literally chewed gum all the time when he was not on the hospital wards. Park remembered him chewing gum at a pathology conference given by William MacCallum, when Dr. Welch was present, and the sight seemed "incongruous beyond description." Perhaps aware of this incongruity in others, if not in himself, Howland did prohibit the chewing of gum by the nurses of the Harriet Lane.

Wilburt Davison confirmed that "In addition to not liking nurses and secretaries, [Howland] was a bit afraid of them. He would never discharge any of them, but would usually leave that job to Park or me, and he would stay away until the job was done."[19] "Once Howland told me he consented to have his number-two secretary, with whom I had to work and who was perfectly terrible, discharged, if I would do the discharging."

The supervising nurse of the Harriet Lane, Amy MacMahon, had been a favorite of Clemens von Pirquet and had been given considerable authority by him. She was an ardent feminist and, anathema to Howland, carried banners in feminist parades. Howland and she clashed on almost the first day. Crowds of nurses inundated the building, making a hubbub and noise. When Howland protested, saying his permission had not been granted, Park reported that he heard Mac-Mahon reply, "Dr. Howland, this is their home."

After this initial clash, Park noted that he found subsequent similar encounters very irritating, as did Howland, Kenneth Blackfan, and members of the junior staff. But Howland left most of the battle to Blackfan and Park. When they approached his office to report, his head would pop out and he would say in a loud whisper, "How did you get along?"

The critical incident occurred one morning when the admitting intern reported that he was unable to admit patients to the dispensary waiting room because MacMahon would not supply a flashlight. He quoted her as having refused to supply one, saying the flashlight belonging to the dispensary, taken out the previous afternoon, must be found and returned. Among the patients backed up and waiting Park found two with diphtheria and one with scarlet fever. A dispensary nurse whispered that the one who had taken the flashlight was Howland himself and that MacMahon knew it. Winford Smith, superintendent of the hospital, withdrew his support of MacMahon and a short time afterward she left."[20]

However, the staff warfare continued with MacMahon's successor, Pearl Stein. From the standpoint of some of the junior staff Stein was even more difficult. For example, Stein and Thomas Rivers collided, as Rivers related later in his oral history:

> I had my personal battles with Howland. One that I still remember began as a skirmish between myself and the superintendent of nurses at the Harriet Lane Home. I had ordered a croup tent for some children that were suffering pretty badly from cough, since the steam provided by such a tent was always helpful. Well, when I made rounds on this particular day, I discovered that Miss Stein, the superintendent of nurses, was using a gas burner to heat the water in the tent. I have always been deathly afraid of fires in a hospital, and particularly in a children's ward and so I ordered the gas burner discontinued and an electric heater substituted in its place. Miss Stein thought I was encroaching on her preserves, and she refused to do it. When I insisted, she went to Dr. Howland to complain, and I understand she complained loud and bitterly.
>
> At the time I was resident, the tennis courts were on the inside of the

Johns Hopkins Hospital grounds—they're not now. I was playing tennis when Dr. Howland came out of the Home, told me about Superintendent Stein's complaint, and asked me to rescind my order. "Dr. Howland," I said, "I'm not going to change that order because I think I have done the proper thing, and when I think I have done the proper thing for the safety of the children, I don't pay any attention to the superintendent of nurses." He demurred, and we had some further conversation on it. Finally I said, "Dr. H., if you have any idea of going in there and countermanding my order, I just want to tell you that, if you do, you'll have to get yourself another resident immediately. I think I'm right and I'm not taking any bossing from the superintendent of nurses of the Harriet Lane Home about something she doesn't know much about. Either I'm running the place or I'm not." The upshot was that Dr. Howland went back and told Superintendent Stein to get an electric heater. I should add that I was quite prepared to leave. I didn't make threats then, and still don't make threats, that I'm not prepared to carry out.[21]

It is unfortunate that the points of view of MacMahon and Stein concerning these two episodes are not available. But the various issues and personalities involved are illuminated. Both Park and Rivers were early in their careers and in new positions of authority at the time. Later on Park moderated his opinion of MacMahon and retracted his criticism of her. Rivers' insensitivity and inability to negotiate were evident on other occasions also. In addition, these two anecdotes suggest a quite uneasy relationship between the first two nursing supervisors and senior members of the medical and house staffs. Perhaps this was a failure on the part of Howland (or even Smith) to better define the hierarchy of authority in this new children's hospital.

Fortunately for peace in the Harriet Lane, Miss Stein was succeeded by a series of superintendents who got along beautifully with everyone concerned.

The Final Journey*

In the last year or two before his death John Howland complained of a lack of energy and not feeling absolutely well. One day in February 1926, Wilmot Jacobsen recalled, "as we were walking down the corridor, [Dr. Howland] hiccupped. He appeared perfectly well but he said

*The text in this section is by John W. Littlefield, drawn largely from the writings of Wilburt Davison.

'I have been doing this for several days. Stimulation of the basal nuclei of the brain can do this. I think I have encephalitis.' "[22] The next morning, according to Davison, "While on the way to the hospital with me, Dr. Howland asked me to hold his clinic because he could not stop hiccupping. The condition became worse that afternoon, and he finally had to stay in the hospital several days."[23] Jacobsen remembered that "Dr. Howland was sent home, but was still stuporous and delirious; and for a week I spent my nights at his home, chiefly as a reassurance to Mrs. Howland."[24]

"The acute phase persisted for many weeks [and] we did not see a great deal of our chief after this," Ashley Weech wrote later. "I remember visiting him at his home and noting that his voice was thick as if he had suffered from a mild stroke. During this period Dr. Howland was not able to be active in his office or laboratory."[25] Davidson noted, "Complete sedation with morphine eventually brought relief, but he was so weak that he decided to go to Europe for a rest and a holiday in accordance with plans made over a year before."[26]

Seemingly recovered, Howland and his wife, accompanied by their longtime close friends Dr. and Mrs. James Gamble, sailed for Europe on March 30, 1926, from Boston,[27] where the Gambles had moved to in 1922. "Charles Howland was then in Greece on a mission for the League of Nations, charged with the repatriation of the Greeks from Turkish territory. The party went first to Greece where Charles, with all the authority and dignity of his position, received and entertained them.[28]

The party then traveled on to Budapest, Zurich, Strasbourg, Paris, and London. From Paris Howland wrote that he was entirely well, but Abraham Flexner, whom they saw in Europe, reported that he looked pale and thin, and complained of fatigue. While the Gambles toured the Basque country, Howland was taken seriously ill in Paris. Mrs. Howland hurried him to England where medical friends awaited. Davison described the sequence of events:

> ... a cold from which he was suffering became worse, a severe cough developed which fatigued him greatly, and he had attacks of what was thought to be indigestion. His condition improved during the next two weeks and he went to London but arrived in an exhausted condition and had two hemorrhages apparently of gastric origin. A tentative diagnosis of duodenal ulcer was made, and as the bleeding continued, an operation

FABRE LINE
MARSEILLE

CIE Cie FABRE
LINE
WINTER
COURSE

on board S.S. Patria
near Boston -

Dear Graham,

I found the flowers that the Staff of the Harriet Lane Home sent me on board the boat, just as we sailed off. It was a very kindly thought for to remember me and I am grateful for it also much to diminish the regret of very comparing out of the fighting world - I'm cannot leave. I hope I'm never nice, how hard it is to pull out of active work, even temperamental, after thirty years of interesting strenuous work - In even

though I am sorry to see things that I have dreamed about and never hoped to see - Even as the municipalize and confiscating municipalized college days I forget over Evan and now approved a great work is to be realized. So much I derived from a clerical education even of the evangelism of the relation is my Hazy.

First I'm please express to the members of the Staff my thanks for their kindly action and wish to wish the best of all things for the next year -

Very sincerely Evan
John Howland -

April 30/26 -

was performed. Marked cirrhosis of the liver was found. That night his condition became critical. The next day the bleeding stopped and Howland rallied but became delirious, coma developed the following day, and he died on June 20, 1926, at the age of fifty-three. Mrs. Howland and Dr. and Mrs. Gamble were with him. He was buried at Walpole, N.H., on July 1, 1926.[29]

Wilburt Davison speculated that "It is probable that the jaundice [Howland] had at Yale [which at the time was presumably regarded as an unusual accompaniment of his typhoid fever] and again in 1919 was what we now know as infectious hepatitis and was responsible for the cirrhosis of the liver which caused his death. It could not be attributed to any other factor as he was a teetotaler, and ate an adequate diet."[30] Less likely alternative possibilities were that his exposure to chloroform and perhaps other hepatotoxins during research with A. N. Richards might have caused the cirrhosis, or even that his "typhoid hepatitis" while at Yale might have done so.

New evidence on the possible cause of Howland's cirrhosis has recently come to light. In his October 5, 1988 letter to Frank Oski, chairman of the department of pediatrics and director of the Harriet Lane Home at the time, Jacobsen stated that the "autopsy revealed severe cirrhosis of the liver and degeneration of the basal ganglia (Wilson's disease). Dr. Howland's early diagnosis had been correct."[31] Efforts to obtain a copy of the autopsy report from among Dr. Jacobsen's papers have been unsuccessful, and all the clinical and pathological records from seventy-five years ago at the University College Hospital in London have been destroyed. Why an autopsy report of such interest to those at the Harriet Lane Home was not available is a mystery, raising the possibility that the pathological diagnosis of Wilson's disease was not conclusive."[32]

When Howland died in 1926, Edwards Park summarized his achievements:

(opposite) A LETTER BY JOHN HOWLAND. In 1926, while recuperating from a serious illness, Howland and his wife set sail for a long-planned tour of Europe. They were greeted in their stateroom with flowers sent by the Harriet Lane staff. In his letter of thanks, addressed to his colleague Wilmot Jacobsen, Howland expressed his frustration about being "forced out of active work, even temporarily, after thirty years of interesting, strenuous endeavor." Howland realized his dream of seeing Greece but did not live to complete the entire trip.

THE UNVEILING OF JOHN HOWLAND'S PORTRAIT. The American Pediatric Society created a lasting tribute to Howland in 1952 when it established the John Howland Medal as its highest award, given each year to physicians who have made significant contributions to pediatrics. In 1958 several of Howland's former associates gathered at Johns Hopkins for the unveiling of his portrait, among them James Gamble, Edwards A. Park, Elmer V. McCollum, and L. Emmett Holt Jr.

"To Howland's own mind the development of his clinic at Johns Hopkins was his greatest accomplishment. In the fourteen years of his leadership he saw his clinic grow to be the foremost in the country and the first pediatric clinic, in the true sense of the term, the country ever possessed. The children in the hospital wards were skillfully cared for; the students were splendidly taught; on every side were encountered devotion to duty, enthusiasm for science, the spirit of sacrifice for the ideal; from the wards and laboratories came forth one valuable contribution after another to the science of medicine; and from Howland himself went forth one assistant after another to head other departments and to assume other positions of responsibility elsewhere. He was a member of the Board of Scientific Directors of the Rockefeller Foundation for Medical Research, of the Council of Pharmacy and Chemistry of the American Medical Association, a director of the Russell Sage Institute,[33] and a member of numerous societies and medical organizations."[34] These included the American Pediatric Society, the New York Academy of Medicine, the American Society for Clinical Investigation, and the Association of American Physicians. In 1952 Park confirmed and enlarged upon this summary in his major address to the American Pediatric Society.[35]

It was Davison's opinion that "Howland's real career started in 1912 when he was called to Johns Hopkins. Here through his clinical and scientific ability and his personality he made the Harriet Lane Home an outstanding university pediatric clinic.... [He] was the leading pediatrician of this country, if not in the world."[36]

Notes

1. Professor of Medicine William S. Thayer, who was a good friend of John Howland's, provided additional memories on the occasion of the unveiling of a plaque of John Howland. They appeared in the *Bulletin of The Johns Hopkins Hospital* 46 (1930): 156–57.

2. Wilburt Davison, "John Howland: The Seventy-Fifth Anniversary of his Birth," *Journal of the History of Medicine and Allied Sciences* 5 (1950): 199 and 201.

3. Susan Drake, daughter of John and Susan Howland's younger daughter, Louise Howland Drake, remembered that her mother related how "medical students often came to the house to meet with Dr. Howland and would sometimes stay for dinner." Susan Drake to John Littlefield, October 14, 2000. Ashley Weech gave a glimpse of suppers at the Howland household: "There was evidence available to us that John Howland greatly enjoyed a battle of wits with his residents and that he often recounted the triumphs of the day to his family after he was home in the evening. This information came to us through one of the residents (A. Wilmot Jacobsen) who for a time dated Howland's daughter [probably Katharine]. We thus, to our great delight, had an inside line as to what went on in the home." Ashley Weech to Edwards Park, March 5, 1964, RG 4, series B, box 8, folder 22, HLH-AMC.

4. Wilburt Davison, "John Howland (1873–1926)," *Journal of Pediatrics* 46 (1956): 476.

5. Emmett Holt Jr., "John Howland: Turning Point of American Pediatrics," *Journal of Pediatrics* 69 (1966): 866.

6. Wilburt Davison, "John Howland (1873–1926)," 484–85.

7. Ibid., 484.

8. Park here quotes Gamble but without attribution. Edwards A. Park, "John Howland Award Address," *Pediatrics* 10 (1952): 101–02.

9. Katharine [Howland] McGee [John and Susan Howland's older daughter] to Edwards Park, December 8, 1968. In this letter, McGee stated that early in 1915 the Howlands moved from Eager Street to a large house on Oak Place, built by them near the new undergraduate campus of Johns Hopkins University. RG 4, series C, box 14, folder 14, HLH-AMC.

10. Susan Drake and John Howland Drake to John Littlefield, October 14, 2000; John Howland Drake to John Littlefield, September 3, 2000.

11. Katharine [Howland] McGee to Edwards Park, December 8, 1968.

12. In his obituary of Howland in 1926 Park wrote, "Howland never read

a great deal and rarely worked evenings, but the salient points in his reading were always remembered." It seems not unlikely that this comment in the obituary irritated Mrs. Howland. Park, "John Howland 1873–1926," 82.

13. Wilburt Davison, "John Howland: The Seventy-Fifth Anniversary of His Birth," 201.

14. According to Edwards Park, John Howland's older brother, Charles, first achieved distinction in New York City as a corporation lawyer. Charles told Park once that he came to abominate his work in corporation law since it consisted so frequently of devising ways by which big business could evade legitimate responsibilities. Charles had wide interests, not only in world affairs but also in the social movements of the time. He often wrote for the *New Republic, Foreign Affairs, Atlantic Monthly,* and other periodicals. He had become widely known as a liberal. Because of his recognized abilities and interests in world affairs he was selected to be chairman of the Greek Refuge Settlement Commission under the League of Nations in charge of the repatriation of Greeks from Turkey and Turkish Asia Minor after the defeat of Greece in 1924. This complicated and difficult task he accomplished with such signal success that his fame became international. Because of this and numerous kindred activities he was called in 1928 to be Dodge Lecturer in International Relations in the Yale Law School. Among his varied activities he was a member of the Yale Corporation and a trustee of the Rockefeller Foundation. It was not generally known but on the retirement of President [Frank] Goodnow, he was offered the presidency of Johns Hopkins University but declined. The reason explained to Park at the time was that Charles Howland did not believe he possessed the kind of ability required for that office. On a rainy night [in 1932] near his home in New Haven he was struck and killed by an automobile. He was then sixty-three years old.

15. Adolf Meyer came to Johns Hopkins in 1910 and oversaw the development and operations of the Henry Phipps Psychiatric Clinic, which opened in 1913. A. McGehee Harvey, Gert H. Brieger, Susan L. Abrams, and Victor A. McKusick, *A Model of Its Kind: A Centennial History of Medicine at Johns Hopkins,* volume 1 (Baltimore: The Johns Hopkins University Press, 1989), 297.

16. After graduating from Goucher College in Baltimore, Margaret Handy obtained her MD degree at Hopkins in 1916, trained at the Harriet Lane Home, and left in 1918 to practice pediatrics in Wilmington, Delaware. In 1921 she became chief of pediatrics at the "old" Delaware Hospital in Wilmington, retiring from that position in 1946, but continuing to practice until a few years before her death in 1977 at the age of eighty-seven. In 1953 the Chamber of Commerce of Delaware awarded her the Josiah Marvel Cup as "the most distinguished citizen of the year" for her "devotion for the children of Delaware." She also received honorary doctor of science degrees from the University of Delaware and Goucher College. Her friend Andrew Wyeth painted her twice, the better-known portrait being called *The Children's Doctor.* In 1953 at the Marvel Cup award ceremony she said, "I have spent thirty-five years doing the thing I wanted most to do. It was not a life of sacrifice, but a life I have enjoyed every minute of."

17. Park recalled that "When Ashley Weech was resident, the assistant resident was his great friend Katherine Dodd. Howland once asked me the riddle:

'What does Weech say when he gets stuck?' The answer was 'Katy, Katy, Katy.' I think many of us would like to be able to cry out for Katy when in difficulties with a sick child." Edwards Park, "John Howland Award Address," 105.

18. Holt Jr., "John Howland: Turning Point of American Pediatrics," 874–75.

19. Wilburt Davison, "John Howland (1873–1926)," 481.

20. Later, Park wrote, "Miss MacMahon had unusual executive ability and the finest standards," and "I could have helped if my attitude had been understanding." Draft memorandum, RG 4, series C, box 17, folder 29, HLH-AMC. After leaving Hopkins, MacMahon had an impressive nursing and administrative career throughout World War I. In 1914 she opened the hospital in England where Sir William Osler became chief of medicine and then served on the front in France with the Canadian Army Medical Corps. In 1919 she was awarded a first class Royal Red Cross by the King and received a book from the Queen at Marlborough House. Coming back to North America, she turned her skills to public health. After reviving a Baby Welfare Clinic in Waterbury, Connecticut, she returned to her native country to start a school and involve herself in welfare work on Prince Edward Island. Eventually she retired to live in Toronto. Biographical file, "Amy MacMahon," CMA.

21. Saul Benison, *Tom Rivers: Reflections on a Life in Medicine and Science*, an oral history memoir (Cambridge: M.I.T. Press, 1967), 46–47. Davison confirmed this event, according to Park: "Rivers once told Howland that if he did not discharge the head nurse, he would resign and take all of his house staff with him. Howland remarked later to Park, 'Rivers would do it, too.'"

22. A. Wilmot Jacobsen to Frank Oski, October 5, 1988, RG 4, series C, box 17, folder 28, HLH-AMC.

23. Wilburt Davison, "John Howland: The Seventy-Fifth Anniversary of His Birth," 200.

24. A. Wilmot Jacobsen to Frank Oski, October 5, 1988.

25. Ashley Weech to Edwards Park, March 5, 1964, RG 4, series B, box 8, folder 22, HLH-AMC.

26. Wilburt Davison, "John Howland: The Seventy-Fifth Anniversary of His Birth," 200.

27. The only letter in Howland's hand in the Chesney Archives was written to A. Wilmot Jacobsen on April 1, 1926, as the Howlands' steamship departed. In it he thanked his staff for flowers placed in his stateroom. HLH-AMC, RG 5, series A, box 1, folder 1.

28. They did not, however, go to Germany. James Gamble stated that "Howland's postwar dislike of Germans was implacable," and that Howland "gave a grim 'No' to my suggestion that we visit Von Pirquet in nearby Vienna." James L. Gamble, "Remarks at the Presentation of the Portrait of John Howland," *Pediatrics* 21 (1958): 659.

29. Wilburt Davison, "John Howland: The Seventy-Fifth Anniversary of His Birth," 200. Immediately after Howland's death Dr. John McNee, a physician (or perhaps surgeon) at the University College Hospital, London, wrote to Wilburt Davison. This letter chronicled in detail the inexorable sequence of events after the Howlands reached London. Sir John McNee and his wife Lady McNee had known the Howlands in Baltimore, and probably

Dr. McNee was the London physician whom the Howlands in Paris urgently asked for help. J. W. McNee to Wilburt C. Davison, June 20, 1926. Lewis Weed Papers, RG 1, box 9, Alan Mason Chesney Medical Archives, The Johns Hopkins Medical Institutions, Baltimore, MD.

Edwards Park concluded his description of Howland's untimely death by noting that "When John Howland died and the very bottom of her life dropped out, Susan Howland showed an unconquerable spirit. But she seemed to live in the past. She moved back to New Haven, where she died of cancer in 1932, surviving her husband by only six years." Draft memorandum concerning Howland's life and career, 1873–1911, [erroneously labeled "Howland Period 1912–1926"], RG 4, series B, folder 11, page 44, HLH-AMC.

30. Wilburt Davison, "John Howland (1873–1926)," 476.

31. A. Wilmot Jacobsen to Frank Oski, October 5, 1988. Wilson's disease (or hepatolenticular degeneration) is an uncommon autosomal recessive condition, first described in 1912, which affects the metabolism of copper.

32. Wilburt Davison, "John Howland (1873–1926)," 479.

33. According to its Internet Web site, "The Russell Sage Institute is devoted exclusively to research in the social sciences. One of the oldest private foundations in the United States, [it] was established by Mrs. Margaret Sage in 1907 for the improvement of social and living conditions in the United States. In its early years the Foundation undertook major projects in low income housing, urban planning, social work, and labor reform. The Foundation now dedicates itself exclusively to strengthening the methods, data, and theoretical core of the social sciences as a means of improving social policies." But at the time Howland was involved, it was particularly interested in infant hygiene and mortality.

34. Edwards A. Park, "John Howland 1873–1926," *Science* 64 (1926): 80–83.

35. Edwards A. Park, "John Howland Award Address," *Pediatrics* 10 (1952): 82–108.

36. Wilburt Davison, "John Howland: The Seventy-Fifth Anniversary of His Birth," 197.

Larger than Life

Edwards A. Park 1927–1946

By Henry M. Seidel

One day in the early fall of 1927 when the clear American air seemed the essence of life itself, I stepped into the gloomy hall of The Johns Hopkins Hospital, and enquired from a formidable lady receptionist who sat under a still more formidable white marble statue of Christ where I might find Professor Park. I was directed to the Harriet Lane Home and proceeded down a number of corridors, through glass swing doors, and turning right found myself in an outer office in which sat a young lady with dazzling eyes. She rose at once and received me with such charm that the nervousness which had steadily increased for the last five minutes left me. Miss Richards, for it was no other, passed me on through an inner door into a second room where a tall rugged man dressed in a very white coat was standing talking to another person dressed similarly. The tall man held out a great hand and took mine with much friendliness: I looked at a bronzed face and two of the kindest and most comprehending eyes I had ever seen, and realized with sudden prevision that I was in the presence of a nobleman of his country, a man of Lincoln-like greatness who wore no mask and whose only protection from the world was a shield of absolute honesty through which the darts of malice could hardly pierce. So immediate and vivid was the impression of the scene upon my mind that now after twenty-five years I can see it clearly, even to the very photographs upon the walls of his study.[1]

So Robert Collis keenly recalled his first encounters at the Harriet Lane Home when he was a new faculty member just arrived from England. Eighteen years later, when I myself arrived in 1945, the Harriet Lane Home was thirty-three years old. (That seems young to me now but the building looked old to me then.) It had a history but I didn't

PORTRAIT OF EDWARDS A. PARK WITH MICROSCOPE. Park was Harriet Lane chief from 1927 to 1946. His charismatic personality convinced well-established clinicians and scientists, as well as promising young doctors just launching their careers, to join the ranks of the Harriet Lane Home. Although he had been a loyal member of John Howland's team for several years, Park had his own ideas about running the Home; when he became its chief, he made significant changes.

know it. There was for me, a third-year medical student, a vague sense of importance about the place. And then, there was Edwards A. Park.

An Exquisite Metaphor

Consider the time: World War II didn't end until August 1945 so hospitals at this time were staffed by the very young and by those too old for the military. That was why Dr. Park was my everyday preceptor when I first entered the wards of the Harriet Lane Home. My classmates and I had his full attention for hours. I remember infants nestled in his huge hands (and one hand occasionally going to his cheek to give ease to his tic douloureux), and the questions with which he constantly, yet gently, prodded us. He was tall and I literally had to look up to him. I knew very quickly that I wanted to be like Park, and if that meant being a pediatrician, so be it. I did not know the role he played in American pediatrics, or the significance of his title of "Professor," or that this eminent physician would be my lifetime lodestar. At the time I was unsure he was even human. I know all this now.

Park had presence and always commanded the room. His quiet charisma and his sensitivity, intelligence, and longevity assured his role in the history of the Harriet Lane Home and of academic pediatrics in the United States. While others followed John Howland, Park was unique. The academic pediatric community recognized his distinctive contributions by bestowing on him the first John Howland Award. Park built on the work that Howland began and he modified and expanded the department of pediatrics at Johns Hopkins to such a degree that it became a model for what we expect today. In addition, Park was the major catalyst for the remarkable research and service efforts of many men and women. He was unafraid of the criticism that his conscientious and sensitive discussion of social issues attracted. Withal, there was the insistent power of his presence as teacher and exemplar.[2] Park's career is an exquisite metaphor for the time in which academic pediatrics in the United States was coming of age.

Park was born in 1878 and spent his childhood in Gloversville, a village in upstate New York set above the Mohawk Valley at the southern tip of the Adirondack Mountains. Called "Ned" by his family, he enjoyed hunting, fishing, skating, and tobogganing in his youth. His sister, Marion, remembered theirs as a simple environment with "few excitements and no spectacular crises of pleasure or pain." The family lived in a comfortable but plain parsonage on Main Street.[3]

Park's father, William Edwards Park, was the Congregational minister in Gloversville and both of his parents were the children of faculty members at the theological seminary in Andover, Massachusetts. Ministers were expected to marry into their own profession in those days and, indeed, there were long lines of New England ministers on both sides of Park's family. The conservative faith evident in William Park's sermons was practiced at home. Still, the elder Park was an eager amateur historian and his children heard sermons laced with references to Alexander, Caesar, and Napoleon. Park also heard his mother read aloud to her children the poems she loved, including the *Faerie Queen* and *Paradise Lost*. She had learned from her father the value of knowing poetry by heart—"a poem a Sunday, with a family recital Sunday evening"—and her children followed suit over their lifetimes.[4]

Park's mother seemed to her children to be intelligent, wise, affectionate, and amusing, according to Marion Park. She was devoted to her children, especially Ned. We know about some of his childhood experiences because she kept an informal record of his remarks in a notebook. There had been ministers aplenty in the family, and farmers, lawyers, teachers, and colonial officials, but no doctors. Yet, Park gave perhaps a hint of the future when he asked, "If a man had 'ralgia, and leprosy, and the disease the man had who tried to get the bed away from Jesus, would he die?"[5]

Park was schooled at home for a time and then sent to boarding school in the Berkshires followed by Phillips Academy for a year. Yale University was the next step because his father had gone there. Park's sister did not remember her brother as a serious or absorbed student but he was popular and socially involved. He graduated from Yale in 1900 and spent a year tutoring in New England.[6]

Family tradition seemed to mandate that Park become a theologian. His father had desired an academic career in history but did not pursue one. So when his son betrayed the same restlessness, his father wished that his son would deny his desire for medicine as he had for history, but Park did not. Medicine, like religion, was a profession in the service of people. Perhaps medicine better suited his more deterministic thinking and theological dogma was less compatible with his analytic mind.[7]

A letter written more than half a century later to Harold Harrison, a friend and a faculty member he had recruited, may suggest the gist of Park's thinking in youth. The letter referred to a copy of the Dead Sea Scrolls that Harrison had sent to Park:

> Since old enough to think, I have believed the Christ story a legend appealing to emotional conviction through its drama. But the Scrolls indicate strongly that the teachings of Christ and the theological conceptions and practices,—life after death, reward & punishment, baptism, etc. were the development of a Jewish sect 100 or more years before Christ and that he [sic], a man of mystery, surrounded by clouds of obscurity put the conception in a form which coming in a period of world misery & oppression made a great popular appeal—suffering borne in this life with freedom and equality in the next. The Scrolls are a blow to the Christian conceptions comparable to evolution and the probability is that the theologians will find some evasion, which

will forswear the status quo. It is astonishing that reason is so weak an instrument. People say this is so and go on just the same. [8]

Park applied to the School of Medicine at Johns Hopkins, which was relatively new at the time, because it was less expensive than other schools and not because he felt that it was in any way superior.[9] He did not have the funds to meet the expenses of medical school, however. The support of a cousin enabled his study at the College of Physicians and Surgeons at Columbia University.[10] After graduation in 1905 Park served two years of internship at the Roosevelt Hospital in New York with six months in pathology at Welfare Island.[11] It was during a two-year internship at the New York Foundling Hospital that he first met John Howland, an attending physician there at the time.[12]

Upon completing his internship in 1909 Park returned to the College of Physicians and Surgeons as a junior member of the faculty where he taught pediatrics and medicine. From 1909 to 1912 he was in private practice as an office assistant to Dr. Theodore Janeway, the Bard Professor of Medicine at Columbia. Janeway was an attentive and sympathetic mentor for Park, who introduced him to the laboratory and early studies on the role of epinephrine in the maintenance of blood pressure.[13] Janeway urged Park to accept an offer to become director of outpatient service at the Harriet Lane Home at Johns Hopkins[14] but first he suggested that Park spend a few months in the laboratory of M. B. Schmidt, a distinguished pathologist and world authority on rickets in Marburg, Germany. Park agreed and it was there that he confirmed his lifetime interest in bone.[15] He also met "that lovely young English girl," Agnes Bevan, during the summer of 1912. Six weeks later he went to England, proposed to her, and then departed immediately for Johns Hopkins.[16] They married in London the following summer and embarked on a new life that was particularly challenging for Agnes in a new country. "Together they built in Baltimore a home of warm hospitality where their many friends and associates were welcome."[17]

Incontrovertible Evidence

Park's scholarly inclination to observe, conclude, and then write was nurtured at the Harriet Lane Home. He wrote approximately forty-four papers during the nine years (beginning in 1912) he worked under Howland's directorship at Harriet Lane. Park's interests included various anomalies of the lung, measles and infectious endocarditis, poliomyelitis, extirpation of the thymus in guinea pigs, hypersensitivity to cow's milk, and rickets.[18] World War I intruded on his research from 1918 to 1919 but even while he worked with the Belgian Red Cross in France he continued to write.[19]

A determination to understand rickets underlay Park's career-long interest in the growing bone. Howland shared this interest and nourished it, putting Park in touch with Elmer V. McCollum at the Johns Hopkins School of Hygiene and Public Health. Park and his colleague Paul Shipley provided the skills and understanding that McCollum needed for his research. McCollum knew nutrition. Park and Shipley knew clinical rickets and the pathology of bone. The pediatricians could read the slides and decide whether or not rickets was suggested. Their pathological interpretations were complemented by the measurement of calcium and phosphate in the blood of rats before and after treatment with cod liver oil. Howland and Benjamin Kramer, an early recruit to the Harriet Lane faculty, developed microtechniques that enabled the chemical study of children's and infants' chemistries using a minimum of blood.[20] Park's histologic studies established incontrovertible evidence that the bone changes were caused by diet, evidence that guided the discovery of the cause of rickets.[21]

Park continued to explore other aspects of bone disease, particularly scurvy, lead poisoning, and nutritional disturbance. He was able to correlate the histologic changes in bone with clinical, biochemical, and radiologic findings. This effort was complicated by the significantly large volume of mineralized matrix, an impediment to the microscopic study of bone.[22] Eventually, it was possible for Park to provide adequate correlation of structure with x-ray findings, the key to proper radiographic interpretation. Typically, he did not assume that the dense band at the metaphysis of the long bones in lead poisoning was solely the result of the deposition of lead. He found the trabecular structure of bone to be altered as a result of the disturbance in bone growth and remodeling. The trabeculae were more closely packed at the growing ends and that, too, added to the density of the "lead line."

Park's modesty and honesty were evident in his refusal to be acknowledged in a major paper on rickets. He left Baltimore in 1921 to start a new department of pediatrics at Yale and he did not want his name on work that described final experiments performed in 1922 in which he had not participated. He had, of course, made essential contributions to hundreds of collaborative experiments. McCollum considered the final experiments to be more of the same but Park did not waver.[23] Park also insisted on ascribing primary authorship for a paper on malformations of the skull to Grover Powers, a colleague at Hopkins who would eventually succeed him at Yale. Powers overruled this generosity of spirit and Park's name was listed first.[24]

In the end, McCollum wrote, "We concluded that this rickets-preventing property was distinct from vitamin A. Since it was the fourth vitamin to be discovered, we called it by the corresponding letter of the alphabet, vitamin D."[25] McCollum and Howland, complemented by Park, Shipley, and Kramer, thus initiated the understanding of rickets that prevails today. Park's major role was evident in papers on the subject where he was the sole author.[26] He also shared joint authorship on some of the more than twenty-five articles that reported on the effort, most of them in the *Journal of Biological Chemistry*.[27]

Park became the first chairman of the newly created department of pediatrics at the Yale University School of Medicine on July 21, 1921. Milton Winternitz was just one year into his deanship at Yale and was intent on cultivating a superior school, which he accomplished during his tenure.[28] He and Park had been colleagues at Johns Hopkins. Winternitz's steady support for pediatrics allowed Park the leeway to explore ideas that had been nascent in Baltimore. Park's vision of academic pediatrics differed in many ways from that of the charismatic and somewhat intimidating Howland. Yale gave him the opportunity to explore that vision, and the years there foreshadowed his tenure at Hopkins.

Support and approval in New Haven were unconditional for Park and he was awarded one of the newly created and prestigious Sterling professorships. The physical setting was not particularly impressive[29] but Park commanded the space. There was no doubt that he was *the* professor and *the* pediatrician-in-chief. Tall and wearing his white coat, he led his group on rounds. Never pedantic, he asked questions constantly and anyone in his range could be a target, be they student or senior colleague. It did not always bother him if his target did not know the answer as it meant that something could be learned.[30]

Clearly, Park established the professional demeanor for which he was so well known at Yale. At home, however, he seemed "moody and difficult." Perhaps he realized that academic leadership would constrain his own research. This is conjecture; no documentation has been found that reveals Park's attitude about leaving New Haven after five years and returning to Baltimore. In any event, when the move back to Johns Hopkins was imminent, his daughter Sally remembered him as "happier."[31]

Larger than Life

John Howland died in London on June 20, 1926 at the age of fifty-three. Wilburt C. Davison, then a senior member of the Harriet Lane faculty,[32] was made the acting head of the department of pediatrics. A committee chaired by Warfield T. Longcope, chief of the department of medicine, that included William MacCallum, William Welch, Lewis Weed, and J. Whitridge Williams was asked to find Howland's successor. This group from internal medicine, pathology, anatomy, and obstetrics had difficulty finding someone who inspired the committee's unanimous support. They even toyed with the notion of naming a non-pediatrician but the advisory board of the School of Medicine wouldn't hear of it. The committee ultimately and almost inevitably concentrated on physicians in New York and New Haven and they unanimously proposed Edwards Park.[33]

Park headed the department of pediatrics at the Johns Hopkins School of Medicine and was the pediatrician-in chief at the Johns Hopkins Hospital from 1927 to 1946. He had an acute understanding of his era's problems and a clear vision for the future. Howland established the first full-time department of pediatrics in the United States, where American pediatricians could earn a living doing research, seeing patients, and teaching—the so-called "triple threat." Park, James Gamble, Grover Powers, and Kenneth Blackfan were at the heart of Howland's effort, but when Park took over he changed things in ways that brought about the approach we use today. No one had a greater impact on academic pediatrics than Park, and there is no evidence that a similar dominance will occur in the foreseeable future.[34]

Park arrived in Baltimore at a time when the nation was struggling. The "Roaring Twenties" were a prosperous time for some. But more than 40 percent of the families in the United States had annual incomes of less than a thousand dollars and for many of these people the inner city, with its segregated neighborhoods, was home. The right to vote, earned by women in 1920, was not often exercised by women or men in poor neighborhoods and the political process was minimally supportive of their needs.[35] In 1929 the U.S. stock market crashed and the socially and economically disenfranchised suffered additional hardship as a result. The devastation was prevalent in East Baltimore, where much of the population was dependent on the Johns Hopkins Hospital for their health care.

In fact, the hospital had been a "neighborhood doctor" from its beginning. Then, as now, this world-class, model institution depended on its impoverished neighbors for its success just as much as these neighbors depended on the hospital. Park's actions over time suggested that he understood this relationship. It is fair to say that he did his best to serve poor children well without limiting the investigative and teaching enterprise essential to the purposes of the institution. Relatively liberal in his social and academic attitudes, he proved able, within the context of a conservative institution, to fashion academic pediatrics as we now know it.

One possible source for Park's unique ability could be the influence of his ministerial family. He was intensely intellectual and, in the view of many, he judged people at least in great part on their intellectuality.[36] James Gamble recalled that Park had "the rare gift of being able to dissociate, with remarkable clarity, idealism, which he serves, from ideology, which he abhors."[37] His daughter Sally thought him "larger than life" as a child and even as a grown-up. "His thoughts, his actions, even his physical gestures, were noble, heroic."[38] That, too, was my first impression upon meeting him. I would not have believed then that his children called him "Punk," and that he would revel in that because they had "found him out."[39]

It was probably not too difficult to "find him out," at least in some ways. Park seems never to have dissembled and he appears to have lived a life dictated in large part by the experience of growing up in a small town. Simplicity and sincerity dominated his life. He lived without pomp and pretension and money was not plentiful for him. Park felt that "there seemed to be enough for the important things." Indeed, money was never his compelling interest. He had no funds at his retirement and was rescued by his sister, Marion, a former president of Bryn Mawr College, who never married and who left all her money to him. Remarkably, two wealthy friends, William Ladd and a close colleague, James Gamble, added to this, providing enough money for a lifelong stipend.[40] Friendship played a role in this practical tribute but so did

Park's constancy and extraordinary regard for colleagues, respect for intellectual honesty, and sensitivity to the human condition beyond the bounds of his immediate environment. He was utterly honest and he did not live life with hidden agendas. Hence, "Punk."

There was a pervasive intellectuality in Park and a need for precision. Two days before his death, his daughter-in-law sat with him. He asked what she was reading. "*War and Peace*, Punk." "Where have you gotten, Janey?" "I'm reading about the death of Andre. Natasha is waiting for the arrival of Andre's sister, Anya." After a long silence in which Park appeared to have drifted into sleep, he responded in a soft, firm voice, "Janey, I think you are mistaken. Andre's sister was called Maria." Punk had read the book at least fifty years before; Jane had read the passage the day before. "He was exactly correct, as usual."[41]

Park's precision may have been excessive at home but it was not perceived as such by Park's colleagues. It was certainly daunting to his daughter and younger son. Sally Park Scattergood wrote that her father "was in love with the truth" and that he had an "uncompromising, punishing attitude" in this regard.[42] She and her younger brother had ambivalent feelings toward "Punk," which were not shared by their older brother. Rollo Park was candid in saying that "it was clear from way back" that he was their father's favorite child. "It was a favoritism not deserved," he said, but it was clear to his siblings and they resented it.[43] And yet, Sally could write after Punk's death, "I recall with pain and joy things that really happened, and he still visits me regularly in my dreams. These visitations are vivid and delightful. I wake up happy, smiling or even laughing aloud as we so often did with him in real life. The negative feelings I had towards him seem never to be there; for this 'dream father' fulfills all my wishes of what I wanted our relationship to have been."[44]

Their mother Agnes, nicknamed "Moo" by her children, was a leavening influence, always the doctor's wife, always there, constant and without "craggy" emotions like Park, but Park seemed to be the most powerful force in their lives. Agnes believed that all bodily requirements were met by ingesting a daily teaspoonful of "foul, smelly cod liver oil."[45] The hospitality of her home was legendary among their friends and colleagues around the world and her gentleness extended to the myriad guests who came and went and even stayed for years. Punk would call to let her know—never to ask because he knew that would be superfluous—that he was bringing visitors home and she usually had everything ready upon their arrival. Park seemed to take his indispensable, commonsensical, and devout wife for granted. Her love and care allowed Park to achieve great personal and professional satisfaction. But he did not necessarily or truly understand this or, in the long run, even understand her.[46] His colleagues were not aware of this side of Park, and yet, it was very much in the substance of the man.

An Incisive, Outspoken, and Tenderly Warm Mentor

Park was an avid student of Howland's and like any good student, Park transcended his superb teacher. Park continued to rely on the nucleus of colleagues assembled by John Howland—Gamble, Blackfan, and Powers—and their professional intimacy was unconstrained by their departures to Boston and New Haven. Two others were Park's close confidantes, Barry Wood at Hopkins and Charles Janeway at Harvard.[47] And everyone, regardless of status, became extensions for Park's inquiry and his service.[48]

Service, education, and research, Park knew, are intimately related; each constantly influences and is dependent on the other. He also recognized that his domain was but a part of the whole and that it was subject to the needs and whims of an external environment that stretched around the world. He reached out constantly to that external environment, the world beyond academia, and, at times, did not hesitate to lecture it.

Edwards Park never tried to be Howland, who seemed to lack humility and the degree of respect for colleagues that were among Park's hallmarks.[49] Park felt constrained by Howland, an intimidating man and a "triple threat" with extraordinary competence and, Park said, "Most of the other doctors felt the same constraint."[50] People worked *for* Howland. Park preferred that people work *with* him. Indeed, Howland might be characterized as having a more "conservative" stance and Park, a more "liberal" one. Park acknowledged that he "… used to think that Howland's method of organization of the department was not the best for its fullest fruition. We underlings were never allowed experiences essential for the development of ideas and we had no opportunity to carry out the ideas we did have. With the exception of a clinic for the treatment of congenital syphilis, Howland would not allow any special clinics or the formation of any sub-departments, but the organization had great advantages, particularly for him. His policy kept the Department small and completely under his immediate control."[51]

Nevertheless, while reflecting on a scholarship established in his honor more than a decade after his retirement, Park acknowledged his debt to and respect for Howland. "I secretly wished the fund could have carried the name of my great predecessor, Dr. John Howland," Park wrote. "He instituted the first University Clinic in pediatrics in this country and started a new era in this continent in the study of disease in children." Then, in very plain language, he declared, "I, like others of his associates, was created by him. My debt to him is tremendous." But Park was worried. "His great influence in turning the direction of pediatrics into scientific channels is in danger of being forgotten.[52]

Park was imaginative and rigorous in his research. His probing questions, always at the heart of his teaching, provoked the same rigor in others. The inexact and the approximate were anathema to him.[53] Contemporaries, young faculty, residents, and students were all nourished by this perspective and by his abiding interest in them. He allowed them the opportunity for experiences essential to the development of ideas and the opportunity to carry out their ideas. Building on Howland's fundamentally biochemical and mechanistic approach, Park persuaded pediatricians to recognize the variables in life that convert disease (perhaps mechanistically measurable) into illness (requiring an understanding of possibilities and probabilities, and a mature comfort with the uncertainty implicit in variability's resistance to measurement).

Park was initially disturbed by what he considered Howland's "haphazard" approach to teaching, which considered only those problems affecting the patients at hand (with the exception of nutrition), thereby leaving lacunae in the full consideration of the range of pediatrics. Park recalled:

> If a certain disease was not represented, it was not taught. This...troubled me when I first joined Howland's staff. But I soon learned to appreciate that the important object to be attained by the teacher is not the transfer of facts but to show the students how to think. If he learns how to organize his mind so as to approach a medical problem effectively, the acquisition of the facts of a given disease is a simple matter. It should be

EDWARDS PARK POINTING TO BLACKBOARD. Park believed that the central mission of education was teaching medical students to think.

131

***

Larger than Life

remarked, however, that the cases in the Harriet Lane wards occupied a very wide range, so that the omissions were not great.[54]

Still today, there is a random quality in the experience of the individual student. It does depend in large part on the patients the student happens to see during any rotation. Nevertheless, the acquisition of information is a simple matter. Knowing how to think, to imagine, to formulate questions, to plan ways of finding answers, and to evaluate the meaning and the validity of information persist at the heart of the teaching/learning experience.

While Park may have resented Howland's constricting style, Park concluded that the potential for error in allowing a colleague freer reign in the pursuit of new knowledge was worth the gamble. He believed that the balance of risk and gain would be positive if that individual knew how to think.[55] Those Park mentored surely appreciated his urging them to exploit their own talents independently and his unreserved support.[56] They knew that he read people well and that his judgments were incisive, outspoken, and constructively critical but without malice. His honesty was consistently leavened by tender warmth.[57]

Daniel Darrow, who was an intern under Park at Yale, came to understand his chief's approach:

> He always wanted to know first what other students of disease had written on the subjects suggested by a patient. Second, he wanted to know how observation of the patient could advance the knowledge of disease. I felt that the minute observations were often futile and of necessity inadequate to acquire the necessary facts. However, nothing could be better in revealing inadequacies of our knowledge to students and house staff. The observations were within the grasp of the students and the difficulties of gathering information so apparent that the curious were driven to other means of study. I believe we all got the feeling that each patient presented an opportunity to learn from the literature and, if we were smart enough, from planned observations of the patients or in laboratory experiments."[58]

Park did not display his knowledge but preferred to coax others to answer. He asked questions of faculty, house staff, and students. This gave the impression at times that he did not know very much and visitors were sometimes distressed at the great man's seeming deficiencies. That amused but did not concern him because he believed that this kind of inquiry was the prelude to learning. His ego was untroubled.[59]

Park's need to know was consistently centered on his understanding of what was happening to the patient and was evident early in his career. When he was asked to work in the laboratory and to teach in the spring of 1919 after his World War I service in France, he was troubled because he believed that teaching without direct clinical responsibility created an impossible situation. The best care for the patient was his guiding light.[60] He stressed that "Hospitals should always seek to become teaching institutions as the surest insurance against obsolescence and decay. Teaching is the greatest single stimulus to good medical care."[61]

The desire to improve the lot of the patient drove the quiet insistence Park brought to effect changes that he thought necessary. Donald Proctor, then a young, resourceful otolaryngologist, recalled a time in the early 1940s when children who might be helped by bronchoscopy were not given the procedure at Harriet Lane because of a rule, instituted by a senior faculty member in the department of otolaryngology, that every child thought to need a bronchoscopy must first have a tracheotomy. Park agreed with many pediatricians that this was a far too invasive requirement that added significant risk to the procedure with little gain. As was his typical fashion, he moved slowly. First, he asked Proctor to give a Grand Rounds talk on the subject. Much was made in that discussion about the extensive, safe use of the procedure at the Children's Hospital of Philadelphia. At Park's urging Proctor went to Philadelphia to learn more.[62] But the barrier to change persisted. Samuel Crowe, the chief of the department of otolaryngology, would not suspend the requirement for tracheotomy. Park gently urged Proctor, then a part-time faculty member, to proceed but only at the nearby Church Home and Hospital and other venues in which he worked rather than at Harriet Lane. Park assured the somewhat tentative younger man that "Sam Crowe is a smart man who isn't afraid to admit he's wrong and who will change his mind when he sees that it's working." Crowe did, and Proctor went on to help numberless children of all ages with atelectasis, cystic fibrosis, foreign bodies, and more. He joined the full-time faculty, taught many others his skills, and worked intensively with Horace Hodes at Sydenham Hospital, Baltimore's infectious disease venue, and Janet Hardy in the premature nursery and the tuberculosis clinic at Harriet Lane. "We could really get out that thick, viscous stuff and make the children with cystic fibrosis feel a lot better, at least for a while. They learned fast not to be afraid and to welcome what it [bronchoscopy] did for them." Park had effected the change in his usual understated and patient way. Proctor remembered sixty years later that "Park had the talent of picking out who he wanted, giving them the responsibility, and then backing out of the picture, not wanting or taking credit."[63]

A Diverse Organism

Departments of pediatrics in the early twenty-first century are structured very much as Park ordained. He anticipated an enormous growth in specific knowledge. That prescience suggested the need for divisions in various specialty areas. His early effort in that direction was the most substantial in pediatrics, although the Children's Memorial Hospital in Chicago (then associated with the University of

Chicago) and the Children's Hospital in Boston had clinics devoted to syphilis, heart disease, allergy, nephritis, and tuberculosis, among others, in the mid-1920s, and there was before that a similar effort at Yale during Park's tenure there.[64] Actually, by the 1920s there was a snowballing tendency among Hopkins' full-time staff and even the part-time staff in medicine and surgery, to specialize. The younger faculty then began to apprentice themselves to the "specialists."[65] Howland, however, was resistant to specialization. He thought the dispensary a proper place for teaching students and residents and he was not much enamored of the idea of specialties or specialty clinics.

Park, in one of his several disagreements with Howland, thought that a general dispensary was too random, did not offer the best potential for good care for those with chronic disease, and did not encourage the development of new knowledge. Park did not share the concern of some of his faculty that a departmental organization that compartmentalized effort would weaken the dispensary. Instead, he was convinced that such an organization would free faculty, particularly the promising young members, to be themselves, to grow and develop as clinicians and investigators with far greater freedom to think and to innovate—but not without mentoring. The goal was to tap their promise and to provide settings in which there might be better continuous care for the chronically ill, improvements in care for poorly understood clinical problems, and increased sophistication in clinical investigation. The care of patients could not be static; it had to improve. Park felt that new knowledge derived in a systematic way in a clinical setting would be just as essential as the knowledge gained in the laboratory.[66]

Park sensed, too, that medical education and the continuing education of physicians was wanting.[67]

> I think the education of students in the medical schools and the self-education of physicians has been too much of the same order. We have schooled ourselves in the study of the heart and the lungs or to estimate the condition and functioning power of the liver or the stomach or of the peripheral nerves until we have come to think too much in terms of parts, losing sight of the animated whole. To borrow the language from one of Lasky's essays, we have been so bent on the "analytic comprehension of a special realm of facts that the power to see that realm in the perspective of totality has been lost."[68]

CROWDED WAITING ROOM. Edwards Park introduced the concept of specialty clinics, where doctors could concentrate on patients with particular conditions. At first there was concern that the character of the dispensary's work might change and its reputation might suffer. On the contrary, the numbers of patients continued to swell, as evidenced by this view of the dispensary waiting room, c. 1945.

Park discarded Howland's methods because he thought they were too authoritarian. "If ever there was a 'one man department' it was pediatrics under Howland at the Harriet Lane Home," Park remembered. John Howland "took sole care of the children on the wards. He also took charge personally of all the private patients. He used to do certainly two-thirds of the teaching and of course all of the administration."[69]

Park understood the interdependency of care and teaching and the various avenues to the development of new knowledge better than Howland. Park was disturbed by Howland's approach, which "kept the department small and completely under his immediate control. He was able to spend every afternoon in the laboratory."[70] Park would have none of that. He created specialty clinics, rudimentary at the start, and he anointed their directors as "specialists."[71] Rejecting Howland's sepa-

ration of the laboratory from the bedside, Park's goal was to bring together clinical and research efforts so that improvement in the care of
serious illness might be better achieved. He considered the laboratory
to include not only the wet bench but also the clinic and the bedside.
Park realized that specialty clinics might attract greater numbers of difficult problems but that the young investigator's skills might be better
honed in a clinic with interests that were not scattered. [72]

The blending of research with care went slowly until a critical mass
of patients and problems was achieved. The earliest clinics, started in
about 1927, were devoted to tuberculosis, psychiatry, epilepsy, and the
heart. At first, the clinics were not well received at Hopkins. Medical students enjoyed the dispensary and seemed to be learning a good
deal there. The fear was that the dispensary would lose patients and
teaching would suffer. Also, the concept seemed inconsistent with
Park's holistic views but the clinics were not rigidly bound and the
freedom and frequency of their interactions overcame the strictures
of specialization. Park made sure of that. He held fast and patient care
improved, teaching did not suffer, and patients continued to come to
Harriet Lane.[73]

Imminent Change

The gestalt of the Harriet Lane Home and of the Johns Hopkins
Hospital at the end of Park's tenure reflected their past. One had to
look hard to find glimmers of the future. This was particularly evident
in the hospital's doctors' dining room. An informal center for decision making at the medical institutions, the dining room was located
between the now long-gone Thayer wards and the still-used Marburg
Pavilion. (The present Park Building is on its approximate site.) The
room had many smaller, round tables at which lesser lights and house
officers ate. At the far end and to the left, there was a long rectangular
table, the province of those who had authority and prominence. One
did not sit at that table casually.[74] Park ate there but not every day. He
offered advice there, as elsewhere, only when it was sought. His advice
was thought integral by many and vital by some, in all areas of the hospital.[75] The past still prevailed in that setting, although unanticipated
changes in medicine and in the institution were imminent.

I started my residency on April 1, 1946, one in the last group to
be selected for training by Park. Francis Schwentker took over the
department of pediatrics on July 1 of that year. The house staff (sixteen

interns, five assistant residents, and the chief resident, mostly men but as always also a few women) included veterans of the recent war and youngsters like me, whose medical school experience had been limited to three calendar years. It was necessary for us to find mentors among the war veterans. Frank Kibbe, Barton Childs, and Jack Peck were splendid, gentle teachers who guided with a gentle hand.

Some others were not as helpful to those with less experience. Interns were expected to notify parents of the death of a child and to ask for an autopsy, although we had not been prepared for this delicate responsibility. In one instance, my plea for the help of an assistant resident brought the rejoinder, "She's your patient, Doctor," and the click of a telephone being hung up. That child's parents did not deserve the ensuing conversation. Medical education in those days did not dwell much on what were considered "soft" issues.

My young colleagues and I were, for the most part, happy and we wanted to learn. Our tendency was to think in concrete terms and to ask for specific direction in specific circumstances. Park would not allow us to be so circumscribed. He asked questions constantly, exploring proximate and ultimate causes for problems, and encouraging consideration of the context of the child's life and experience. "Medical Notes," a collection of short papers addressing situations relevant to the demands of a given moment, was the hallmark of Park's persistent inquiry. The notes included his memos of telephone conversations and letters to him from experts around the world. Faced with a problem, Park would call such a person immediately to ask questions and he would record what he discovered. He also asked many of us to write notes. Narrow approaches were not appropriate. We were expected to explore beyond the fringes of our knowledge. Those notes reflected the intellectual tone set for us in 1946.[76]

Park's impact on the house staff continued after his retirement; he did not abruptly change his old habits. For example, shortly after my chief residency (1952–53) began, I passed Park in the Harriet Lane corridor. He had retired several years before, but he still remembered my name, at least my last name. "Seidel, have you ever wondered what causes those 'growth lines' we see in the bones of young children?" he asked. I admitted that I had not. And I did not know that he had given the question considerable study. Still, he had asked me a question and I responded by going over each day's x-rays (easier to do then than now), relating what I saw to what I knew of the child, and keeping a notebook. It was almost a year before I saw Park next and, once again, it was in the corridor. "By the way, Seidel, did you ever learn anything about those growth lines?" he inquired. The notebook was in my pocket. Sadly, my observations did not add to our base of knowledge but he had once more taught me to wonder, to ask questions, and to seek answers.

Much later on I learned that Park knew a great deal about those lines, better described as "growth arrest lines." Normal bone formation proceeds vertically. Park demonstrated that disease and nutritional disturbance arrest the maturation of cartilage, causing it to grow horizontally so that a dense horizontal line of bone appears when growth is resumed. These lines tend to disappear by adult life. Dr. Park must have been seventy-four or seventy-five when he questioned me in the hall. He received the Goldberger Award in recognition of this work when he was eighty-five years old. His last paper, published in 1964, was a summary of what he had learned about bone growth. He considered those lines to be the "imprinting of nutritional disturbances on the growing bone."[77]

There was much good in medicine in the mid-1940s and much, too, that was wanting. My colleagues and I were quite self-absorbed—learning, trying to do well for the children, but making little effort to work for real improvement in patients' experiences. Park had integrated the wards in 1928, but water fountains and rest rooms were still labeled "colored" and "white." Visiting hours were limited to two one-hour periods a week, one on Sunday afternoon, the other on Wednesday evening. (We had the option to put a severely ill child on the "critical list" and thus allow unlimited visiting.) There is no evidence that house officers during those years sensed emotional issues or took an active part in addressing them. In 1943, however, when Helen Schnetzer, chief nurse in the Harriet Lane Home, began an effort (which evolved into the Child Life Program) to make the children's experiences in the hospital more tolerable, Park was supportive.

After his retirement, Park summarized his conviction that a pediatric clinic should be:

> …a place where sick children get the best medical care available anywhere and well children obtain the best guidance on how to remain well; where teaching is accepted as an integral part of the day's work; where thought keeps overflowing into new channels of curiosity and takes prac-

tical form in study and experimentation; where the spirit which prevails is one of intense burning zeal for the truth, which means constantly to seek to learn more and to do better things; where the human side of things is never lost sight of or made subordinate to the rest; where there is a broad social outlook and a consciousness of obligations to the community, not only to the individual members but to the community as a whole, so that the clinic is accepted by general consent as a great directing influence.[78]

This template was Park's constant guide; the potential for positive change was explicit.[79]

A Golden Rectangle

In 1946 the Harriet Lane Home was much like it was in 1912, a golden rectangle set on an east-west axis facing a park-like quadrangle. The Henry Phipps Psychiatric Clinic was to the east and the Wilmer Eye Institute and original nurses' home were to the west. The center door of the Harriet Lane opened on the quadrangle and several buildings opposite. Most often, the staff entered the Home from the west through the hallway that connected the HLH to Wilmer and the long U-shaped corridor that united all of the hospital.

The first floor of the Harriet Lane Home was busy. Those passing through from Wilmer and Phipps collided constantly with Harriet Laners and their patients. The director's office was immediately on the right as one entered the building and across the hall a mailroom frequently afforded a meeting point. Outpatient clinics were centered to the south. The corridor, flanked by the x-ray rooms, led to a large registration and waiting area, which was somewhat partitioned by social work and administrative cubicles, a small pharmacy, and a room that provided a bit of quiet when necessary in the midst of the usual chaos.

The areas devoted to care spun from there. One to the east was designated as isolation for acute-care cases in the belief that it was possible to limit contact with contagion. Three appendages at the rear of the building (observation rooms I, II, and III) were for scheduled care for both clinic and private patients. The cardiac clinic was attached to the rear of the observation rooms. There were bedrooms for house staff atop III and the child psychiatrist's office was upstairs in I.

The architecture of the central stairway was striking. The steps went halfway to the second floor before dividing so that the climber might go to right or left—and so on to the top or down to the basement. The middle level on the way to the basement provided access to the amphitheatre from the east or west and also to the fluoroscopy room under the eastern bank of amphitheatre seats (and one wonders at the amount of radiation delivered to the many occupants of those seats.) A short stairway from the waiting room with a step elevator (coaxed by Helen Taussig from the Women's Board of the hospital) also led there. The director had a private entrance from his office.

The amphitheatre, styled after classic Greek design, was at the heart of Harriet Lane. Arranged in a semicircle of concrete tiers looking down on the "pit" where the action took place, it brought Harriet Laners and many others together five days a week. The comfort of the "audience" was barely improved by the hard, wood shell-like seats that were intended to protect them from the concrete. Park usually entered from the left and sat in the first tier on the right, and patients were brought in from the right. Acoustics were never a problem. Park's provocative and thoughtful questions assured good discussion.[80]

The Harriet Lane elevator was just to the east of the central door. Eva—inappropriately, we never learned her last name—ran the elevator in the daytime and anyone needing it ran it at night. There weren't buttons to push but, rather, a lever that controlled its start and stop. If the elevator happened to be on the first floor and it was needed elsewhere, the steps were used to find it. On occasion, it had a mind of its own and would ever so gradually sink to the basement.

The second floor contained rooms for private patients generally under the care of Harriet Guild or surgeons, principally otolaryngologists who, in those days, were relatively unconstrained in electing to do tonsillectomies. At some point in the 1940s, a premature nursery directed by Janet Hardy was added to the south end of the second floor.

It was on the third and fourth floors where the house staff quite literally reigned. The wards were large rooms to the east and west: Infants up to two years were treated on 4 and children aged two to fourteen were on 3. On both floors, the nurses' station and a counter for the house officers were in the center, framed by glass, with an unobstructed line of sight to the beds on the open floor, to glassed-in, so-called isolation cubicles, and a utility cubicle straight ahead. The central hallways opened on isolation units, small kitchens and, originally on the fourth floor, rooms for the wet nurses. House officers would invade the kitchen on the fourth floor at night to make hors d'oeuvres using canned baby meats—liver was the favorite—and crackers. The

NURSING STUDENTS FEEDING CHILDREN. Students at the Johns Hopkins Hospital School of Nursing often made up the majority of the workforce of the Harriet Lane Home. Nursing students assisted during medical procedures, accompanied doctors on rounds, and cared for the young patients on night shifts as well as during the day. Fondly remembering the training they received there, many young nurses vied for openings on the Harriet Lane staff when they graduated. Photograph by the Blakeslee Group and reproduced here with permission.

chief resident's office on the 4 East hallway opened to an outside deck with the Baltimore harbor visible in the distance.

These were the floors on which the chief resident made daily morning rounds (at eight o'clock on HLH 4 and at nine o'clock on HLH 3), dragging a chart rack from bed to bed, accompanied by nurses, interns, and residents. This was a caring, decision-making group with the senior faculty at hand if consultation was necessary. Each month there was an attending physician who made teaching rounds three days a week at eleven o'clock, with the agenda set by the house staff. The house staff ran the wards in the fashion established by Howland and continued by Park. Accountability was addressed in the Friday conferences at which each patient's problems and care were presented and also on occasion at the clinical pathological conferences run by Arnold Rich, chief of the department of pathology.

RESIDENTS AND A NURSE WITH PATIENTS ON A WARD. The breadth of experiences offered in the wards of the Harriet Lane Home was extraordinary. Interns and residents treated many diseases and conditions firsthand that doctors in other hospitals knew about only from textbooks. Interacting with patients was merely part of the challenge for residents. Here, resident Dick Dormont gave instructions to a visiting parent holding her child while his colleague and a nurse cared for other toddlers.

Very early on the morning of April 1, 1946, a freshly scrubbed, brand-new intern, dressed in the then mandatory white suit and wearing saddle shoes, approached the nurses' station on HLH 3 East rather tentatively, ready to begin his career. The nurse stood immediately, almost coming to military attention. I was taken aback and quite uncomfortable but soon I became familiar with the hierarchical structure that predominated in the hospital. Six years later, then the chief resident, I learned of the powerful substructure of the hierarchy. Each morning, very early and well before rounds, I went to Head Nurse Frances Abernathy's office, sat silent in a corner, and listened to the overnight change of shift report and to "Miss Abby's" insightful comments that consistently found their expression in the everyday effort of the Harriet Lane. It was inevitably the patients' gain when her wisdom was later quoted at rounds.

Those open wards, with the ability to see everything from the nurses' station, were very helpful one night in the late 1940s when I was still an intern. A baby had just died. I stood on one side of the bed and the distraught father on the other side. The father, crying and angry, pulled a small handgun. I froze but Neil Lysaught, the assistant resident, saw it all from the station and, in a moment, was all over the father, disarming him. There were no recriminations. We sat together, talked it through, and cried together.

Tuberculosis, meningitis, and cyanotic heart disease were frequently among the problems affecting the infants. During one terrible night in the era before intensive care units, five babies died between eleven o'clock and five the next morning. The parents of one of the babies had been phoned to alert them to their child's discharge the next morning. That baby's death, the last of the five, left us spent. Lysaught and I retreated to an empty side room where Lysaught offered me a cigarette. It was my first, and it tasted good. A few puffs brought a bit of ease and a return to the demands of the ward. (My wife saw to it that the habit did not last long.)

The fifth floor was the laboratory floor. Lawson Wilkins and other investigators shared space there with the chemistry laboratory. The tiny offices were rudimentary by present standards but we didn't know that then. Similarly, there was no grumbling about the history room in the basement run by Mrs. Zimmerman and her staff. We were able to go there freely and hunt through the stuffed shelves for a chart, particularly at night. The library, with its limited collection, was near the history room and contained Park's "Medical Notes." A large, oval table suitable for long-running poker games and two or three comfortable chairs for reading or napping filled the room.

This basement library was also the birthplace of Harrison Spencer's idea, which eventually resulted in *The Harriet Lane Handbook*. Spencer, who was chief resident in 1950–51, counted on his successors to implement the concept when he left for private practice in Virginia. Will Waring (1951–52) and Henry Seidel (1952–53) completed the task, devising a small, pocket-sized, three-ring notebook. The assistant residents, however, did the real work, writing at the oval table. The *Handbook* became an unimagined success when Robert Cooke had it published. The library and the oval table are gone but Hopkins' senior residents in pediatrics still revise the *Handbook* and the chief residents still edit it, allowing for new editions to be published every three years.

The quadrangle that lay outside the front door served as the front yard of the Harriet Lane Home. Bounded on three sides by hospital buildings and on the fourth by an iron fence with a gate that looked across Wolfe Street to the School of Hygiene and Public Health, it was a splendid little park with tennis courts, benches, crisscrossing pathways, and grass. House officers would often take a few moments of respite there. The wives and children of residents could tarry and play, joined sometimes by husbands and fathers. Dating couples found it a good place for a rendezvous, and the tennis courts served, of course, for frequent matches but also as the "racetrack" for the turtle derby run annually by the house officers. The derby was an event where turtles were raced for a monetary prize and skits that lampooned the hospital administration and the senior faculty were performed. The rest of Baltimore seemed far away.

The Social Aspects of Medicine

Park considered Howland to have been an inward-looking man and was critical of him as one who "had little interest and paid little attention to the child welfare movements in pediatrics." Howland considered those pediatricians who embraced child welfare as inferior."[81]

As Howland's successor, Park approached things differently. He understood and welcomed the compelling need for new knowledge and the particular abilities of the "full time man" in the diagnosis and care of the unusual. But he noted that the academic pediatrician had the full panoply of the various resources in the hospital supporting him. The man who "live[s] by practice" Park felt, had

> …an immense experience with illness of minor severity and a multitude of little things of immense importance to know and understand. He sees disease at its beginning—one might say almost before its beginning— meaning before it has declared itself in recognizable form. Moreover, he has constant contact and great experience with the problems of childcare arising in the home, involving the comfort and happiness of the child, the management of the parents, and adjustment of the environment. He is an adept in the psychology of pediatrics, in holding the confidence of

the family when the situation seems dangerous and is confused, and he learns how to say just enough and no more. He has no one to fall back on but himself. He does not have the impregnable walls of a hospital behind him to take the impact of responsibility and of failure. He is required constantly to act on insufficient evidence. Finally, the practicing pediatrician has a unique experience in preventive medicine and long range prognosis which is denied the full time pediatrician working in a hospital.[82]

Park wrote this about six years after he retired. He recognized the complementarity of the full-time academic pediatrician and the practitioner and he realized the necessity for and the valuable contributions of both. Despite his efforts, an attitude of inferiority (sometimes implied and sometimes explicit) toward the non-academic practitioner persisted. There was still derision among the house staff for the LMD (local medical doctor), a demeaning implication that was not vigorously disputed by their elders.[83] This persisted in spite of a group of splendid practicing pediatricians who were encouraged by Park, to the extent possible, to participate in the activities of the department— without remuneration, of course.

Park tried, however. His approach was obvious during his time at Yale. Grover Powers, Park's successor in New Haven, confirmed that "The highlight of Dr. Park's service to pediatrics at Yale lay in the fine quality not only of the scientific study of disease but in the emphasis on the broad implications, social relationships, and public health correlations of child care.... [Ward rounds] constituted the forum in which ideas were brought forward and concepts and principles crystallized."[84]

In 1945 Park persuaded the American Academy of Pediatrics to let him write a column to be published periodically in the *Journal of Pediatrics* (and later in *Pediatrics*). The column became known as "The Pediatrician and the Public." His writings covered the gamut of social issues affecting children and included the subjects of race and religion in medicine. The organization of medical care was centermost. The broader issues he brought to the fore were given lip service in some quarters but the reality was still far off his desired mark.[85]

In his very first column, titled "The Social Aspects of Medicine," Park wrote that pediatricians had "an advanced point of view which should enable them to face the future in a particularly liberal frame of mind." He made it clear that "from inheritance and from the requirements of their daily professional lives," he believed that "they are the ones who should be leaders in the social reorganization of medicine which is bound to come." Park predicted the increasing role of government in medical research, education, and patient care. "No one can foresee just what the changes in medical care will be, but it is safe to say that, whether we like it or not, they will be considerable and they will be initiated and dictated largely by the lay public, that the preventive aspects of medicine will have a much more important place than at the present time, and that medical care will be extensively reorganized and increasingly regulated and controlled by centralized authority."[86]

Events in the United States, Park noted, were similar to earlier changes in England and Europe. For example, the Wagner-Murray-Dingle Bill before Congress in 1945 (and later defeated) suggested possibilities for federally supported health insurance and the distribution of resources—including doctors, hospitals, and academic centers—guided by community need instead of, as Park put it, "the location of money."[87] He cautioned that the American Medical Association's losing efforts to forestall the development of the Group Health Association in Washington, D.C. and the Kaiser program in the West foretold the future loss of the autonomy of physicians in the medical decision-making process. Obviously, scientific inquiry was much more sophisticated than the social mechanisms that served the people. The new knowledge gained by the academic community was not made available to all who needed it because of the economic barriers that prevented access to care for far too many people.

Physicians had the power to "guide the forces of change" but, in Park's opinion, "very little power to stop them."[88] If they were to provide appropriate guidance then they needed to be well informed, keep an open mind, and make selfless choices—a tall order because of the fear of change. Park wanted his readers to avoid prejudice against new ideas just because they were new and strange. Intense discussion and disagreement did not dismay him. Ultimately, his determined exploration of medical care systems around the world and of the changes incipient in the United States did not achieve the freedom from bias that he sought. Nor did he forestall the prejudice against new ideas that he wanted so much to allay.

Park wrote a column in 1947 entitled "Changing Medical Care in our Changing National Life," in which he noted that

A few weeks ago President Truman requested the Federal Bureau of Investigation to investigate all government employees in order to discover and eliminate Communists. I sometimes think that governments are more in need of psychiatrists than individuals. The way to free this country from Communism is not by Gestapo espionage and persecution, methods which history has shown over and over and over again merely drive ideologies underground and give them increased impetus by repression and dispersion, but to make our own people so much better fed, housed, clothed and educated and happier and freer than others, that Communism will wither and die for lack of soil of misery and discontent to grow on. I can think of no better beginning than with the least possible delay to reorganize medical care so that in full measure and in most modern kind it would be available to each citizen with all its benefits."[89]

In 1949, when Park stopped writing "The Pediatrician and the Public" column in *Pediatrics*, it was quite clear that he had irritated the pediatric public. He was, however, unrepentant: "I am aware that the column has been under criticism in Academy circles even in high places, but I am aware that if it had not awakened feeling it would not have accomplished its purpose. Its failure to receive a completely sympathetic hearing from all members of the Academy was inevitable since the field of discussion is one in which there is such wide disagreement and which is so mined with emotion."[90] Park's goal was to provide facts "as a basis for intelligent judgment and action" and he discussed efforts at improving access to medical care in countries around the world.[91] His audience was not enchanted. The concern with the other—other peoples, other political systems, other medical approaches—overwhelmed a dispassionate approach to understanding and descended into a deeply felt bitterness. The pediatric community at that time despised the idea of "socialized medicine." Park stood firm, however, and denied conscious bias in his writings. His idealism did not degenerate into ideology.[92] But he spoke too soon and the majority of the pediatric community would have none of it.

Park's colleague, Dr. Paul A. Harper of Johns Hopkins' School of Hygiene and Public Health, took over the column. Park, however, never let go of his firm conviction that those who work in a children's clinic must have a "broad social outlook and consciousness of obligations to the community, not only to its individual members but also to the community as a whole so that the clinic is accepted by general consent as a great directing influence."[93] This was certainly at variance with Howland, who seemed to Park to have been "aristocratic and autocratic, brilliant and strong-willed, stimulating and demanding, and aloof."[94] Howland was chief when medicine's preoccupation with the morbid anatomy of disease was giving way to biochemical analysis. He initiated much change and Park was at first seen as a transitional figure with the mission to sustain Howland's effort. He did that but he also initiated change as the preoccupation with biochemical analysis grudgingly began to give way to a responsibility that went beyond the understanding of morbidity, the skill of diagnosis, and the quest for cure.[95] Park reached beyond the contained world of an academic department and achieved much that has lasted—but his accomplishments were short of his own goals. He was not resentful, however, and he appeared comfortable with the price he had paid. He understood that agents of change must expect resistance and deferred—and sometimes unrealized—gratification.

Ninety-six Summers

In 1945 Park indicated his intention to retire a year hence. He was sixty-eight years old. Not ready to fade away, he avoided being an encumbrance to his successor, Francis F. Schwentker. Schwentker had asked him to teach but Park refused, "I just can't do it. I'm really a biologist now. If I were to take clinical responsibilities, I would have to keep abreast of the current pediatric literature and just don't have the time. It wouldn't be fair to the resident staff."[96] The solution was a workspace in the department of pathology, still in the hospital but as far away from Harriet Lane as possible. There, he continued the study of bone pathology, rickets and scurvy, and the attempt to achieve more equitable universal health care. Indeed, his determined pursuit of truth as he defined it never wavered, be it in the laboratory, at the bedside, or in the world about him.

During his retirement, Park took on an altogether new task. His conviction that the establishment of the Harriet Lane Home represented the watershed of American academic pediatrics motivated him to assume the mantle of department historian. (Perhaps he felt the same pull toward history that had captured his father's imagination a generation before.) Blending his own sentimental reminiscences with a careful examination of primary and secondary sources, Park made a solid start at capturing the accomplishments of his predecessors and colleagues, as well as the philanthropists who made the Harriet Lane Home possible. Although he did not complete his task, he convinced Taussig to join the effort, and he inspired others to continue the work to its completion.

At that time it was not the university's habit to assure financial ease during retirement, even for its stars. There was worry about it, however, and a suggestion of the problem in a letter Park wrote to Johns Hopkins University president Isaiah Bowman in 1948, in response to the receipt of a check for fifteen hundred dollars from an unknown donor:

> Although I am so thoroughly appreciative of what my friend or friends have done, I feel that I cannot go on accepting aid.... Although all which devoted thoughtfulness could devise has been done to prevent embarrassment, I am embarrassed ... the self consciousness of which I spoke—to receive even from the kindest friend and I can get along on the income I have, if some burden like Mrs. Park's illness is not added to the usual ones. So please tell these splendid friends of mine that, with all the appreciation which one would feel to another, next year I must fight my own fight.[97]

We do not know how often such gifts arrived but the letter suggests that they were not uncommon. We know that Park was never impelled by money and that he was little more successful in raising support for the Harriet Lane Home (as Schwentker was to discover) than he was for himself.

In any event, Park, by his own design, was no longer a substantial presence in the Harriet Lane Home. It was not where he wanted to be. That was in Nova Scotia on the Margaree River, which flowed in a peaceful valley dotted with sheep and wildflowers and berries. He studied the Margaree during most of the ninety-six summers of his life in the same way he studied a research problem and the needs of children: thoroughly and perceptively. There was a sense that he approached fishing in the way that he approached the care and feeding of students, staff, and faculty. The flies he made by hand and his mastery of fly-casting put him on an almost equal basis with the salmon and trout. The fishing people of the Margaree Valley knew that his casting was the work of an artist. His daughter recalled,

> His line would fly back from the bent rod, describing a figure eight at the
> exact level of his shoulders; then it would unwind slowly, sailing forward

over the water until the fly dropped lightly, delicately over some spot where his keen eye had detected the shadow of a salmon lying in the deeps, with undulating fins, its head pointing upstream into the currents.

When he wasn't wading in it, or walking along the banks of the river, on summer days he would mostly sit in the cabin at a crude table on which were all manner of fish hooks, spools of thread, assorted clamps, tweezers, glue, tropical feathers, furs, monkey tails spread out under a strong light. With these ingredients he fashioned dainty trout and salmon flies. To make the insect's body, he would painstakingly wind silk thread around hooks thin as pins. He wound so carefully that no strand crossed another. Small feathers and individual hairs were laid on this foundation, and bound in tiny knots. Finally, the whole thing was cemented by a brushing with shellac. Each little insect lure was of an exquisite perfection. These flies represented hours of intense and patient concentration, and were so fine that it seemed hardly possible his clumsy-looking, huge hands could have created them.[98]

Those huge hands linger in my memory. I saw, at rounds, how gently they held each baby. This man as much as any shaped the future of pediatrics. And this man, when his pacemaker was wearing out and needing new batteries in 1969, determined that he would die in the Margaree Valley. He did, and his death was so painful that his son and daughter agreed that the shot of morphine he begged for should take away consciousness for good. "After that 'compassionate blow,' my father left this world without pain, in peaceful quietude," his daughter remembered.[99] Typically, Park died leaving a question about the "rightness" of mercy medication, and, typically, the answer is not an absolute: "I can tell you that it was very difficult and has remained that way all my life," his son, Rollo, admitted.[100]

Having a Wonderful Time

Park's influence on those whose lives he touched was thought by them to be his greatest gift. Taussig, preparing her address on the receipt of the Howland Medal in 1971, wrote to A. Gorman Hills, a friend of Rollo Park's and of the Park family (who, at the time, worked in the Electrolyte Research Laboratory at the University of Miami) and asked Hills to share his recollections of Park. Hills began by saying, "His influence on me was, needless to say, profound, and it was not narrowly scientific or professional."[101]

The Chesney Medical Archives at Johns Hopkins are replete with similar testimony. Antonio Waring, chief resident in the early 1940s, recalled that a particular child had upset him thoroughly. "Dr. Park remonstrated in his usual, accurately gentle manner, 'If you ever find yourself in conflict with a child, you've lost.' This thought has kept me on base many times, and I pass it on as a tried and useful concept."[102] John Birmingham, another of Park's residents, wrote of a visiting mother who complained vigorously to the chief about the condition of the wards. "You know what a shambles HLH 3 becomes during a mid-morning play period—paper scattered about, kids smeared with finger-paint, a scratched record on an old Victrola making the noise more confusing; add to this, Easter just past and three baby chicks running about." After he heard the mother out, Park went to see for himself and reported back. "You are right," he agreed. "There is paper on the floor; some of the children are covered with finger-paint, and the toys haven't been picked up—but isn't everyone having a wonderful time?"[103]

No part of the human experience was isolated from another in Park's mind. Helen Hewitt Arthur recalled an afternoon in the dispensary when she had been an intern for barely a week: "The place was, as usual, filled to overflowing with patients and mothers. I was (also as usual in those first few weeks) in a complete daze." Park, standing at the entrance to a cubicle in Observation I, to her "horror" beckoned to her. She went to him fearing "whatever thunderbolt was in store." He leaned toward her and, pointing to "a fat, resolute-looking colored woman standing with folded arms and outfitted in a rakish hat and flowing dress," whispered, "Who does she remind you of?" Arthur was too astonished to answer even if she guessed his thinking but Park went on, "She looks exactly like the Duchess in *Alice in Wonderland*, don't you think?"[104]

Park had early on rejected Christian orthodoxy but "he never succeeded in exorcising from some corner of his consciousness the appalling possibility that an angry god would after all arrange for a reckoning after this life."[105] Perhaps to appease that possible anger, he rejected immodesty and remained humble. Julian Price, a Harriet Laner in 1927, remembered an incident in South Carolina. "We went on a hunting trip as the guest of a farmer friend of mine. The farmer had a little girl who was a spastic and he was very anxious for the 'great doctor from Hopkins' to see her. Realizing that Dr. Park was on a bit of a vacation, the farmer was somewhat timid about making his request but he did. As though a great privilege had been bestowed upon him, Dr. Park picked up the child and held her on his knee. With that courtesy and gentleness for which he is famous, the pediatrician examined the little girl. Then he turned to the parents and talked to them in simple and comforting words. It was a scene which I will never forget; the great man was at his best in the home of a simple farmer. What to others might have been a bothersome chore was to him an opportunity for service."[106]

John Washington, a house officer from 1931 to 1937, remarked on the visit of a distinguished refugee physician. Park was guiding the visitor around Harriet Lane when they arrived at the door leading into the dispensary. "Both halted. Dr. Park motioned the visitor to go ahead. The visitor clicked his heels and said, 'No, you are the professor.' Dr. Park said, 'Oh no, you are my guest; you go first.' More 'oh no's' and 'oh yeses' followed. Finally, the professor seized his guest by the shoulders and lifted him ahead of himself through the door and the tour continued."[107]

Certainly, Park would reject for himself an image of secular sainthood. "He was one of the world's great backsliders," Gorman Hills reminded Taussig. "I recall, from the time I was privileged to live in his house, how often he would fail to do the work in the evening he had planned to do, or would show impatience or insufficient courtesy, at least in his own eyes, or else just plain flee from some person or duty." Still, there was a Calvinistic "remorse and depression which these backslidings invariably evoked; I am sure that each one of them helped in its humble way to keep alive the grim old specter of damnation which these backslidings invariably evoked."[108]

Park's wife, Agnes (Moo), often rescued her backsliding husband. She was his willing caterer, forgiving for the most part his absent-mindedness and frequent lack of thought about her needs—but only to a point, and she exercised a firm hand when it was necessary. Moo's death deprived Park of cosseting and left him somewhat at sea. There are intimations of this in his 1965 Christmas letter to Robert Mason, the Parks' internist. Moo was ill and he lamented the need to disturb Mason about problems for which there seemed to be no real help. "At this pre-Xmas moment, I express my heartfelt gratitude to you for your devoted care of Moo. If you had several home patients for whom you would like to do much and so little can be done, you would be a wreck. I find myself without the power to respond beyond attempts at comfort which become worn out."[109] It was about a year after her death when he said, "You know, without Agnes I really have no more business here."[110]

Park's dependency on Moo and others was not often revealed. Yet years before Moo's death Park indicated his powerless regret at onrushing old age. He wrote Mason in 1959, "I was terribly saddened by the death of my great friend, Jim Gamble. He was my closest and dearest friend and I quite worshipped him. Life will not seem the same without him. It is terrible to have reached a time in life when one great friend after another topples and goes. There are very few of my contemporaries to whom I am devoted who are left. I can understand how old people suffer from loneliness."[111] Park was then eighty-two.

On the other hand, Park could be uncharitable at times in his view of others. On reviewing his correspondence with a journal editor, he said of the man, "I should get the impression that he was self-centered, limited, and rigid, not a gentleman, and not competent as an editor of a journal representing a society of fine people."[112] This immoderation was usually kept under control and, recognizing the imperfect humanity that underlies science, he negotiated the academic arena with remarkable aplomb. He sacrificed a good deal of his own research opportunity but he nourished the careers of others, often advocating their appointment to prestigious positions. He found it difficult, however, to steer those with less promise to more productive paths. Robert Collis wrote that "some people said that Park's only real weakness was a failure to dispose of failures in his department, that he helped his good assistants to get better jobs elsewhere and was always left with the second rate."[113]

Reality suggests otherwise. The department Park built was distinguished by its people and, in a very real sense, they sat at his feet. He was an intellectual prod, not an abstract theorist. A constantly curious pragmatist, he had a genuine feel for the essence of a question. The obvious and the esoteric, seldom noted by others, urged him to think and to ask questions that moved others to action. No one escaped his queries, students or senior staff. What he noted and questioned concerned far more than the immediacy of Harriet Lane. Howland had initiated the first full-time system in academic pediatrics in this country with its emphasis on the pathogenesis of disease expressed in biochemical terms and the sense that the development of new knowledge would

153

Larger than Life

require an intense commitment to a specialized area. Park did nothing to dispel these notions. He continued that philosophy when he began to anoint individuals as specialists, and he thought "outside the box" in a way that Howland did not, inviting social workers into Harriet Lane and giving them a secure footing there, looking out from the hospital to the community, espousing child welfare, preventive medicine, and a form of national health insurance. He assured that Harriet Lane would be desegregated and, unlike many in his time, welcomed women, physicians trained abroad,[114] and Jews (but not yet blacks) into the professional fold.

In sum, Park built on Howland's fundamentally mechanistic approach by leading pediatrics into the arena of the social and economic context of medicine. Park recognized the diversity in life that converts disease, perhaps measurable, into illness with all of its variability. Park was well ahead of his time in much of this and, too, in his advocacy of "socialized medicine." Living long, he met rebuffs and lost a degree of favor that Howland possibly had avoided by dying young. Unhappily, the environment of Johns Hopkins did not always foster "Parkism" in the time of Francis Schwentker.

In the end, it may be Park's love of nature that defined him best. Much has been made of his close observation of practically everything, and this was certainly evident in his love of the woods and fields and streams, the plants and animals, and, of course, the fish—particularly the salmon. He knew and understood the salmon. The fisherman is occupied in a way that does not allow time to rush.[115] His is a quiet calling that permits close observation and the opportunity to ask questions and to wonder, why? It gives, too, the chance to experiment—to discover the perfect lure for the salmon—and to teach others who want to know. Edwards Park could do all of that. It was appropriate that, as his life ebbed, he was close to his streams.

Notes

1. Robert Collis, "The Chief," *Journal of Pediatrics* 41 (1952): 664–68. Miss Richards was Park's secretary at the time but left by the time I arrived in the mid-1940s.

2. Barton Childs, "Edwards A. Park," *Journal of Pediatrics* 125 (1994): 1009–13.

3. Marion E. Park, "Childhood Days," comments made at the presentation of the Kober Medal to Edwards A. Park, *Journal of Pediatrics* 41 (1952): 660.

4. Marion E. Park, 662.

5. Marion E. Park, 661. The "'ralgia" Park mispronounced was presumably neuralgia.

6. Marion E. Park, 662.

7. Helen Taussig, "Pediatric Profiles: Edwards A. Park 1878–1969," *Journal of Pediatrics* 77 (1970): 722.

8. Edwards A. Park to Harold Harrison, January 20, 1956.

9. Helen B. Taussig, "Dr. Edwards A. Park, Physician, Teacher, Investigator, Friend," comments made at the dedication of the Edwards A. Park Building at the Johns Hopkins Hospital, February 23, 1973, *Johns Hopkins Medical Journal* 132 (1973): 370. Helen Taussig was a graduate of the Johns Hopkins School of Medicine who entered her residency in the department of pediatrics after being turned down by the department of medicine at Hopkins. She achieved worldwide fame as a pediatric cardiologist.

10. Charles Coffin never accepted repayment. Edwards A. Park to Barry Wood, January 21, 1958, "History of the Home, transcribed tapes of Dr. Park," box 12, folder with manuscript draft entitled "Dr. Park, March 5, 1969," HLH-AMC. Columbia then, unlike now, was not particularly noted for excellence in teaching. It became necessary for Park, like John Howland before him, to supplement Columbia's teaching with Dr. Ellsworth Eliot's two-hundred-dollars-a-year quiz courses. Park noted that all he learned in medical school came out of the four years of Eliot's courses. Helen B. Taussig, "Dr. Edwards A. Park, Physician, Teacher, Investigator, Friend," 371.

11. Edwards A. Park curriculum vita, biographical file, "Edwards Park," Alan Mason Chesney Medical Archives, The Johns Hopkins Medical Institutions, Baltimore, MD, hereafter referred to as the AMC.

12. James L. Gamble, "Presentation of the Kober Medal to Edwards A. Park," *Journal of Pediatrics* 41 (1952): 641–42. Gamble had a distinguished career at the Harriet Lane Home and Boston Children's Hospital. He was particularly noted for work with electrolyte balance and his diagrams, known affectionately as "Gamblegrams," explaining that balance.

13. Ibid., 641. Examples of the work Park did with Theodore Janeway are evident in: Edwards A. Park, "Observations with Regard to the Actions of Epinephrine on the Coronary Artery," *Journal of Experimental Medicine* 16 (1912): 532; Theodore C. Janeway and Edwards A. Park, "The Question of Epinephrine in the Circulation and Its Relation to Blood Pressure," *Journal of Experimental Medicine* 16 (1912): 541.

14. James L. Gamble, "Presentation of the Kober Medal to Edwards A. Park," 641.

15. Edwards A. Park curriculum vita.

16. Sara Scattergood (Edwards Park's daughter) to author, December 18, 2003.

17. Helen B. Taussig, "Dr. Edwards A. Park, Physician, Teacher, Investigator, Friend," 372.

18. Edwards A. Park curriculum vita.

19. *Archives de Medecin des Enfants* 22 (1919): 393.

20. Barton Childs, "Edwards A. Park," 1011.

21. Helen B. Taussig, "Dr. Edwards A. Park, Physician, Teacher, Investigator, Friend," 374.

*Larger
than Life*

22. A. McGehee Harvey, "The First Full-Time Academic Department of Pediatrics: The Story of The Harriet Lane Home," *Johns Hopkins Medical Journal* 137 (1975): 41.

23. Barton Childs, "Edwards A. Park," 1011.

24. Grover F. Powers, introduction to "Edwards A. Park: John Howland Award Address," *Pediatrics* 10 (1952): 83.

25. Elmer V. McCollum, "An Adventure in Nutrition Investigation," in *Essays on History of Nutrition and Diet* (Chicago: American Dietetic Association, 1967), 37–39; T. E. Cone Jr., "Unraveling the Pathogenesis of Experimental Rickets at the Johns Hopkins Hospital, 1918–22," *Pediatrics* 57 (1976): 186.

26. Edwards A. Park, "The Etiology of Rickets," *Physiological Review* 3 (1923): 106–63; Edwards A. Park, "The Influence of Severe Illness on Rickets," *Archives of Diseases of Children* 29 (1954): 369–80.

27. Barton Childs, "Edwards A. Park," 1010.

28. Grover F. Powers, "Edwards A. Park, Yale Professor 1921–1927," comments made at the presentation of the Kober Medal to Edwards A. Park, *Journal of Pediatrics* 41 (1952): 651.

29. Ibid., 652.

30. Ibid., 653.

31. Author's conversation with Sara Scattergood, March 5, 2002.

32. Davison later became the first director of the department of pediatrics at Duke University.

33. Thomas B. Turner, *Heritage of Excellence: The Johns Hopkins Medical Institutions, 1914–1947* (Baltimore: The Johns Hopkins University Press, 1974), 124.

34. Barton Childs to Joseph M. Garfunkel, August 9, 1993, and August 21, 1993.

35. "Self Help in Hard Times," in *A People's History of the United States, 1492–Present,* ed. H. Zinn (New York: Harper Perennial, 1995), 368–97.

36. Barton Childs, "Edwards A. Park," 1009.

37. James L. Gamble, "Presentation of the Kober Medal to Edwards A. Park," 644.

38. Sara "Sally" Scattergood, "My Father: An Unpublished Memoir," 6.

39. Lawrence Wissow and John Littlefield conversation with Rollo Park, Edwards Park's eldest child, July 5, 1999. In an interview on March 23, 2004, Barton Childs told me that Park often said that a good reason "not to blow your own horn" was that "it is better to be discovered than found out."

40. Ibid.

41. Sara "Sally" Scattergood, "My Father: An Unpublished Memoir," 1.

42. Ibid., 15.

43. Conversation with Rollo Park.

44. Sara "Sally" Scattergood, "My Father: An Unpublished Memoir," 4–5.

45. Ibid., 7–8.

46. Ibid., 21.

47. W. Barry Wood joined the Hopkins faculty after graduation in 1936 with a residency in internal medicine. It is likely that his relationship with Park began at that point and that it continued unabated during his service as

chief of the department of medicine at Washington University from 1942 to 1955. He returned then to Baltimore and assumed major roles in the hospital and School of Medicine. Charles Janeway was the son of Theodore Janeway, Park's mentor during his early years in New York. Charles, younger than Park, became a lifelong friend.

48. Barton Childs, "Edwards A. Park," 1010.

49. Helen Taussig, "Pediatric Profiles: Edwards A. Park 1878–1969," 725.

50. Ibid.

51. Edwards A. Park, "John Howland Award Address," *Pediatrics* 10 (1952): 92. There was a bit of a petulant note in this address delivered in homage of Howland, as if Park was telling the assemblage that he had decided long ago to do it differently from Howland if ever he had the chance.

52. Edwards A. Park to Barry Wood, January 21, 1958.

53. H. E. Harrison, "Edwards A. Park, an Appreciation of the Man," comments made at the dedication of the Edwards A. Park Building at the Johns Hopkins Hospital, February 23, 1973. *Johns Hopkins Medical Journal* 132 (1973): 365.

54. Edwards A. Park, "John Howland Award Address," 94–95.

55. Ibid., 100.

56. Barton Childs, "Edwards A. Park," 1011.

57. H. E. Harrison, "Edwards A. Park, an Appreciation of the Man," 364.

58. Grover F. Powers, "Edwards A. Park, Yale Professor 1921–1927," 653.

59. Barton Childs, "Edwards A. Park," 1012.

60. Ibid., 725.

61. Edwards A. Park, "The Preservation of the Ideal in a University Children's Clinic" *Canadian Medical Association Journal* 66 (1952): 483.

62. Donald Proctor, conversation with author, August 5, 2002.

63. Ibid.

64. Grover F. Powers, "Edwards A. Park, Yale Professor 1921–1927," 654. S. A. Halpern *American Pediatrics: The Social Dynamics of Professionalism 1880–1980* (Berkeley: University of California Press, 1988), 113.

65. Thomas B. Turner, *Heritage of Excellence: The Johns Hopkins Medical Institutions, 1914–1947*, 150.

66. S. A. Halpern, *American Pediatrics: The Social Dynamics of Professionalism 1880–1980*, 114–15.

67. This was evident when Park cited the early education of Herakles, detailed in Theocritus's "Beautiful Idyll XXIV" at a professional conference: "We are informed that 'under his mother's care' Herakles was reared 'like a young tree in a vineyard.' The ancient Linos taught the boy his letters; 'to draw the bow and send the arrow to the mark,' Eurytos was his teacher; Eumolpos taught the lad to be a minstrel 'and to the boxwood lyre disciplined either hand'; the tricks of foot in wrestling and arts of boxers, Harpalykes taught, 'whom no man beholding even from afar could find the courage boldly to stand up to in the lists, so grimly scowled the brow that hung over his savage face'; but to 'drive forth the horses yoked with chariots and guide the

nave of his wheel safely around the turning post,' Amphitryon taught his son himself; finally, Kastor taught him 'how to marshal a phalanx and to measure with his eye an enemy's charging squadron.'" Edwards A. Park "Methods, Results and Opportunities of Four Years' Liaison Between Pediatrics and Psychiatry," *Proceedings of the Third Conference of Psychiatric Education* (New York: The National Committee for Mental Hygiene, Inc., Division of Psychiatric Education, 1935), 5.

68. Ibid., 6.

69. Edwards A. Park, "John Howland Award Address," 88.

70. Ibid.

71. A. McGehee Harvey, "Helen Brooke Taussig," *The Johns Hopkins Medical Journal* 140 (1977): 138.

72. S. A. Halpern *American Pediatrics: The Social Dynamics of Professionalism 1880–1980*, 114–15; Francis F. Schwentker, "Dr. Park as a Teacher," *Journal of Pediatrics* 41 (1952): 637.

73. Helen Brooke Taussig, "Tetralogy of Fallot: Early History and Late Results," *American Journal of Roentgenology* 133 (1979): 425–26.

74. Thomas B. Turner, *Heritage of Excellence: The Johns Hopkins Medical Institutions, 1914–1947*, 247–48.

75. Ibid., 125.

76. Edwards A. Park, "Medical Notes," 433923337, Edwards Park Papers, AMC.

77. Edwards A. Park, "The Imprinting of Nutritional Disturbances on Growing Bone," *Pediatrics* 33 supplement (1964): 815.

78. Edwards A. Park, "The Preservation of the Ideal in a University Children's Clinic," 483.

79. A. McGehee Harvey, "The First Full-time Academic Department of Pediatrics: The Story of The Harriet Lane Home," 42.

80. Barton Childs, "Edwards A. Park," 1012.

81. Edwards A. Park, "John Howland Award Address," 105. In 1928 Alfred E. Cohn, a cardiologist and senior member of the Rockefeller Institute for Medical Research, echoed Howland's stance. He wrote a retort to the Boston physician, Francis Peabody, who had said in a letter to Warfield Longcope at Johns Hopkins that "the primary function of a department of medicine is to teach students those things that will enable them to practice the best contemporary medicine" and that the best place to simulate the world of actual practice would be the clinics and wards of the academic hospital. Peabody did not see the role of the professor of medicine as primarily in research but he certainly recognized the value of new knowledge and he urged that the young in medicine be educated in a way that would allow them to grow with it. (Thomas B. Turner, *Heritage of Excellence: The Johns Hopkins Medical Institutions, 1914–1947*, 154–55.) Cohn, alarmed, felt that the academic enterprise was threatened by Peabody's perspective. "The difference between Peabody and me is that to him the center of interest in medicine is practice and the care of the sick; to me it is the enlargement of the confines of knowledge. His is not an unworthy object. But its center of gravity is not one which places the medical clinic in the heart of a University. His might be a preparatory or an apprentice school. It makes of the Professor the father of his children and of

knowledge a decoration. But in a University knowledge is not a decoration but a passion and indeed life itself." (A. E. Cohn to Simon Flexner, August 1, 1928, cited in Saul Benison, *Tom Rivers: Reflections on a Life in Medicine and Science*, an oral history memoir (Cambridge: M.I.T. Press, 1967), 105–07.) The lines were thus drawn and Cohn's view was at that time already embedded in the heart of academic medicine. And it persisted. Town and gown were nowhere near rapprochement then and, to this day, it is usually economic necessity that brings them together.

82. Edwards A. Park, "The Preservation of the Ideal in a University Children's Clinic," *Canadian Medical Association Journal* 66 (1952): 484.

83. When I was the chief resident in 1952–53, I was only dimly aware of the extent of this prejudice. It sank in, however, when I sought career advice from Francis Schwentker, Park's successor as HLH chief. My concern was my inability at that moment to decide between going into practice and taking a fellowship in one of the subspecialties. Schwentker's response: "If you even think about practice, you don't belong here." I began my career in practice.

84. Grover F. Powers, "Edwards A. Park, Yale Professor 1921–1927," 653.

85. Barton Childs, "Edwards A. Park," 1012.

86. Edwards A. Park, "The Social Aspects of Medicine," *Journal of Pediatrics* 27 (1945): 202.

87. Ibid., 203.

88. Ibid.

89. Edwards A. Park, "Changing Medical Care in our Changing National Life," *Journal of Pediatrics* 31 (1947): 615.

90. Edwards A. Park, "The Pediatrician and the Public—An Open Forum: Communication from Dr. Edwards A. Park," *Pediatrics* 4 (1949): 689.

91. Ibid.

92. James L. Gamble, "Presentation of the Kober Medal to Dr. Edwards A. Park," 644.

93. Edwards A. Park, "The Preservation of the Ideal in a University Children's Clinic," 483.

94. "Commentaries: Edwards A. Park," *Pediatrics* 44 (1969): 899.

95. Barton Childs, "Edwards A. Park," 1010.

96. Francis F. Schwentker, "Dr. Park as a Teacher," 639.

97. Edwards A. Park to Johns Hopkins University President Isaiah Bowman, August 18, 1948.

98. Sara "Sally" Scattergood, "My Father: An Unpublished Memoir," 16–17.

99. Sara "Sally" Scattergood, "My Father: An Unpublished Memoir," 3.

100. John W. Litttlefield and Lawrence S.Wissow conversation with Rollo Park, July 5, 1999.

101. A. Gorman Hills to Helen Taussig, December 28, 1970.

102. Antonio Waring inscription to Edwards Park, February 24, 1951, author's files. On March 4, 1952, Edwards Park's successor, Francis Schwentker, sent this memo to me and many of my colleagues:

"Dear Doctor:

"At the time of the Johns Hopkins Medical and Surgical Association meetings last year, Dr. Park was presented with a desk pad on each sheet of which had been written an anecdote of greeting from his former staff members and colleagues. Some of the anecdotes were read at the luncheon and a number of people asked whether they might not be mimeographed and distributed. I am sorry that it has taken so long to complete them but we are enclosing a copy which we hope you will enjoy.

Looking forward to seeing you at our next reunion, I am

Francis F. Schwentker, M.D.
Pediatrician-in-Chief."

103. John Birmingham inscription to Edwards Park, February 24, 1951, author's files.

104. Helen Hewitt Arthur inscription to Edwards Park, February 24, 1951, author's files.

105. A. Gorman Hills to Helen Taussig, December 28, 1970.

106. Julian Price inscription to Edwards Park, February 24, 1951, author's files.

107. John Washington inscription to Edwards Park, February 24, 1951, author's files.

108. A. Gorman Hills to Helen Taussig, December 28, 1970.

109. Letter, Park, EA to Mason, Robert, 12/22/65.

110. A. Gorman Hills to Helen Taussig, December 28, 1970.

111. Edwards A. Park to Robert Mason, June 15, 1959.

112. A. Gorman Hills to Helen Taussig, December 28, 1970.

113. Robert Collis, "The Chief," *Journal of Pediatrics* 41 (1952): 667.

114. Notably, Victor Najjar, Laslo Kajdi, Walter Fleischmann, and Leo Kanner were among those trained abroad who found secure positions with Park's department. Najjar first reported the Crigler-Najjar syndrome, an inherited disorder of the bilirubin system, with John Crigler, a fellow who worked with Lawson Wilkins. Najjar continued his distinguished career at Vanderbilt. Fleischmann worked on the early studies of hypothyrodism and growth development during the first few years of Lawson Wilkins' endocrinology clinic. Kajdi's effort was based on the study of epilepsy. He worked in that clinic with Edward Bridge and Samuel Livingston.

115. The sense of Edwards Park's character is perhaps best evoked in a short essay composed by Park and shared with us by Park's personal physician, Robert Mason. Mason called this piece "Punk's Description of Landing a Salmon": "About a week ago I fished the garden pool from the roadside and quite low down took out a grilse [a young Atlantic salmon]. He leaped nine or ten times and I felt sorry for him but not sorry enough to return him to the water. I then crossed over ... narrowly escaping being washed down and having both boots filled with water at the crossing above the Blacksmith's Pool. After I had dried out a little in the sun, I walked down to the Garden Pool, fishing it from the side away from the road. There I had a curious experience. A fisherman had just been over it and I was casting it without any expectation

of raising a fish when suddenly I felt a tug and saw a splash and realized that I had encountered a salmon. I thought to myself, that fish will never take my fly again, but when I reached the spot of the rise, the same thing happened all over again. The tug was very definite. I then was perfectly convinced that it was useless to cast for that particular fish, However, I worked my fly down to the place where I thought the rise had occurred and nothing happened. The fly was on a very light hook and I thought, inasmuch as the current was quite swift, that I had better change to a heavier hook. I put on what amounted to a buck tail of black caribou hair, actually the fly which had taken the fish in the Little McDonald. Nothing happened at the spot where I thought the rise had occurred. Over and over again I fail to mark the exact location of the rise. In this instance I tried to remember it in terms of the current instead of some mark on the shore and found myself confused because the current seemed to repeat its pattern for some distance. When I reached the spot with my fly, which I thought was some ten or fifteen feet below the point of the rise, I suddenly found myself fast. The salmon rushed up to the top of the pool, taking out backing, and then came back with such speed that I had great difficulty in keeping my line taut. He then repeated the performance and, the second time, I could not reel in fast enough, but from the behavior of the line felt fairly sure that the salmon was still on. The salmon then made a run across the pool and again took out backing. I had no difficulty in reeling him in and he came close into shore, bumping the rocks, apparently completely exhausted. I could not beach him because the pebbly bank made too abrupt an angle and determined to use the gaff. I was much hampered by having a leader much longer than my rod. However, the Hardy gaff is very long and by maneuvering I was able to reach him. I made a tremendous lunge and missed him entirely. He was so exhausted that he moved only a short distance away and I had the opportunity to try to gaff him a second time. That time my gaff slid off him and when I tried to use the gaff the third time, again the gaff slid off. The salmon now began to back downstream and I continued to hold him with a very short line, standing high up on the bank. Presently I realized that a poplar tree had fallen into the water about 20 feet below me. I determined that I would not lose the salmon in the tree and so waded out into the river up to my middle. I had on wading shoes and slacks. At the deepest point the current was quite swift and I did not know whether I could make the other side but I succeeded. In any event, I was able to get the salmon around the tree. I then found myself on the road side standing in about 2 feet of water. I looked for a beach and saw one about 100 yards down. If you remember the anatomy of the pool, there is a bar on the bottom of it on the road side and a fairly deep run on the far side. I determined to try to draw the salmon down to the bar, where he would be forced to turn over on his side. This I tried to do for at least one hour. I never encountered such resistance on the part of a salmon. All the time he was swimming against the current and all the time the pressure from me was downstream at an angle of about 45 degrees. When I would succeed in drawing him into the shallower water, he would suddenly become aware of the danger and zoom always upstream. However, I did succeed in bringing him a little closer to the bar. Suddenly he gave up and I pulled him into the shallows without any resistance. He weighed 16 pounds."

Edwards Park's Legacy

By Henry M. Seidel

EDWARDS PARK'S LEGACY is visible in the innovations he enabled when he refashioned the inner workings of the Harriet Lane Home. He helped orchestrate the careers of many of the men and women who were already on the staff when he took charge of the Home as well as those whom he recruited to Johns Hopkins. He was confident in his actions and he did not hesitate to implement ideas that improved the care provided by the Home. His efforts as chief had a remarkable ripple effect on the institution and the people who were part of it. The effects of his tenure could be felt not only during his time but also long after his retirement and can still be detected today in the people and the hallways of the Children's Center at Johns Hopkins.

The Outpatient Experience

Webster's dictionary defines "dispensary" as "a place where medicine or medical or dental aid are dispensed to an ambulant patient."[1] There is little to suggest that the dispensary in the Harriet Lane Home commanded much attention or respect in its early days and no evidence that Clemens von Pirquet or John Howland attended patients there.[2] But all that changed when Edwards Park assumed control.

Park was in charge of the HLH dispensary until Grover Powers took over in 1917.[3] Under Park and Powers, it was essentially an emergency clinic for children. This arrangement continued through Park's and then Schwentker's tenures as director of the Harriet Lane Home. Park chafed at the dispensary's unsatisfactory space arrangements which made isolating children with infectious diseases difficult.[4] Those who worked with him, particularly the nurses, appreciated his efforts. In 1932 Harriet Lane nurses D. M. Young and K. B. Kinkle described the

STAFF OF THE HARRIET LANE ON FRONT STEPS. Each year Edwards Park consistently attracted an outstanding group of physicians to Baltimore to work with him. Some stayed for only a year or two and then moved on to other positions in pediatrics and other specialties. Others, such as Hugh Josephs (third from the right in the front row, standing on Park's left), made their careers at the Harriet Lane.

dispensary in detail in an article in the *Johns Hopkins Nurses' Alumnae Magazine.* They cited constructive changes and noted optimistically, "Even more changes will be made so that we will be able to give our patients the attention and consideration they deserve under better and less crowded conditions."[5]

Park was ambivalent about the value of the outpatient experience for students and residents but he was concerned that working in the dispensary made it impossible for them to attend Howland's rounds.[6] Indeed, he could not mollify some of his colleagues who thought that both outpatient care and private practice were inferior to the trainees' experiences with inpatients. This attitude pervaded the house staff and was often expressed in derisive comments about practitioners on the "outside." Outpatient care was a major component of the residency experience but it was based principally on immediate problems and only nominally on the continuing care of sick or well children. A resident completing training in the 1950s was better suited to be what we now call a "hospitalist" than a primary care physician.[7]

Early in his tenure, Park worried about the structure of the clinic and its financial base. In January 1928, he put Hugh Josephs in temporary charge of what he then called the "pay clinic in the pediatric dispensary," with the intention of having Josephs "test out the value" of such a clinic (using a similar effort in the department of medicine as a model) and providing a salary of two thousand dollars a year for its chief. The clinic was to have a strong social work staff not only to better serve the needs of the patients but also, quite practically, to explore the patients' ability to pay. Parents coming into the dispensary were interviewed by the social worker. "Those patients who can pay $2.00 for the first examination and $1.00 each for subsequent examinations are referred by Miss Emery to the pay clinic," according to the established rule.[8] Park replaced Josephs with Alexander Schaffer, a 1923 graduate of the Johns Hopkins School of Medicine and Howland's last chief resident,[9] but a "pay clinic" as such did not go on to play a significant role in the Harriet Lane Outpatient Department.

The dispensary was consistently busy. It was staffed by residents who were supervised by an additional chief resident for the outpatient department (OPD), plus a succession of older faculty members. Each evening they pored over the charts of the day, made their notes, and gave feedback to the house officers concerned. Their presence along with that of the chief resident for the OPD assured consistency of care and teaching. There was immediate support both day and night and also the resource of the chief residents on other services, particularly surgery and ophthalmology. A range of subspecialists were just a few steps away, and once or twice a month a dermatologist would visit to give advice. The physical setup at Harriet Lane assured that informal consultations occurred because people were constantly bumping into each other.

Concern in the dispensary for the needs of the patient was genuine, although there were barriers to appropriate care because of a minimum of cross-cultural understanding. The world of the Harriet Lane staff and the world of those who lived in East Baltimore abutted but did not merge constructively except for the dependent relationship established when a sick child was brought for care. Many important questions concerning possible causes of major illnesses arose, but the "Why did this happen?" questions—with answers rooted in the cultural and societal environment—were rarely asked. Unfortunately, this was also true with lesser problems confronted in the dispensary. Those may well have had roots in behavior that was not adequately explored or understood.[10] Issues related to behavior, social environment, and family relationships were seldom part of the conversation with the parent or child, nor were they a substantive part of the residents' training. The search for cultural or societal causes had little priority in the determination of a health management plan. Routinely, the ability of a family to follow through on recommendations or to fully understand those recommendations was not well explored.

Park was not unaware of these factors. He did not want the clinic to be a backwater in an otherwise sophisticated milieu in which research and care of the hospitalized patients were the valued pursuits and he tried to make the outpatient experience better for both the children and the medical residents. He did so in the manner of his time, however, leaving so-called well-baby care to private pediatricians and the scant resources of the Baltimore City Health Department.

By today's standards, the dispensary then was an inadequate training ground for primary care of children. Yet, in my memory visions linger of late nights and weary times when I sat on a bench in the corridor thinking that all the patients had been seen. Then I caught sight of yet another obviously tired mother with her infant coming slowly toward me. Or, at other times, it was a father trailed by a reluctant toddler. I remember, too, with guilt, the flash of resentment I felt as I wondered why they waited until just then to arrive. That resentment always disappeared quickly.

Listening to the Children

When Park took over as director of the Harriet Lane Home in 1927, he found several conditions at the Home disturbing. He thought the physical ambience of the floors was a problem. He wanted a new design so that the "institutional character of our wards will be changed and a more home-like atmosphere introduced."[11] It is not apparent that there was any such change. But much was accomplished during Park's tenure with regard to the child's emotional experience in the hospital. His decision in 1928 to integrate the Harriet Lane wards was

CHILDREN AND NURSING STUDENTS READING TOGETHER. The stories read by these nursing students in the third-floor playroom in 1939 don't seem to have been very successful in cheering up the patients. In 1943 head nurse Helen Schnetzer, concerned about the stressful impact of long hospital stays on children, proposed a more comprehensive effort to promote play activities, and chief Edwards Park agreed.

perhaps his earliest positive contribution. The nature of the illness—infectious or non-infectious—became the determinant for the location of a child's bed, and not race. There is no evidence of meetings or requests for permission. It happened smoothly and without commotion. He just did it.[12]

A particularly important contribution had its origins toward the end of Park's tenure. The head nurse in Harriet Lane then was Helen Schnetzer. Her office was just a few feet along the first floor corridor from Park's, separated only by a narrow hallway. A tall, slender woman with a rather stern mien, she had his ear and his interest. It is hard to imagine that they ever shared small talk. But it is easy to imagine Schnetzer telling Park that the experience of children in the hospital should be far better than it was, and that it must improve. How that might occur was suggested to Schnetzer by Onica Prall, head of the department of child development at Hood College in Frederick, Maryland. Park's recognized the need too, and this allowed Schnetzer to instigate change. The year was 1943. That summer, Prall worked with several of her senior students in a demonstration program on Harriet Lane 3 East. Their approach to the older children was to provide structured play activities. The children and the nursing and medical staffs responded eagerly. Prall was asked to stay but she chose to remain at Hood. One of her first graduates, Mary Hawkins Johnson, became the HLH's first play director, probably sometime in 1944 on Harriet Lane 3. From the beginning the premise was that sensitivity to the stages of child development and the use of play can help children and their families cope more successfully with the hospital experience. Before long there were staff managing children's play activities on the private patient floor, Harriet Lane 2, and on the surgical floor for older children, Halsted 3. The Women's Board of the Hospital provided the initial funding for these efforts and continued its support for many years though the Johns Hopkins Hospital School of Nursing and the nursing service of the department of pediatrics were ultimately responsible for the program.[13] This program, while not the first of its kind in the United States, was certainly one of the earliest. We do not know if Schnetzer and Prall were aware of the scarce literature on the subject available at the time or of the established similar efforts at Babies Hospital at Columbia-Presbyterian and Bellevue Hospitals in New York, and at the University of Michigan.[14]

Gerald Powell, the chief resident in 1964, pointed out that "The psychological impact of an illness and subsequent hospitalization varies... in type and degree from one patient to another." The young doctor observed that these factors "may have a determining influence on the course of the adjustment to the disease, but more particularly it may have an influence on the child's future emotional development." In fact, the resident worried that "Although the illness may be of a temporary nature, an adverse emotional reaction may be far more lasting." Powell noted that doctors were often associated with uncomfortable examinations and nurses with painful injections, so it was important for "someone to supply the security, the comfort, and the interest that the child needs."[15]

CHILDREN PAINTING AT EASELS AND TABLE. Over the years, the Child Life Program evolved into an essential part of caring for patients in the Harriet Lane. These animated youngsters were just a few of the thousands of patients who expressed themselves through art, writing, and games. It was also during Edwards Park's directorship that all the Harriet Lane wards became fully integrated, although—like almost all of Johns Hopkins Hospital—the Harriet Lane had always accepted patients regardless of race.

Jerriann Wilson, the long-time director of what is now called the Child Life Program, described a spectrum of activities that have evolved over the years:

> At one end of the spectrum, familiar activities are provided for the children so that the hospital does not feel like a foreign country to them.... Play is a most important tool that Child Life utilizes.... At the other end of the spectrum, we think about ways to help children cope once they are relaxed enough by explaining what may have happened to them and showing them what's going to happen to them. Our feeling is that

if children understand what will happen to them when they are in the hospital and how they are going to get through all of that, and if they have a chance to participate in the coping process, they will be stronger and they will benefit from the hospital experience. It is not our intention that kids laugh all the time or that we are trying to have a smile on every child's face.

Obviously, not every child wants to smile.... But we think that with talking with children about why they are in the hospital, eliciting their understanding, really, about why they are in the hospital or why they have come, or in an emergency after the fact about why they were brought to the hospital, then we can start where they are and we can build on that, asking them questions to clarify our understanding of what they understand and help clarify their thinking.... So, our approach is not necessarily to teach children, to talk at them, but to learn what they understand and build on that.

Then, probably the most important thing is to talk with them about how they are going to cope with whatever it is, whether it's just being in the hospital or getting through a spinal tap, what is it that they can do to make the process easier and more bearable for them. We picture the circumstance and rehearse it with them. We practice with them, and once they've had the experience, we talk about it afterwards. "How was it for you?" We believe that helps the children and it also helps us to learn at times if we have misjudged the situation.[16]

These were not the prevalent practices in 1943 when Park responded to Schnetzer's suggestions. Children were separated from their parents on admission to the hospital and were allowed visits for one hour twice a week unless they were critically ill. Helpful attention to their emotional state was random at best, and there is nothing to document that the faculty or house staff protested or that with any constancy they added to the emotional support primarily provided by the Harriet Lane nurses.

The progression to the present Child Life Program, while steady, was not always smooth. There was obvious support from the nursing leadership but, as time passed and the "play ladies" grew in number, took on greater responsibility, and became more confident of their ground, the controlling influence of the nurses began to chafe.[17] The play director and her colleagues had to wait for the tenure of Robert Cooke to achieve the degree of autonomy they wanted.

Nurturing Social Service

Harriet Lane has always served children who live both nearby and far away. But the primarily black children who lived near Johns Hopkins were the heart and soul of the care, teaching, and learning experience at the Harriet Lane. Park sensed the need to understand the patients' home environments if their out-of-hospital care was to be well managed. Trusted professionals were needed to provide outreach that would complement the efforts of the pediatric staff. Within a decade, Park had ten to fifteen social workers who served as many as a thousand patients and made up to five thousand house calls a year.[18] Park was unafraid to challenge the role previously thought to be the sole province of physicians. This was evident in a commentary he wrote in 1946 in anticipation of a discussion on social planning at an American Academy of Pediatrics meeting:

1. Let us not waste time saying that physicians are superior ethically to other occupational groups. Physicians by and large probably do not differ much from the general run of human beings. It is much safer to assume that anyway.
2. Let us not waste time, either, in saying how enlightened pediatricians are. The pediatricians have been most forward in the practice of preventive medicine, but that development was a corollary to our work and need not go to our heads.
3. Also, let us not waste time in pointing to achievements in medicine of the last twenty years as if they implied that the public need have no voice in determining medical care. The achievements in medicine merely parallel those in chemistry, physics and mathematics; they are just part of a general advance in science. The essential point is that the advances in medicine have far outstripped their social applications and have created new needs and possibilities.[19]

Park's sense that the specialty clinics he was nurturing needed social service support is reflected in his April 11, 1928, letter to the Harriet Lane trustees:

You will be delighted to hear that the Commonwealth Fund has given to the Department $1,800 for a social worker... for the Cardiac Clinic to take effect on July 1, 1928, and has promised to renew the gift if this year's work proves sufficiently profitable, and has suggested the possibility of making the gift permanent. You will also be pleased to learn that the Maryland Tuberculosis Association has given us $2,000 for the salary of a social service worker in tuberculosis with the prospect of renewal if our work on tuberculosis patients proves sufficiently valuable... ; Miss Mc-Culloch has been transferred from the Social Service Department to this special [epilepsy] clinic. You will see, therefore, that the plans for the special clinics offered to the trustees at their first meeting last fall have been consummated and that by July 1 next the dispensary will have in operation a clinic for children with heart disease supplied with a special physician and social worker; one for tuberculosis supplied with a special social worker; one for epilepsy supplied with a technician and social worker... ; one in syphilis now in full operation, supplied with a special physician who gives his services, Dr. Schaffer, and a special social service worker, Miss Baetjer.... As a result of the acquisition of three new social service workers, the Department of Social Service under the extremely able leadership of Miss Bond will be greatly strengthened. The addition[s]... will release the other members of Miss Bond's staff for social work of a general nature."[20]

These social workers visited the home and helped the patient carry out the doctor's recommendations.[21] That, however, was only part of it. It was an important foot in the door, which often enabled a more complete understanding of a child's needs and a better effort to satisfy them. In that era the social worker went where the physician often did not lead.

The influence of Park can be seen in academic departments of pediatrics even today. Physicians, nurses, and social workers—and now many other professionals whose skills have flourished in recent decades—provide care to patients in a setting that respects and coordinates the contributions of each and allows service to be complemented by the need to gain new knowledge and to teach that knowledge. Park insisted on this arrangement, and he designated outpatient clinics as full partners with the inpatient floors in this regard. He thought beyond the confines of the hospital when considering the needs of the patient—a new concept in his time. He taught us that there were numerous moments when questions needed to be asked and answers sought. Most important, he selected men and women for these special tasks who proved to be seminal in their fields. They secured Park's legacy.

Helen Brooke Taussig and the Cardiac Clinic

It is likely that Helen Taussig would have preferred to have attended Harvard Medical School and then have become an internist and adult cardiologist. But Harvard did not accept women in the 1920s. When she graduated from the Johns Hopkins School of Medicine in 1927 the department of medicine had a quota of only one woman a year in its residency program, and it was based on grade point average. Taussig's rank was two-tenths of a point shy of one of her female classmates. Warfield Longcope, the department of medicine chief, went strictly by his rules and Taussig went to Harriet Lane.[22]

Taussig had a will that some viewed as iron and others interpreted as stubborn. As a result, not every one thought as graciously about Taussig as did Catherine Neill, her long-time colleague. Neill recalled Taussig's "combination of great humanitarian skill and a piercing intellect that enabled an extraordinary ability to see the big picture."[23] Taussig did have an unshakable determination, a steel hand in an occasionally velvet glove, that was relentless in pursuit of her goals. It is now more comfortable for me to speak of her as "Helen." Although she suggested long ago that I address her familiarly, I could not then. It was always Dr. Taussig or Dr. T. Now, so many years later, "Helen" feels right.

Taussig was born to academic privilege. Her father, Frank Taussig, was a prominent economist at Harvard. Growing up in Cambridge, she followed for a while the expected path in her schooling—the Cambridge School for Girls, then Radcliffe for two years. She broke the mold, transferred to the University of California at Berkeley, and graduated in 1921 with an A.B. degree and a Phi Beta Kappa key. Her first intention was to go to medical school but this was a time when teaching or nursing were the recommended options for a young woman. Her father suggested a career in public health, and proposed the newly opened Harvard School of Public Health. She tried to parlay an experience there into a degree in medicine and suggested that possibility to the dean at her interview. He was constrained by President Abbott Lawrence Lowell's insistence that women had no place at Harvard Medical School. Taussig remembered her angry response: "Who is going to be such a fool as to spend two years studying medicine and two more years in public health and not get a degree?"[24]

This, however, left Taussig without a clear pathway to medicine.

Her first step was a course in anatomy at Boston University, where Alexander Begg offered a beef heart for Taussig to dissect and then urged her to learn the larger organs of the body. Begg also advocated that she apply to the Johns Hopkins School of Medicine.[25] The pre-eminent Harvard physiologist, Walter Cannon, wrote a glowing letter of recommendation, assuring Hopkins that she would most certainly be admitted to Harvard if Harvard admitted women.[26]

After graduating from the medical school at Hopkins and the re-buff from the department of medicine, Taussig began her residency at Harriet Lane. Since residencies then did not have the same rigid structure as now, she also worked with Dr. Edward P. Carter in the adult cardiographic laboratory. Park's commitment to specialty clinics led him to conversations with Dr. Carter and the appointment of one of Dr. Carter's senior fellows as the pro-tem director of the new Harriet Lane Cardiac Clinic. It was in that clinic that Park first met Taussig on December 7, 1927.[27]

In 1930, when she was thirty-two years old and just three years out of medical school, Park appointed Taussig director of the cardiac clinic. She agreed with Park that a better understanding of disease would evolve from careful follow up of patients and precise recording of their progress over time. She also profited from his eager advocacy of the latest in medical advances. Park was aware that in New York, Dr. May Wilson had taken advantage of the fluoroscope to clarify the understanding of left ventricular enlargement. As a result, Park had a fluoroscope installed in 1930 in a room under the Harriet Lane amphitheatre and made it available to faculty and house officers.[28] The small room had no windows and a canted ceiling corresponding to the ascending tiers in the amphitheatre. More than two observers crowded the place. Just one leaded apron hung on the door. It was usual for observers to cluster behind the fluoroscopist, poorly—if at all—protected from the radiation

On the day the fluoroscope was installed Park announced, "Now, Dr. Taussig, you are going to learn congenital heart disease." "But I thought I was to study rheumatic fever," she demurred. "You cannot run a cardiac clinic and not learn congenital heart disease any more than Dr. [Leo] Kanner can run a psychiatric clinic and not study mental retardation," Park retorted. "When you do, it will be a great day."[29] And, Neill pointed out, "Helen did not ultimately make a real contribution to rheumatic fever but, in that time, no one else understood the heart as well."[30]

CATHERINE NEILL AND HELEN TAUSSIG STUDYING AN X-RAY. Taussig, right, was thirty-two when Edwards Park tapped her to lead the new cardiac clinic. In the 1940s she proposed a surgical procedure to correct tetralogy of Fallot. After Alfred Blalock performed the first "blue baby" operation, their names were linked to this pioneering procedure, the Blalock-Taussig shunt. Photo by the *Baltimore Sun* and reproduced here with permission.

In the new cardiac clinic clinical observation of patients was supplemented by blood pressure determinations, three-lead electrocardiographs, x-rays, and the fluoroscope. Fluoroscopy included at least three positions: antero-posterior, left and right obliques (after a barium swallow), and, often, a lateral view. Special attention was paid to pulmonary vascularity— was it increased? normal? decreased?—and also to pulsations in the chambers of the heart and in pulmonary arteries. X-rays recorded the size and shape of the heart. Dr. Maude Abbott's earlier studies of congenital heart disease provided the basis for Taussig's work on tetralogy of Fallot, the so-called "blue babies." Abbott, at McGill University in Montreal, had classified congenital disease as cyanotic and acyanotic, and had recognized that the onset of cyanosis was not always immediate at birth, in which case it is termed *cyanose tardive*.[31]

Taussig's well-prepared mind took advantage of that observation. No matter how young, the cyanotic babies referred to her were given the same workup as children and adolescents with rheumatic fever. Repetitive fluoroscopies revealed a seeming consistency: a right ventricular hypertrophy as a characteristic of the cyanotic. Then, in 1933, she cared for an infant who showed no evidence of a right ventricle on fluoroscopy and whose electrocardiogram indicated a left axis deviation. Taussig made the diagnosis of absent right ventricle and reasoned that the baby was kept alive by a patent ductus arteriosus, which allowed some of the blood from the aorta to enter the pulmonary artery for oxygenation. This observation was repeated three weeks later with another cyanotic infant. Two children with the same malformation in that short span! Each died when his or her ductus arteriosus closed. At postmortem, it was discovered that the first baby had an absent right ventricle and the second, a vestigial one. Both had pulmonary artery atresia.[32]

The house staff initially was skeptical of diagnoses based on interpretations of observations with which they were unfamiliar. The autopsies persuaded the house staff but, more important, they persuaded Taussig that specific malformations of the heart can be identified by characteristic changes in the size and shape of the heart. She realized that these consistent patterns made possible accurate diagnosis of both anatomy and function in life, and that babies with congenital malformations died of inadequate oxygenation of the blood and not of cardiac failure. The infants lost adequate blood flow to the lungs because of the gradual—or not so gradual—closure of the patent ductus. But how to keep the babies alive? The challenge now was to figure out how to keep the ductus open, or how to replace it.

At the Boston Children's Hospital in 1939, Robert Gross had tied off the patent ductus arteriosus successfully in children in whom it did not close normally. This persuaded Taussig that if a patent ductus arteriosus could be tied, it might be constructed in order to increase pulmonary blood flow. She spoke with Gross about this but he was unenthusiastic. Indeed, she even suggested a possible move to Boston because of her father's illness. Gross told her to stay in Baltimore where she was "wanted."[33]

Alfred Blalock successfully operated on three patients with a patent ductus arteriosus at Vanderbilt. Assisted by his longtime technician Vivien Thomas, he had developed (in the dog laboratory) the ability to anastamose the subclavian artery to the pulmonary artery. In 1941, Blalock was called to Baltimore to be chief of the department of surgery at Johns Hopkins, and he invited Thomas to join him. The first time he ligated a patent ductus arteriosus at Hopkins, in 1942, Taussig was in the operating room. She told Blalock how impressed she was by his surgical skill. "I stand in awe and admiration," she complimented him. Then, she offered a caveat, "... but the truly great day will come when you build a ductus for a cyanotic child, not when you close a ductus for a child who has a little too much blood going to his lungs." "When that day comes," Blalock responded, "this will seem like child's play."[34]

No single person can be credited with the basic idea for the surgical correction of tetralogy of Fallot. There were consultations, moments of epiphany, and repeated efforts in the laboratory. Taussig and Blalock were central, but Vivien Thomas in the laboratory and Park, for the exchange of ideas, were vital facilitators. Blalock experienced a failed trial operating on dogs when he cross-clamped the aorta in order to anastamose a coronary artery into it to try to repair coarctation. The dogs' hind limbs were paralyzed. Park reminded him that there was still ample blood flow to the brain and asked if the carotid artery, a long, straight vessel, might not be used to bypass the coarctation. Taussig grasped the moment: "If you could put the coronary artery in the descending aorta, couldn't you put the subclavian artery into the pulmonary artery? That is all I want."[35]

The effort to create a model of the tetralogy of Fallot in dogs was difficult, but after some two hundred operations, Blalock was confident. "I am convinced that I know how to do the operation," he announced.[36] The effort with infants began and with this the specialty of pediatric cardiovascular surgery was firmly established. The Blalock-Taussig operation for the tetralogy of Fallot was successful, although the initial efforts were made difficult by grave illnesses in the children and the need to learn more about their care. Taussig discovered the beneficial effects of morphine during a cyanotic episode. Penicillin became more readily available. The techniques of cardiac catheterization and angiography, in their infancy in 1946, were adapted to the study of these patients with significant help from the Hopkins laboratories of Richard Bing and Robert Cooley.[37] But foremost, the operation worked. I remain in awe of the incalculable benefits. One summer night on Cape Cod in the 1990s, my wife and I heard the pianist

Samuel Sanders play a Beethoven sonata. He was one of Taussig's first "blue babies."

The ensuing acclaim did not change Taussig. Her demeanor was low-keyed, always reasoned, not arrogant but quite assertive. Only a very few thought her at all abrasive. She had unqualified respect and was able to command attention. In the 1952–53 academic year Taussig wanted to take an African-American physician, Effie O'Neal Ellis, as a fellow. This would be a distinct departure at Hopkins, but the choice was made easy when it became apparent that Ellis came or Taussig went.

Taussig continued to make her mark as she aged. Her fellows and staff enabled the development of pediatric cardiology nationwide and those she mentored moved on to leadership positions in many places. Among the first: Mary Allen Engle went to Cornell, Gil Blount to Colorado, Ruth Whittemore to Yale, Robert Ziegler to Henry Ford Hospital in Detroit, Frank Dammann to the University of Virginia, Edward Lambert to Buffalo, Daniel McNamara to Houston, and James Manning to Rochester, New York—and these were but a few.[38]

Since medical school, Taussig had been sufficiently hearing impaired[39] to need an amplification system for her stethoscope, which was rather bulky. Once, intrigued by what she had heard, she asked me to listen and handed me her stethoscope—but she forgot to turn down the amplification. The sounds boomed and I jumped. She laughed, made the necessary adjustment and went on to a careful, several-minute interpretation of what I was hearing. Indeed, Taussig constantly interpreted, observed, correlated, and recommended. She confronted any complications and errors in diagnosis forthrightly. Her publications were frequent and thoughtful. The first edition of her 1947 book, *Congenital Malformations of the Heart*, reflected her experience in words and, importantly, illustrations.[40]

The cardiac clinic adapted an important Park innovation—the services of a social worker. The need was apparent in the 1930s; there were so many patients with rheumatic fever, so few beds in hospitals, and so much care was necessary. Taussig made house calls with the help of a social worker and learned that treatment of the disease was insufficient without attention to the context in which the patient lived.[41] Even today physicians need to be reminded constantly of this valuable resource in the care of patients, since we remain stubbornly resistant for the most part.

Taussig never really rested. Certainly, she relaxed at her Cape Cod cottage and she enjoyed teaching her many visitors the art of the properly prepared lobster, the blueberry muffin, and beach plum jelly.[42] But she remained a physician to the world. One night she phoned me, as she had in the past and would again on many other nights. "Henry,"— unlike Park, she invariably used my first name—"may I talk with you about thalidomide?" she asked. And so it went.[43]

Honors for Taussig abounded. Physicians and other professionals from around the world sought her counsel. But formal recognition of her talent came more slowly from Hopkins.[44] The institution was hampered by an academic rule imposed at its origin: only the chief of a department could be a full professor. Taussig was promoted to associate professor in 1946 but the step to full professor had to wait until 1959. Ultimately, she became the first woman and the first pediatrician to become president of the American Heart Association. In the 1970s, she became a Master in the American College of Physicians and was invited to membership in the National Academy of Sciences and the American Philosophical Society. Her awards, medals, and honorary degrees are too numerous to count.[45]

Lawson Wilkins and the Endocrinology Clinic

Lawson Wilkins seemed like one of the romanticized physicians of old, one who gave calm assurances and felt deeply the potential for tragedy in life. Clearly, his twenty-five years in the private practice of pediatrics governed his subsequent efforts with children. He never stopped asking whether what he was doing had any significant relationship to outcomes. The need to answer this question underlay his exceptionally close observation of each child and the flowing records he kept. He seldom seemed uncertain or in a deeply reflective mood. Occasionally, though, his hand would go to his face and his fingers would tap his chin ever so lightly.

A 1918 graduate of the Johns Hopkins School of Medicine, Wilkins' earned his degree while doing "elective time" as an orderly in the Johns Hopkins Hospital Unit in France during World War I. His residency began when the war ended. His first choice of internship may well have been influenced by Wilkins' great regard for his father, a physician who could not understand a medical life devoid of intimacy with the sick, something more common in private practice. Thus, the new graduate took an internship first in internal medicine at the New

Haven Hospital, and then returned to Hopkins, to the Harriet Lane Home.

The young Wilkins found it difficult to tolerate what he thought was a rather haphazard approach to the care of poor children, who were primarily the responsibility of inexperienced interns at the time. The Harriet Lane and, indeed, Johns Hopkins, had yet to learn the advantages of organization in clinic care, good recordkeeping, and appropriate follow-up. It is fair to say that, in the Harriet Lane at least, Wilkins was the first to make these changes. He started a clinic for children with congenital syphilis, organized their care, and even obtained the service of a social worker for the clinic. In the early 1920s it was the only "specialty" clinic for children. Howland was not particularly enthusiastic about the clinic but his recognition of the potential in this intern prompted him to offer Wilkins an assistant residency—a sure path to a career in academic medicine. One can imagine Wilkins' difficulty making this decision, a problem shared by many even today. He declined Howland's offer and began private practice in Baltimore.

While patient need was great, the work hard, and the days and nights long, Wilkins continued to be a consistent presence at Harriet Lane. At first there was no particular pattern to the issues that attracted him. He wrote a number of review articles at the bidding of Louis Hamman, a respected part-time Hopkins internist, and these articles revealed Wilkins' eclectic interests. Then, in the early 1930s, he took over the care of a child with epilepsy who was in treatment with the ketogenic diet. This prompted Park to suggest that Wilkins work with Edward Bridge, then director of a nascent epilepsy clinic. This collaboration resulted in a paper published in 1937 titled "Epilepsy in Childhood: I. A Statistical Study of Clinical Types; II. The Incidence of Remissions; III. Results with the Ketogenic Diet."[46] Wilkins proved to be a sound clinician blessed with sharp observation, intellectual curiosity, and abundant common sense.[47]

The concept of an endocrinology clinic did not originate with Wilkins. Park, probably influenced by Lewellys Barker in the department of internal medicine at Hopkins and by adult clinics at the Mayo Clinic and the Massachusetts General Hospital, realized its potential. Wilkins, still in practice, thought that it was a field intended for charlatans. At least, that was his first response when Park asked him to form such a clinic.[48] Fortunately, Park prevailed. Before Wilkins took over in the mid-1930s children with endocrine problems had been cared for

LAWSON WILKINS. For years Wilkins blended private practice in Baltimore with his responsibilities in the endocrinology clinic he formed at the behest of Edwards Park. Wilkins emphasized exact recordkeeping and introduced numerous innovations in his approach, particularly in treating thyroid conditions and the study of patients with the adrenogenital syndrome. Photo by Greystone Studios (New York).

at Harriet Lane in random fashion. To support his family, he continued parallel practice until 1946, working nights and weekends on clinic duties. For the first ten years, the studies in the clinic were funded by a grant from the Commonwealth Fund. There was no salary, however. Park was not reluctant to recruit a practitioner he valued with the promise of professional growth but without financial gain.[49]

Wilkins knew his patients well and he recorded their individual experiences graphically. Observations became data and data became charts, the running story of objective, subjective, and temporal findings. Serial photographs of patients enriched the charts. His reasoning was influenced by close observation of the patient and he was not intimidated by the literature of the time. Wilkins did not look to others to suggest how he might think.

At meetings of the American Pediatric Society in 1937, 1938, and 1940, Wilkins presented his early reports concerning thyroid deficiency and its influence on growth, bone, and mental status. Wilkins knew that it was not enough to replace the deficient hormone; it was also necessary to explain how the hormone acted and what might be the risk as well as the gain in replacing it. He recognized that blood chemistries must be measured, just as weight and height were. He took advantage of the developments of Benjamin Kramer, an early recruit to Howland's faculty who was particularly adept in the laboratory. These developments enabled microstudy of the blood in children. Thus, this pediatrician who was constantly at the front line with the patient and not often in the laboratory added as much to the biochemical understanding of disease as he did to the phenotypic description.[50]

Francis Schwentker, Park's successor as chairman, offered Wilkins a full-time position at Harriet Lane. There must have been at least a moment's pause before Wilkins' acceptance. A considerable loss of income was compensated by the opportunity to read, reflect, and learn better how to complement the clinical effort with the laboratory. This came at an apt time. The advent of adrenocortical steroids and a better understanding of the function of the adrenal-pituitary axis enabled fresh thought about the regulation of adrenocortical dysfunction. Infants with congenital adrenal hyperplasia—boys and girls with ambiguous genitalia—responded positively to the newly available, synthesized adrenocortical hormone, cortisone. Other researchers elsewhere were actively investigating similar issues at the time, but the particular contributions by those at the Harriet Lane established Wilkins' primacy. The careful study of the many infants and children referred to his endocrinology clinic, the masterly recordkeeping, and the integration of clinical care with the laboratory explained the success of cortisone and provided biochemical insights into the many variations of the syndrome. Another profound problem that needed study was that some female infants had been mistakenly identified as male after a too cursory examination of the enlarged clitoris typical of the syndrome. These children had been reared as boys until they were first seen at Harriet Lane. Wilkins and John Money, who was recruited from the department of psychiatry, made the first attempts at understanding disturbances of the usual patterns of growth and sexual development.

The activity of the late 1940s and early 1950s in endocrinology attracted a remarkable group of men and women who became

Wilkins' fellows. They established their specialty widely and put it on a firm footing in this country and abroad. Walter Fleischman was with Wilkins during that first "thyroid decade."[51] The others were younger. In 1963 they met in Baltimore to share scientific thought and convivial moments. This group of pediatricians was probably Wilkins' greatest contribution. Wilkins died a few months after that meeting, but his former fellows continued to come together and, in time, they established the Lawson Wilkins Pediatric Endocrine Society and installed Claude Migeon as the first president in 1971.[52]

Wilkins had a presence unlike Park's. Wilkins was a colleague who was in it with us all the way: vigorous, outspoken, sleeves rolled up, eager. Still, his direct, no-nonsense approach, emphasized by his ebullient voice, was always tempered by his understanding of the fragility of the human condition. I remember a corridor conversation with him in the early 1950s. I asked Wilkins about the steroid dosage for a little girl with a severe bullous skin condition. "I'm not sure," he said. "Try this." His answer was scribbled on a bit of paper. I had the comforting sense that this was the right thing to do. And I remember, too, the minutes he spent that afternoon in thoughtful reflection, standing at the foot of the child's bed. Memory assures me that, ultimately, she did well.

Wilkins met once a year with those of us who were interested in talking about what private practice was like. There were part-time faculty members with whom the house staff had interactions—Charles Donovan, William Stifler, Alexander "Buck" Schaffer, Wilson Grubb, and John Askin among others—but it was Wilkins who gave us the flavor of their world. He loved that part of his life and he was ambivalent about having left it. He would lean forward and his voice would take on intensity when he described the value of house calls. There was a certain glee as he talked of the long, sharpened fingernail recommended by Howland for the direct incision of a retropharyngeal abscess. "Simply hold the child upside down and do it!" (We never heard that Wilkins ever actually did it.) Wilkins validated a life in private practice despite the academic environment in which we were maturing, which was unsupportive of the idea.

Wilkins proved Park right. Specialty clinics devoted to particular disease added considerably to new knowledge. They intertwined the clinic with the laboratory and allowed the study of the problems of patients over a long period of time. Meticulous recordkeeping provided continuity that offered a better understanding of outcomes. And outcomes became more readily evident as these children became adults, still in the care of the clinic.

An assistant professor in 1936, Wilkins became an associate professor in 1942. He received the few distinguished awards given to pediatricians before he was finally promoted to full professorship in 1957, after he acted as interim departmental chairman pending the arrival of Schwentker's successor.[53] By then, his book *The Diagnosis and Treatment of Endocrine Disorders in Childhood and Adolescence*[54] was the standard reference book on the subject, and he himself was the standard for pediatric endocrinologists, and many others, the world around.

Harriet Lane house staff and faculty members were frequent visitors in the Wilkins' home. These parties reflected his personality. They were informal, spread out on the lawn, a tad boisterous with much singing—sometimes even in tune—and dominated always by Wilkins' hefty voice. We went home feeling good and feeling that we had been in the company of a colleague and a brother, fully as much as that of a mentor and a father. Lawson Wilkins was all of these.

Leo Kanner and the Behavior Clinic for Children

Leo Kanner saw patients in a small office on the second floor of Observation I, an appendage to Harriet Lane's first floor. He was a gentle man with an ever-present cigar. We were all rather closely packed, the child, parents, Kanner, and the house officer. As a result, everyone in the room smoked that cigar. But the important lesson from Kanner that persists still for me is respect for patients and how essential it is to hear what they say. Kanner's discussions were never obscured by jargon and always reflected the fact that he had listened closely and without preconception.

Kanner was anointed as a child psychiatrist and put at the head of the Behavior Clinic for Children in 1931.[55] Park thought, unfairly, that repetitive error leading to certainty of conviction was more likely in psychiatric child care than in other pediatric specialties. The way to avoid this, according to Park, was to recognize that the behaviors of children assume repetitive patterns that can be "analyzed, rationalized, and understood." These insights could then be reported and taught so that the tendency in those years to prescribe repression of unwanted behavior (for example, lying, thumb-sucking, stealing, and masturba-

LEO KANNER. Psychiatrist Leo Kanner assumed the leadership of the Behavior Clinic for Children in the Harriet Lane Home in 1931. He wrote for both his colleagues and the general public, and helped to demystify behavioral issues common to children and adolescents. Kanner, a pioneer in the recognition of autism, gained local prominence as a champion for the mentally retarded in Maryland. Photo by Greystone Studios (New York).

tion) might give way to a search for and treatment of the underlying cause.[56]

As a psychiatrist, Kanner resisted intimidation by common wisdom or dogma. His approach was based on observation and description of the child and the context of the child's family and environment. His insistent message was to "describe."[57] He shared Park's concern about the perceived inadequacies of busy pediatricians untrained in the seemingly arcane gestalt of behavior and psychiatry. "Knowledge of technique is just as necessary for psychiatric as for neurological examination," Park wrote, and he believed that the real enemy in developing the skills was time:

> Probably no kind of medical work... is so time devouring as thorough psychiatric examination, and in no work is success so proportionate to

the time plus pains. It is necessary not only to interview the child but also parents, teachers and others.... More than that, one must win from all conviction and support. Then, in addition, complicated readjustments within or outside the home must be effected, and these may demand visits and interviews. Finally, the child cannot be forgotten; he must be kept under supervision, as must those in his environment. The busy hospital pediatrician, single-minded, has not the leisure to do all this, even if he does possess the knowledge and desire.[58]

Park wrote this in 1938. Kanner had been at his task for seven years and Park's thoughts were a mix of the reasons that led to the establishment of the clinic and of what Kanner had taught Park in those seven years.

Adolph Meyer, the first chief of psychiatry at Johns Hopkins, was also the first in the United States to stress that people are mentally integrated individuals. He fostered the concepts that define emotionally ill individuals as improperly functioning persons needing understanding and not mechanical diagnoses rigidly constrained by symptom lists. A seminal book by Clifford Beers, *A Mind That Found Itself*, conceived as early as 1908 and encouraged by Meyer, eventually led to a widespread effort to encourage mental health education by 1930.[59]

Although Kanner felt that the time was ripe for him when his clinic opened in 1931, skeptical pediatricians continued to impose barriers to change. Many did not yet recognize that knowledge of pathology and biochemistry was not enough to care for the full range of problems of childhood. Kanner's way to deal with this was to be at the front line with the patient and with the skeptics. He worked with his pediatric colleagues in their clinics—on their territory—and he used their language. He and his co-workers were on constant call at Harriet Lane wherever they were needed, and each house officer was with him three days a week for two months. They acquired an "attitude, a knowledge, and a method."[60] In time Kanner was fully accepted and his discipline earned respect.

Kanner continued to learn throughout his career, satisfying an intellectual curiosity that had been nourished in his childhood. He was born in Klekotow, Austria, in 1894 to a mother who valued education and insisted on secular schooling in addition to the religious training expected of a Jewish boy in late-nineteenth-century Austria. This did not go down well in the Orthodox community. The family endured the criticism and young Leo learned early to value individual choice and to resist intimidation. Kanner was an exceptional student who made decisions that suggested little fear of risk. His studies in Berlin were interrupted by service in World War I in the Austrian army. Granted his MD degree in 1919 from the University of Berlin, he began practice with an interest in the new field of cardiology and supplemented his income as a part-time assistant at Charite Hospital in the German capital. But postwar life in Germany was difficult, with rampant inflation just one of many problems. An American physician studying in Germany urged the budding cardiologist to go to the United States. He took a position in 1924 on the staff of the State Hospital in Yankton, South Dakota, where there is now a Leo Kanner Memorial Building.[61]

Kanner's English needed improvement so he improved his language skills by doing the *New York Times* crossword puzzle and by observing, thinking, describing, and writing in his new tongue. His publications on paralysis associated with syphilis in Native Americans, blood pressure response to adrenalin in functional psychoses, and a monograph on the folklore of teeth (a study begun in Berlin) reflected his eclectic interests.[62]

This broad range helped Kanner compete for a Commonwealth Fellowship at the Henry Phipps Psychiatric Clinic at Johns Hopkins for the years 1928 to 1930. Adolph Meyer, the chief, interviewed him and in a follow-up letter told Kanner that he was just the kind of man Meyer was looking for but that Kanner was also just the kind of person desperately needed in a state hospital setting like Yankton. But this compliment did not deter Kanner for one moment. He telegraphed Meyer asking if a certain date for arrival in Baltimore was suitable. The response was positive.[63]

The academic community, as judgmental as ever, responded well to Kanner's intellect, which was unencumbered by conventional thinking, and to his gentle, hubris-free demeanor. Ambitious and assertive without being abrasive, he moved with unintimidated ease in the world-famous hospital. Although Kanner had no substantial experience in child psychiatry, Park, supported by Meyer and grants from the Josiah Macy, Jr. and Rockefeller Foundations, determined to put him in charge of the new Behavior Clinic for Children in the Harriet Lane in 1931.

Kanner taught himself the ropes and then he taught succeeding generations of house officers and colleagues. An exploration of world medical literature complemented his experience and led to the publication in 1935 of *Child Psychiatry*.[64] The first textbook with that title to appear in the United States, it was free of dogma and given to common sense.[65] His book for the laity, *In Defense of Mothers*, was just as wise and just as accessible; it remains one of the best in the plethora of advice books that have overtaken the bookshelves since then.[66]

A syndrome that Kanner wrote about in 1943 as "autistic disturbances of affective contact" and later called early infantile autism or, occasionally, Kanner syndrome, may be the effort most associated with his name.[67] Although he described children who differed markedly in poorly understood ways, Kanner was likely not the first to describe features of autism. Today there is disagreement with his original characterizations but he prompted renewed thought and better understanding as time went by. We know more today but the cause, thought by many to have a strong genetic component, is still in dispute and many of these children are still painfully dependent and not well understood.

A better remembrance of Kanner would dwell on his attention to the problems of the mentally retarded. With the support of Park and the aid of Mabel F. Kraus, a social worker, Kanner documented the exploitation of the mentally retarded by their families, lawyers, and judges, who rendered helpless the superintendents at the Maryland State Training Schools for the Retarded. Children at the school were often released with a writ of habeas corpus and put into domestic servitude, then discharged because they could not perform well. Commonly, they ended up in a "sad peregrination through the whorehouses and flophouses of the slums" with all that that implies.[68] Kanner's and Kraus' work was heralded in the *Baltimore Sun* on April 8, 1938, and the needed changes ensued.[69]

Kanner's social conscience was evident in his riposte to a physician who suggested that euthanasia might be appropriate for the retarded. In 1942 Kanner responded:

> Let us try to recall one single instance in the history of mankind when a feebleminded individual or group of individuals was responsible for the retardation or persecution of humaneness in science. Those who caused Galileo to be jailed were not feebleminded. Those who instituted the inquisition were not mental defectives. The great manmade catastrophes resulting in wholesale slaughter and destruction were not started by idiots, imbeciles, morons, or borderlines. The one man, Shiklgruber, whose

I.Q. is probably not below normal, has in a few years brought infinitely more disaster and suffering to this world than have all of the innumerable mental defectives of all countries and all generations combined."[70]

He was consistent in his defense of those whose humanity was threatened, particularly when colleagues urged him to stop his aid to Hitler's victims because the arrival of too many Jewish immigrants in the United States might arouse latent domestic anti-Semitism.[71]

Like others at Hopkins, Kanner came late to a full professorship, achieving that status in 1957, just two years before he became emeritus. That did not deter worldwide recognition and a host of honors, however. He was eighty-seven when he died after a splendid career and sixty years of marriage.

Horace Hodes and Sydenham Hospital

Diphtheria was epidemic in Baltimore in the mid-1940s. Patients with infectious disease were isolated at Sydenham Hospital, a branch of the Baltimore City Health Department. Horace Hodes, the medical director, constantly there, was what we define today as a hospitalist. The Harriet Lane house staff, who rotated to Sydenham, was Hodes' house staff, supported by occasional rotators from other institutions.

Since the Baltimore City Fire Department would not transport patients with presumed infectious disease, the house staff drove Sydenham's "ambulance." Not well equipped, it looked like a bread truck painted red. Inevitably, it was witness to drama. On one run to Mercy Hospital to fetch a young woman with poliomyelitis, a young man accompanied his stricken fiancée. We transported him one week later. She lived but he did not. A teenager with probable diphtheria, well over six feet tall and two hundred pounds, hid in the bathroom when we made our call. It took the arrival of a policeman with a club to bang on the door to get him out. I remember still my 5-feet-8-inch self with the policeman behind me, pleading with that young man to open his mouth: "Please, Bill! Let me see what your throat looks like, please!"

Hodes took charge when patients arrived at Sydenham. A splendid clinician, he provided and supervised patient care and taught the house officers with calm consistency. The decision to go ahead with tracheotomy if a laryngeal obstruction or a complicating bull neck threatened the patient with diphtheria was made quietly, unhesitatingly, and without fanfare by Hodes.[72] He was undeterred by conventional wisdom

HORACE HODES. Hodes became director of Sydenham, Baltimore's infectious disease hospital, in 1938. In a time before vaccines made it possible to prevent numerous conditions and antibiotics were available to treat others, Sydenham was the only facility in the city where patients suspected of having infectious conditions could be taken. The Harriet Lane house staff worked under Hodes as he explored ways to deal with the life-threatening conditions of their patients.

that did not have the force of genuine evidence. There had been some unsupported teaching that the use of digitalis might be disadvantageous in the treatment of diphtheritic myocarditis. He used it often but with caution during Baltimore's diphtheria epidemic of the 1940s, and the results assured that there was benefit without inappropriate risk.

Selman Waksman at Rutgers had discovered streptomycin during the 1940s. Hodes was able to corral a few vials of the precious drug for the trial treatment of the almost invariably fatal H. influenza B meningitis. One night, a tired house officer reached into the refrigerator for three bottles for immediate use and dropped them. Hodes consoled the crestfallen young doctor and simply went on to the next task. When I met that doctor years later at a meeting, he spoke of that moment with a clarity undiminished by time, eternally grateful for the sensitivity we all felt in Hodes' nurture of our incipient careers.

Sydenham opened in 1935 with Schwentker (Park's successor at the Harriet Lane as of 1946) as the infectious disease hospital's director. Hodes took over in 1938, an appointment arranged by Park. Born in Philadelphia in 1907, Hodes attended the University of Pennsylvania for undergraduate and medical school. He was the third author on two papers concerned with calcium metabolism by the time he graduated in 1931.[73] (His obituary in the *New York Times* perhaps overstated the claim that, while still a first-year medical student, he discovered that "the main function of Vitamin D is to bring about the absorption of calcium from the intestines."[74]) He was an intern for a year at the Children's Hospital of Philadelphia, went to Harriet Lane as an assistant resident (having attracted Park's interest with the calcium research), and then went back to Philadelphia as chief resident.

Park wanted Hodes to return and offered him an appointment as director of the Harriet Lane Dispensary. It isn't clear when Hodes shifted his research interest from calcium to viruses and bacteria. Perhaps the innumerable problems of children with infectious disease that he confronted during his years in training were a prime reason. In any event, he went to the Rockefeller Institute in New York in 1936 as an assistant in bacteriology. The papers on which he was the lead author during that period were concerned with viruses, and his demonstration that ultraviolet light could render rabies virus avirulent improved vaccination for that disease.[75]

Park brought Hodes back to Baltimore in 1938 to serve at Sydenham, where he complemented his service at the bedside with more than twenty published papers concerning the use of newly arrived chemotherapeutic and antibiotic agents, viral immunity, streptococcal infection, and, of particular note, the isolation of a filterable virus causing diarrhea in calves. Hodes and a colleague at the time, Jacob Light, are now credited with the first recognition of the rotavirus.[76]

A letter to Dean Alan Chesney at Johns Hopkins from Dean L. R. Chandler at Stanford confirmed Hodes' reputation. "I want you to know that we are casting eyes at Dr. Hodes and would like your permission to go ahead and contact him to see whether or not he would be interested in such an opportunity."[77] Chesney was immediately forthcoming: "By all means take a look at Horace Hodes. He is excellent professorial timber and the boys at U.C.L.A. have been casting their eyes at him. He is very highly thought of here... a reserved, softspoken individual, very clear thinking, and has done excellent research. I think that you would make no mistake in appointing him."[78]

It was soon apparent that the "boys" at Mount Sinai Hospital were also interested and in 1949, when he was forty-one years old, Hodes went to New York where he continued to serve until his death in 1989. It is unclear why he did not choose California. It is easy, however, to surmise in him some restlessness and eagerness for new challenges. Mount Sinai intended to start a new medical school where he could be (and was) a major player in its founding. Also, he could not expect that Hopkins during that period would recognize his achievement by promotion to full professor. At Mount Sinai School of Medicine, he was appointed the first Herbert H. Lehman Professor of Pediatrics and Chairman of the Department in 1964. A spate of other honors followed, notably the John Howland Award in 1982.[79]

I remember an incident that may help to explain in some measure Hodes' decision to go to Mt. Sinai. My oldest son was born in October 1946. Eight days passed and the time for ritual circumcision (a bris) arrived. Desperately wanting the time off, I approached Hodes hesitantly. Every bed at Sydenham was full. The pull between family responsibility and desire and patient responsibility was great and there was uncertainty about the chief's response. I worried that maybe he didn't know what a bris was. My concern was misplaced as Hodes, of course, knew what it was. I still remember the broad smile on his face and the admonition, too, that concern for one's family needs should never be ignored. I learned of Hodes' respect for the humanistic tradition that was his heritage.

Sydenham did not last long after Hodes' departure. The hospital was soon closed because newer treatments with antibiotics made it possible to transfer Sydenham's functions to Baltimore City Hospitals and private institutions.[80] It is unlikely that Hodes was passive in the inevitable discussions about Sydenham's closure and there is nothing to suggest that he would resist change. Rather, he likely understood the decision and realized that it was time to move on.

Samuel Livingston and the Epilepsy Clinic

Unlike others whom Park had selected as specialty clinic chiefs, Samuel Livingston was not present at the creation of the Johns Hopkins Hospital Epilepsy Clinic, the first in the United States to limit its patients to those with seizures.[81] The clinic was organized in 1926 at a time made murky by Howland's death. Park realized its potential and made sure that it would survive, relying first on Lawson Wilkins as its temporary head and in 1928 on the recruitment of Edward Bridge, a 1926 graduate of the Harvard Medical School.[82]

The clinic cared for children and, after 1941, adults. This broadening of the age range gave the opportunity, infrequent in those days, for prolonged follow-up and a better understanding of the lifetime impact of a disease. Treatment of epilepsy was wanting even into the 1940s. Few physicians were willing to take on the care of those whose problems were treated by society with the same hush-hush ambivalence as cancer. Hospital emergency departments and general outpatient departments with inadequate resources, gave little, if any, attention to the total care of the patient.[83]

Happily, there was money to support Park's intentions. The university had received six thousand dollars for the care of patients with epilepsy and for research. This allowed major recruitment: a technician from Boston, a social worker from within the hospital, and the clinic's permanent chief, Edward Bridge. With these funds Bridge was able to devote himself entirely to the study of epilepsy.[84] He ran the clinic for the next sixteen years, leaving in 1944 to head the newly established Statler Pediatrics Research Department at the Children's Hospital of Buffalo.[85] A prolific investigator, his research concerned both the mental and chemical state of the patient with epilepsy and extended into aspects of glycogen metabolism.

Bridge did not work alone. Howland had recruited Laslo Kajdi, "a young Hungarian chemist with some knowledge of pediatrics and a far greater knowledge of chemistry... highly recommended by those with whom he has worked in Budapest."[86] Wilburt C. Davison, acting chief of the Harriet Lane during Howland's trip to London, petitioned Dean Lewis Weed on June 4, 1926, for authority to set a salary of fifteen hundred dollars and to make the final arrangements to hire Kajdi.[87] This was granted but Howland's unexpected death led Davison to decide "he did not think it wise to appoint Dr. Kajdi as Instructor in Pediatrics."[88] The record is uncertain but it may have been Park's intervention that assured Kajdi's arrival. Together, Bridge and Kajdi did the initial work contributing to our understanding of epilepsy and its social problems.

The clinic was thus well established when Livingston, then twenty-eight years old, joined it in 1936. He would increase its productivity exponentially but not always with acclaim. Livingston did not have the patina of obvious intelligence and the charisma of so many of his contemporaries. Even the house officers shied from deferring to him as they did with other senior faculty. His small size, indifference to sartorial elegance, quiet reserve, and absolute absence of pedantry belied his energy and intellectual dynamism.

Livingston was accustomed to deferred recognition and rejection. His early life was a struggle. He worked seven days a week as a movie usher to support his high school education at Baltimore City College and as a restaurant menial to get through Georgetown University. An excellent college record did not make it easier to get into medical school. Johns Hopkins, Harvard, and Yale turned him down. Forty-two years after the fact, Robert Cooke (who became director of the Harriet Lane in 1956) suggested that there were "two perfectly possible reasons—one, he came from a Catholic College; two, the Jewish quota."[89]

Livingston, undaunted, took a master's degree in chemistry at George Washington University and applied to Hopkins again. Cooke reported: "He was turned down again. This time the reason was probably just the Jewish quota." Vanderbilt, however, accepted Livingston. He learned there the meaning of play and fun for the first time. "He was a good but not distinguished scholar, but good enough to be accepted at Hopkins by a great man without prejudice, Edwards A. Park, the Professor of Pediatrics."[90]

It took time for Livingston to become confident of his craft. His first paper, concerned with tests of carbohydrate metabolism, appeared in 1942, six years after his appointment to the clinic at Johns Hopkins. Bridge was the second author.[91] Over the next quarter century Livingston published almost ninety papers, primarily in refereed journals, and four seminal books. Epilepsy was the constant theme in his publications and he explored the specific problems associated with drug therapy, the social and emotional needs of the patient, the variety of convulsive disorders, and possible causes of seizures or seizure-like episodes in particular.[92]

Livingston evaluated drugs used for seizure disorders, provided careful instructions for their use, and described various seizure manifestations in the young including febrile convulsions, focal epilepsy, paroxysmal choreoathetosis, and photogenic epilepsy, which clarified considerably the range of disorders. He was unafraid to use the con-

SAMUEL LIVINGSTON. The Johns Hopkins Hospital Epilepsy Clinic was well established when Livingston joined its staff in 1936; ten years later he became its director. In its early years the clinic treated children exclusively but by 1941 adults were also admitted as patients. Livingston wrote dozens of articles and four influential books considering drug therapy and the social and emotional needs of patients with seizure disorders. Photo by Udel Brothers and reproduced here with permission.

troversial ketogenic diet—disparaged by many as too difficult and impractical—that continues to provide significant benefit to many with intractable problems. Livington's clinical efforts and publications were the foundation for his role as advisor to state and national government bureaus and for his contributions to "improving the educational, social, and legal status" of those with epilepsy.[93]

In 1946 Livingston became director of the epilepsy clinic at the age of fifty-eight. Hopkins, still slow in these matters, did not appoint him an associate professor until 1966. The delay in recognition was likely influenced by the fact that he had not been highly trained in neurology and his work was criticized for this by at least some neurologists. Cooke's ardent advocacy, however, prevailed in the long run and Livingston was awarded his appointment.

Livingston believed that patients with epilepsy should not be considered "second class citizens," and that they should be allowed every opportunity to participate, as they were inclined, in the mainstream of life.[94] Livingston regretted that there were still inadequate numbers of epileptologists and even fewer neurologists as late as 1978 who devoted themselves to the total care of epileptic patients and their intimidating range of problems. He took this as a mandate to educate and involve the entire range of primary care physicians.[95] During my many years of practice in Baltimore I witnessed his achievement of this goal.

Miriam Esther Brailey and the Tuberculosis Clinic

The date on which Park established a tuberculosis clinic for children is uncertain but it really began to achieve its potential when he installed Miriam Brailey as its chief in 1941. She grew up in a tiny village in Vermont. After graduating from Mount Holyoke she taught zoology at her alma mater for two years and then worked as a technician and assistant in a doctor's office in Lynn, Massachusetts. In July of 1926, the Mount Holyoke *Alumnae Quarterly* reported: "Miriam Brailey will enter Johns Hopkins Medical School in the fall. She has received a fellowship covering tuition and living expenses for the four years of the medical course, and for a possible fifth year if she wishes to specialize in public health work."[96] Brailey arrived in Baltimore at the age of twenty-six and was immediately chagrined at the quality of life for the patients who lived near the hospital. Already needy, they were beginning to feel the further impact of the nascent depression of the 1930s. The raggedy inner city became subject to even greater decay. Concern for its problems informed the next three decades of her career.

After graduation, Brailey took advantage of her fellowship and earned a doctor of public health degree at the Johns Hopkins School of Hygiene and Public Health, then began her work with Wade Hampton Frost, the first professor of epidemiology in the United States.[97] He applied epidemiological methods to the study of tuberculosis and investigated the experiences of the patients in the Harriet Lane clinic. Brailey's doctoral thesis examined the histories of adolescents in that clinic who had contracted tuberculosis in infancy. In the December 1936 issue of the Baltimore Council on Social Agencies' quarterly publication, *The Councillor,* Brailey supplied the text on which she based her career: "Maryland has 305 tuberculosis beds for Negroes, yet in 1935 there were 614 fatal cases. In contrast to this, 1103 beds were assigned

MIRIAM BRAILEY. Brailey was on the faculty of the Johns Hopkins School of Hygiene and Public Health's department of epidemiology when, in 1941, Edwards Park asked her to lead the Harriet Lane Tuberculosis Clinic. At the same time she also became director of the Bureau of Tuberculosis in the Baltimore City Health Department. Brailey was an ardent advocate for the city's black population, which often received inadequate treatment because of segregation policies in many city health facilities. Photo by Greystone Studios (New York).

to white patients, there being 749 fatal cases in 1935. Although Negroes in Maryland have four times the death rate, sanatorium facilities are one third as numerous as for the white race."[98]

Miriam Brailey was the first female faculty member in the Johns Hopkins School of Hygiene and Public Health's department of epidemiology. Then, in 1941, Park asked her to lead the Harriet Lane Tuberculosis Clinic and she was also made director of the Bureau of Tuberculosis in the Baltimore City Health Department, which signaled a developing relationship between the health department and Johns Hopkins. These positions provided Brailey with the opportunity to improve the well-being of African Americans in Baltimore and complemented her participation with Janet Hardy in the Harriet Lane Study, in which a cohort of children and their families were followed for years.[99]

But Brailey had a parallel life. *The Baltimore Health News*, a publication of the Baltimore City Health Department, reported in April 1945, "Dr. Brailey is a member of the Society of Friends and has a keen interest in interracial cooperation and in world organization to promote a durable peace." Four years later Maryland, not unaware of Martin Dies' House Un-American Activities Committee in the United States Congress, passed the Subversive Activities Act that demanded that state and city employees sign a loyalty oath assuring that they were not and had never been involved in subversive activities. "Subversive" was never well defined. Regardless, on July 29, 1949, the Homewood Society of Friends voted to oppose the signing of the oath. Brailey and two other Quakers who were state employees refused to do so. Health Commissioner Huntington Williams, displaying no support for his colleague, agreed with the state's mandate and discharged her on March 26, 1950.[100]

Brailey's future at Harriet Lane was secure, however. Johns Hopkins was a private institution and, in any event, Park would not have been intimidated. Still, she suffered a substantial loss of income. Her effort to regain her city job back via a lawsuit based on her religious principles went nowhere. Hopkins was, however, helpful. She was appointed assistant professor of epidemiology in the School of Hygiene and Public Health and, not long after, to a similar rank in pediatrics and medicine. She also took over the directorship of the tuberculosis section of the chest clinic of the Johns Hopkins Hospital. She scrounged for clinical and research support and in 1954 the Maryland Tuberculosis Foundation granted her fourteen thousand dollars, citing the need for education, research, and consultation. In this instance the Baltimore City Health Department, aware of the funding, did not back away from acting as one of the program's coordinators.

The Harriet Lane Study was also productive. *Tuberculosis in White and Negro Children*, volumes I and II, was published in 1958.[101] Hardy wrote about the clinical aspects of the disease in volume I and Brailey covered the epidemiological aspects in volume II. It is ironic in present terms that Brailey felt that the era of tuberculosis in the United States was pretty well over because of modern therapies.[102] She could not know, of course, of the future entanglement of AIDS with tuberculosis.

It may be that the promise of control of tuberculosis in the United States underlay Miriam Brailey's decision to leave Baltimore in 1959.

She was, after all, a fifty-nine-year-old single woman who had no resource other than herself. She was a Quaker with a profound concern
for universal justice and peace. She chose to move to the Bruderhof
Community of Oak Lake, near Farmington, Pennsylvania, in which
those ideals and a life based on service to God and humanity were
rooted. Brailey described it to friends as a liberal religious community
where "whole families and single persons as well live together in complete sharing of possessions, making their skills available to the group
and of course working without pay in money."[103]

The strong-minded, often outspoken Brailey joined this closed,
male-dominated society and ceded to it all of her assets. She was candid in expressing her concern about aspects of the life at Bruderhof
and was admired by some and isolated by others. Gradually, her health
dwindled, her vision failed, and Parkinson disease took over. Her courage remained, however. It was reported that she refused to take the
required loyalty oath to the Bruderhof leader and, as in the past, her
conscience evoked a heavy response. She was ordered from the community and removed to a nursing home where she died in 1976. Those
who visited her there recognized her loneliness, her physical frailty,
and her persistent mental toughness.[104]

Janet Hardy and the Harriet Lane Nursery

Janet Hardy came to Harriet Lane from Montreal, Canada, as a
1941 graduate of the medical school at McGill University.[105] Her husband, Paul Hardy, also a pediatrician, joined her in Baltimore after his
wartime military service, later becoming a chief resident in Harriet
Lane. Janet Hardy, one of Park's last academic appointees, was another
young doctor whose career he directed. She recalled that when she was
the physician to the nursery, Park told her "Dr. Eastman and I have decided that pediatrics is going to take over the nursery service as of next
Monday and we would like you to do this." Hardy was amazed. "You
know, one was left with one's mouth sort of hanging open and said,
'yes.'"[106] Park, mindful of the national campaign to reduce the mortality of prematurity, anointed Hardy a second time not very long after
that. "We are putting a new premature nursery in Harriet Lane," he
told her. "With your experience in the nurseries, we would like you to
be in charge of it."[107] Park probably had little more to go on in judging
Hardy as what we now call a neonatologist other than his observation
of her on the wards and his confidence in her abilities. Just out of her

JANET HARDY. Hardy was only three years out of medical school when Edwards Park named her to head the nursery in the Harriet Lane Home. Her interest in patients continued long after their discharge. She conducted in-depth studies on the subsequent lives of children who grew up in neighborhoods around the hospital, and she became prominent for promoting sex education for adolescents in an effort to reduce the number of teenage pregnancies.

residency at Harriet Lane and only three years out of medical school, she was the first pediatrician put in charge of any of the newborn nurseries at Johns Hopkins. She was at the same time director of a long-term study of tuberculosis, working with Miriam Brailey.[108]

Clinically astute and possessed of impeccable judgment, Hardy pressed her points with a quiet, unabrasive but nevertheless assertive approach. This became clear while she was still a house officer, when a baby was admitted with, by Hardy's diagnosis, an intussusception. "To me, it was an absolutely classical case," she recalled. The surgeon, however, grumbling and a bit patronizing of a pediatric house officer, chastised her and said that she "had no right" to make that decision. He and his entourage did the diagnostic barium enema under fluoroscopy and found no intussusception. They left "very disgruntled." Hardy had to chase them down the hall to insist that they again see the baby, whose condition had obviously worsened. She insisted that the infant did have the abdominal mass indicative of the problem, and she was proved right. When the baby was properly cared for, the surgeon smiled at Hardy and graciously admitted that he had been wrong; he never argued with her again.[109]

The premature nursery formally opened on April 1, 1946, built as an appendage on Harriet Lane 3 West.[110] Park and Ethel Dunham, also a Harriet Laner, planned the nursery. At the entrance there was a large demonstration room and nursing station with four nurseries serving as many as twenty-four infants and three workrooms beyond. The nurses were clearly in charge. They took over in the demonstration room, assuring that everyone entering was properly hand-washed, masked, and gowned. Conferences and parent classes—relatively recent innovations—were held there, and a large viewing window allowed families to see their babies. The newest and sickest babies, constantly supervised by the nurses, moved on to the "graduate nursery" as they grew bigger and stronger. Hardy, working closely with the nurses, devised a program that validated the excellence of the nursing service in the Harriet Lane Home, which had been manifest since its early days.

The doctors' expertise would have accomplished little without the minute-by-minute meticulous nursing essential to the babies' survival. Their care was far from routine. For example, babies were not bathed on admission. They had to reach a weight of eighteen-hundred grams before they had their first real immersion, and then only every other day. Before that, the nurses or nursing students cleansed just a few areas, particularly the buttocks and face, with oil. Feeding, too, demanded delicate care. Most of the babies could not be started on a nipple. They needed to be fed by gavage, a tube slipped into the stomach. The nurse could judge a baby's readiness to take the nipple when the tube was sucked vigorously enough during the gavage.[111]

In the 1940s and early 1950s the Gordon-Armstrong incubator was the ordained "residence" for infants under seventeen- or eighteen-hundred grams. It could be maintained at a temperature of eighty-eight degrees Fahrenheit and a humidity of fifty-five to sixty percent. It also served as an oxygen hood and the house staff provided oxygen generously. Our understanding of prematurity was still limited, however. We did not yet know the role of oxygen in causing what was then called retrolental fibroplasia (now, retinopathy of the newborn) and we used it to excess. We also gave frequent blood transfusions. Hardy instructed us in the art of threading a tiny needle into an even tinier vein to deliver as much as ten cc of blood at a time. She supported us and attempted to relieve our frustration at our inability to sustain the very low birthweight infants. Sadly, many died. She even taught me, a non-Catholic, how to administer the last rites to babies when appropriate.

More than fifty years ago major operative procedures on premature babies became somewhat less daunting. Surgeons, enabled in part by the example of Blalock and Taussig's work with infants with tetralogy of Fallot, were inspired to take up additional challenges. William Longmire in the department of surgery worked with Hardy to rescue babies, even prematures, born with tracheo-esophageal fistula. The combination of his surgical skill, her understanding of very young and very small babies, and splendid nursing care saved one child whose progress I was privileged to watch hour by hour when I was an assistant resident.

The subsequent lives of many of the surviving premature infants and other babies from the inner city became one of Hardy's compelling interests. What became of them? What influenced their growth and development? What problems were particular to their circumstances? What could be done to help if help was necessary? These questions inspired her decades-long involvement in the life of East Baltimore's urban community, especially its children and adolescents.

Her first study, begun in the 1960s, tracked inner-city children from birth, indeed, from their in utero existence. Hardy and her team interviewed more than two thousand mothers when they were pregnant and again when the children were eight years old. Follow-up twenty-five to thirty years later was achieved with a dedicated search of hospital records (tracing the next of kin) and motor vehicle registry records. In the end, 1,758 (seventy-one percent) of the children in the initial study—at that point in their late twenties to early thirties—were found. They lived in Maryland and in places as disparate as California and Germany. Some owned businesses and earned as much as $250,000 a year while others lived on a Baltimore street corner or in a jail cell. One, a man who declined to participate, played on a team in the National Basketball Association. All told, substantial numbers of these former inner-city children had become successful adults, but, unhappily, not all were successful. Hardy and her colleagues reported on and discussed innumerable variables that seemed to guide these outcomes.[112]

Further, Hardy the investigator became an ardent advocate, intimately involved in the issues facing the East Baltimore community.

Hardy's quiet demeanor cloaked the ardor of her approach. She ran special programs and clinics that addressed in forthright and accessible terms a variety of issues related to the needs of the poor and she did not back away from sensitive issues like sexual behavior.[113] In 1982 *USA Today* reported on a year-old program headed by Hardy that provided sex education courses and contraceptives to junior and senior high school students at an after-school medical clinic in East Baltimore in an effort to curb the high teenage pregnancy rate.[114] Three years later the *New York Times* gave an account of the success of that work, noting a 15 percent drop in the pregnancy rate during the almost three-year period in which counseling and contraceptives were made available. Hardy asserted, "This data is significant because it really refutes the claims of those who believe that the provision of contraceptives causes kids to become promiscuous."[115]

Hardy never minced words. A letter she wrote to the editor of the *Baltimore Sun* in 1984 began, "I want to express my sense of outrage and concern about what appears to be a shameful lack of foresight on the part of the current administration." The issue in that instance concerned vaccine supplies for Baltimore children.[116] "The price of one bomb would likely pay for all the vaccine needed by poor children and the price of one bomber amply cover both vaccine and the victims. When will we demonstrate our concern for the long-term health of all our children?" she asked plaintively.

Hardy's multifaceted career was more intensely involved in the Baltimore community than most others at Harriet Lane. Johns Hopkins was her base, but she also held a variety of leadership roles with the Baltimore City Health Department over the years. More than most on the School of Medicine faculty at the time, Hardy worked closely with colleagues at the Johns Hopkins School of Public Health. This collaboration provided her with valuable insights and allowed her the opportunity to make vital contributions to an eclectic range of issues as disparate as maternal viral infection in pregnancy, congenital syphilis, and pitfalls in the measurement of intelligence in urban children. She amassed a bibliography that revealed her extensive consideration of society's difficult social and health issues, such as contraception, teenage sexual practices, and adolescent parenthood. She was concerned with the economically disenfranchised well before such interests had become politically acceptable, and she moved beyond research to the implementation of useful programs and involvement in public discussion.

Hardy's career was enormously satisfying to her. "Looking back over my life there are few things I would change." Few would agree, but she believed she "should have worked harder and been more productive." She also acknowledged her debt to Park: "As far as I am aware, I am probably the sole remaining Park faculty appointee. It was a privilege to have known him well and to have benefited from his mentoring and his friendship." She summarized her relationship with her home institution simply and effectively, and she addressed the feelings many of us share when she noted, "I have been fortunate indeed! Hopkins has (and still is) treating me very well and I am duly grateful."[117]

Hugh Wilson Josephs, Pioneer in Pediatric Hematology

The wisdom of Park's invitation to Hugh Josephs to join the faculty was confirmed in 1936 by the publication of Josephs' seminal monograph, "Anemias of Childhood" in *Medicine*. Josephs performed profoundly revealing studies on the relationship between iron metabolism and the anemia of infancy in a rudimentary laboratory, using instruments of his own design and construction.[118] He was a pioneer pediatric hematologist, although he was not considered an initiator of the field as Taussig, Wilkins, and Kanner were. (Louis Diamond at Children's Hospital in Boston, among others, was another powerful presence in pediatric hematology and could lay claim to that description as well.)

Josephs went to medical school intent on the study of disease.[119] His family thought that the prodigiously accomplished young man, like his father a graduate of Harvard College, might just as easily have had a future as a chemist or a concert pianist, or even as a horticulturist. His distinguishing characteristic was a passion for perfection and excellence in all things. In 1915 he started medical school at Johns Hopkins because it seemed to him the place to be for a physician interested in scientific inquiry. After three years as a Harriet Lane resident he moved in 1922 to the University of Chicago to study chemistry. That one year, he wrote, was his "dividing line between youth and maturity... if one can define youth as the period of preparation, and maturity as beginning with the acceptance of responsibility for one's own development."[120] Josephs then returned to Harriet Lane for the rest of his career.

Josephs' contemporaries at Harriet Lane were, like him, bright—

HUGH JOSEPHS. Josephs was a pioneer pediatric hematologist. His studies provided new insights into the relationship between iron metabolism and anemia in infants and children. His clinical wisdom and range of knowledge were vast; his manner was soft-spoken and unassuming.

some were even brilliant—deeply committed, and genuine in their efforts to contribute to new knowledge and new techniques. They were by no means superficial, but there is little evidence that many of them had an understanding of themselves with quite the same depth of insight as Josephs. For example, Josephs took little for granted, certainly not what he read in the scientific literature. "I found it desirable to attempt an analysis of why it was I would reject one article, while accepting another. It soon became apparent that pure objectivity held up as an ideal for scientific work was not only virtually impossible but not even desirable," Josephs argued. Objectivity, then, was misleading and needed a little deflation as a universal scientific goal. Certainly, the roles of emotion, desire, and bias had to be recognized and kept at bay. Given that, he continued, "I find that my opinion of the validity of an idea depends largely on the ease with which that idea can be assimilated. In many cases, after a lapse of time, I find myself easily accepting an idea that I had previously rejected; it is evident that the excellent reasons I had given myself for the rejection no longer hold."[121] Werner Karl Heisenberg, who won a 1932 Nobel Prize for his Uncertainty Principle, might have influenced Josephs in this regard and created a disciple in Baltimore.[122] Josephs valued those who accepted "doubt and insecurity as part of their philosophy of life, and so have lost their fear of it." The scientist has to be wary, though, for "truth is never static, and the danger to those who have attained success is that they may succumb to the delights of security, and in so doing surrender truth to dogma."[123]

Owen Lattimore is associated with an embarrassing episode in the life of the Johns Hopkins University which occurred over a half-century ago when Senator Joseph McCarthy of Wisconsin intimidated the country and, for a while, "McCarthyism" reigned. Lattimore, who was a noted "China expert" and teacher of Asian studies on the Hopkins faculty then, lived next door to the Josephs, sharing a common driveway with letterboxes side by side. The two families had a flourishing relationship when in the late 1940s and early 1950s Lattimore was wrongly suspected because of his expertise and many contacts with people in Communist China. Lattimore believed and later confirmed that there were several bugs on his telephone placed by government agencies. Since he and some of his associates were among the few in the United States who knew the Mongolian dialects, he simply went next door to collect his mail and to use the phone, speaking in flawless Mongolian. Josephs stood by Lattimore throughout this difficult time, although the university did not.[124]

This was, of course, characteristic of Josephs. He was born to a prosperous family in New Orleans in 1892 and educated at Gilman School in Baltimore and Groton in Massachusetts before he attended Harvard. His mother and father encouraged an eclectic experience: formal studies, as well as Josephs' bent for the piano and for gardening. Mornings were spent "moseying on the piano… composing his own scores through which he told a great deal about how he was feeling." This was evident also as Josephs planted and cared for flowers and shrubs in his English-style garden in suburban Baltimore.[125] Josephs was a self-contained man who was sensitive to both beauty and discord and who achieved impressive self-realization. The physician, musician, and gardener in him were able to support his friend Lattimore while giving us considerable understanding of the anemias, as well as other problems of childhood.

In 1926 Josephs married Charlotte McCarthy, a Hopkins graduate and a practitioner of medicine throughout their lives together. After his death in 1980, she endowed a visiting professorship in his name. The rigid Hopkins promotion system had never made Josephs a full professor. But now each year the visiting professorship reminds the department of pediatrics of Hugh Josephs' contributions.

Harriet Griggs Guild and the Harriet Lane Private Service

Harriet Guild, a native of New England and the daughter of a country doctor, was in a sense bequeathed to Park by Howland. "I was in the last group of interns appointed by Dr. H., but then he died just before we got started!"[126] She "got started" at Harriet Lane and she stayed, establishing a career that engendered love in many patients and colleagues, and ambivalence at best in other colleagues.

Guild's interest in medicine was confirmed at Vassar College. "I began majoring in languages with an idea of teaching—French, German, Spanish, even Old English. I took some science just out of curiosity. But when I got into biology I knew more than anything I wanted to be a doctor." Never intimidated by the clock or the calendar, she responded to her father's insistence that she take a year to be sure. She made house calls with him in his horse and buggy and "did some lab work" and convinced him.[127]

Grades were the most important hiring criterion then, particularly if a woman wanted a place on the Johns Hopkins house staff. Guild's record was superb.[128] Typically unhurried, she took a year as an intern in medicine before going to Harriet Lane. "Even though I knew I wanted to do pediatrics, I interned my first year at the Adult Medical Service because I felt I should know something about adult medicine before I turned to children."[129]

After residency and a short period in the dispensary, Guild became in effect the director of the private service on Harriet Lane 2. She devoted herself totally to her patients. They were her children and she believed religiously that, to be a doctor, one "must want to with all

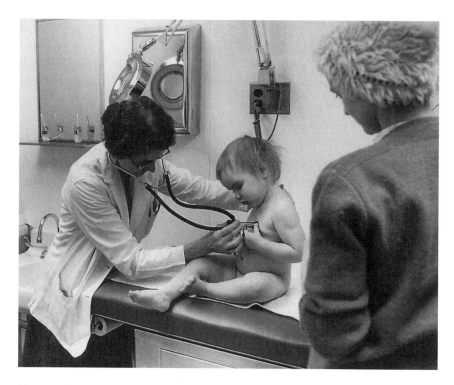

HARRIET GUILD EXAMINING A CHILD. Guild ran the second-floor ward, which was dedicated to the care of private patients, for many years. Her commitment to care was absolute. Photo by the Barton Gillet Company of Baltimore.

your heart and whole self... not half way interest... one must not only have an absorbing interest but one must be willing to forget oneself.... Isn't this exactly what a mother must do?"[130]

And this was how Guild lived. She took on compulsively the care of children with nephrosis and other kidney diseases, Gaucher disease, diabetes, and much else, at a time when our ability to deal with the attendant issues was limited at best. Many recognized her expertise and her patients had a seemingly limitless faith in her. Others saw her differently. Park wrote to a potential colleague that sending "a private patient to Dr. Guild is like blood to a tiger and I am afraid that you will find that she cannot keep her hands off, so that you may have difficulties from [her] barging in after she appears on the scene. She becomes so engrossed that she does not realize she is barging in. She will not deliberately interfere but I doubt if she can help interfering."[131]

I respected Guild's base of knowledge and her meticulous attention to detail. I remember, too, the constant phone calls when I covered for her during her infrequent vacations back home in Connecticut. Others dissented, however, and the resentment toward her approach and the feeling that she over-treated her patients and isolated them unnecessarily became more explicit after Park's retirement. She was, however, well entrenched and I found nothing to suggest that Schwentker paid much attention to her during his troubled tenure. He did organize one noon conference at which he proposed to discuss critically one of her patients but "everybody failed to support him."[132] Guild ran the second floor of Harriet Lane and there were years in which she had house officers recruited only for that domain.

It fell to Robert Cooke to solve the problems that many felt Guild presented. Cooke was rather abrupt in laying down the law. Samuel Asper, then a vice president of the hospital, wrote a memo for the record after Guild had come to him, desperate for help. She was to become emeritus on July 1, 1965, she told him, but she wanted to keep on with her fellowship program concerned with nephrosis and her patient care responsibilities. She had the funding for a fellow and secretaries but no laboratory space. However, Cooke had written her on February 17, 1965, to tell her "that the space presently occupied by [Guild], her fellows and secretaries will be required for other programs, that no fellowships will be permitted, and that [she could] continue her work with private patients with nephrosis, but subject to the usual rules applying to the active part-time staff." Asper noted, "It is apparent that Dr. Guild feels keenly this abrupt removal of her responsibilities and program. Although I think that there is little that can be done about it, I told her I would ask Dr. Turner's [the dean of the medical faculty] opinion."[133]

Nothing was done about it, and Guild went into private practice and moved her office across the street from the hospital. She was honored with an abundance of awards and public avowals of respect. But much was missing. This was apparent in a subsequent conversation I had with her. She said she hoped that my career was satisfying to me but she lamented that that had not been the case for her after she "moved over here, across the street."[134] She lived for twenty-seven years after the move.

Harold and Helen Coplan Harrison and Baltimore City Hospitals

Near the end of Park's tenure, he determined to entice a promising young couple from Yale. Grover Powers, Park's successor in New Haven and his steadfast friend, was a mentor to Harold and Helen Harrison. The Harrisons shared Park's fascination with rickets and had a "lively and sophisticated interest in calcium and phosphorus metabolism."[135] Park envisioned them as colleagues in the studies he planned during what turned out to be his twenty-three years of retirement.

Harold Harrison, born in New Haven and educated at Yale, met Helen Coplan when she was a doctoral student in the department of physiological chemistry there and he was chief resident in Yale's department of pediatrics. There was a patient with unexplained glycosuria, which clearly was not diabetes. Helen happened to have access to a polarizing microscope, which they set up in a small closet off the ward. Together, they proved that the problem was fructosuria, and Harold was a hero at morning rounds. They married in 1936 and their first coauthored paper appeared shortly thereafter.[136]

Park first tried to recruit the Harrisons in 1938. They were then involved with electrolytes, carbohydrates, and adrenal hormones. The Harrisons' developing reputation attracted both Park and Samuel Levine at Cornell. Helen had grown up in Baltimore and graduated from Goucher College there. Still, the pull home was not strong enough and Park's offer was turned down. He was gracious: "I am sorry that you could not join us but I am glad that you have this fine opportunity with Dr. Levine." In a handwritten postscript, Park wrote, "I hope that you will visit us even though you will not wear our colors." [137]

The four years with Levine in New York allowed a renewed relationship with Harry Gordon, once a pediatric resident at Yale, and the chance to explore different paths in research, particularly in phosphate excretion.[138] That friendship probably helped to convince Gordon to take on the leadership of the department of pediatrics at Sinai Hospital in Baltimore not long after the Harrisons eventually made their move to Johns Hopkins in 1945.

Meanwhile, World War II intervened. The Harrisons went back to Yale where Harold worked as a physiologist on a chemical warfare project. Park persisted with his recruitment efforts. His second attempt, with Powers as mediator, began in 1944. Park, at the end of his tenure as chief, had no money and he was hampered by some of Hopkins' inbred practices and prejudices. "After having asked [Powers] to talk to you on the assumption that I could offer you a position in the Department in the very near future, I have found that I cannot do that on account of the lack of provision in the budget," Park wrote to Harold at the end of 1944. "I hope that I can make you an offer on July first but that will be contingent on my ability to raise the funds

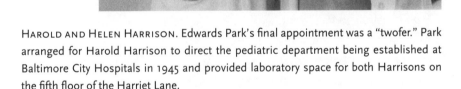

HAROLD AND HELEN HARRISON. Edwards Park's final appointment was a "twofer." Park arranged for Harold Harrison to direct the pediatric department being established at Baltimore City Hospitals in 1945 and provided laboratory space for both Harrisons on the fifth floor of the Harriet Lane.

necessary to obtain for you technical assistance and money to finance your investigative work."[139] Park was defensive: "I am not at all sure that you would care to consider an offer from me. In the first place, I am sixty-six, almost sixty-seven years old. The age limit here is seventy years and I have urged on the President to replace me, whenever it seems advisable to do so.... As the result of my age, two conditions, therefore, arise: First, I could not offer you an appointment of longer duration than my own; in other words, when I am retired, your future in the Department would be in the hands of my successor." The second condition concerned Hopkins' habitual reluctance to be generous with academic appointments. "Second, I could not offer you an Associate Professorship but only the position of Associate." And then, the money: "The salary which I could offer you, also, would not be large; it would be only four thousand dollars. Of course, living is not as expensive in Baltimore as in New York City."[140]

"There is a curious situation in the Department," Park continued, suggesting a way to get what he wanted. "There is a pediatric service at the City Hospitals in progress of being developed. I hope that it will develop into a pediatric service that will rival the one here." After describing the situation at City Hospitals in positive but not overstated terms and reminding Harold Harrison that the service at City was under the "jurisdiction" of the Johns Hopkins School of Medicine and staffed in part by its pediatric residents, Park wrote that taking a post there "would be a gamble" on Harold's part but "... nevertheless, it might be worth taking."[141] Clearly, Park was frustrated by the proposal he was making: "It was not with the idea of placing you at the City Hospitals that I had you in mind as a member of our staff but rather to place you in the Harriet Lane proper where I could give you responsibilities in teaching and ward work.... This place has been a fine searching place for pediatric talent; a good many men have gone out from us to important positions in medical schools and laboratories. I think that if you came here, you would be in the full flow of pediatric advancement."[142]

Finally, Park revealed the central reason for suggesting Baltimore City Hospitals in the first place: "Then there is the opportunity at City Hospitals, which you might not like at all, but it would be your own kingdom and I believe a good chance for you to take, in particular, in view of difficulties confronting your race in University advancement." Then Park shared his own bias. "I might add that I have never had any sympathy with discrimination against Jews and am inclined to think that I am fonder of some of my Jewish assistants of the past than of the Aryans."[143]

It took Park more than six months to confirm his offer with the assurance that funding had been arranged for both Harrisons.[144] Harold went on to create a splendid program at City Hospitals in which patient care, teaching, and intellectual inquiry were of exceptional quality. It may be that the program did not achieve Park's intimation of equality with Harriet Lane in public perception but those of us involved even at the periphery recognized its excellence.

Settling in was not easy in 1945. The Harrisons' son Stephen was still quite young when they moved to Baltimore and Richard was born not too long afterward. Helen did not take over in the laboratory for at least a year, and Harold had to deal with the bureaucracy of the City Hospitals and the City of Baltimore. He was offering "personal interest, great breadth of knowledge, dedication and high standards of conduct and of service to offset the handicaps then largely inherent in community hospitals"[145] The administrators did not fully appreciate this or the man himself at first, but they came around.

Park, however, was quick to take advantage. He used Harold's presence to attract Daniel Darrow of Yale as a visiting investigator for a study of "summer diarrhea" in children.[146] This was vintage Park. He marshaled resources, primarily human, as best he could and provided the relentless push that brought so much to fruition.

The laboratory Park provided for the Harrisons on the fifth floor of Harriet Lane was part of the push. Helen returned to her collaboration with Harold. Their effort clarified fundamental aspects of calcium and phosphorus metabolism in numerous ways and the significance of their steady stream of groundbreaking publications was recognized in 1961 by the granting of the American Academy of Pediatrics' Borden Award, and the American Pediatric Society's Howland Award in 1983.

Harold was a superb mentor, much like Park in style: rigid in his expectation of maximum effort and gentle in his instruction if failure followed on that effort. But Harold could be short with sloth. Everyone knew exactly where he stood and he lived up to the standard he set. He dragged the City Hospitals "kicking and screaming into the twentieth century and eventually to a level of excellence not often seen in similar institutions."[147] Helen, too, served the community on various committees of the School of Medicine, the board of trustees of her sons' private school, and as a prime mover in the development of the chamber music concert series on Johns Hopkins' Homewood campus.

Park had a warm and sometimes intimate relationship with the Harrisons. His letters to them, mostly handwritten, noted the ways in which their lives touched. The husband and wife team became Park's friends and, at times, his confidants.[148] At home and at the laboratory bench, their contributions to new knowledge, their exemplary family, the many contributions to the community, and the warmth of their response to him confirmed the success of Park's last recruitment.

A Personal Note

The sense of privilege that I felt as I wrote this chapter is shared, I am assured, by all of us who were contemporaries during the years these men and women were fashioning academic pediatrics in the United States. It amazes me still to think that a kid from a mill town in northern New Jersey could have been witness to their effort and to have been shaped, at least in part, by their examples. And it is gratifying to reflect on their contributions, to acknowledge their very human frailty, and yet to think of them in almost saintly terms. Hagiography is not our purpose. Still, these individuals and their efforts are the essence of Park's legacy and, to the extent that this legacy lives in those of us who were its beneficiaries, it will endure.

Notes

1. *Webster's Third International Dictionary*, unabridged (Springfield, Massachusetts: Merriam-Webster, Inc., 2002).

2. And yet before them, the Revered William Osler, the first physician-in-chief at the Johns Hopkins Hospital and professor of medicine at the Johns Hopkins University until 1905 (when he left to become Regius Professor of Medicine at Oxford University) saw patients in the Hopkins' dispensary for children that was set up in the department of medicine. He was interested in the medical care of children, participated in the formation of the American Pediatric Society, and published many articles on this subject. Benjamin H. Robbins and Amos Christie, "Sir William Osler, The Pediatrician," *American Journal of Diseases of Children* 106 (1963): 124–29.

3. Park returned to the Harriet Lane in 1919, but Howland wanted him to do research on bone structure and he wanted Powers to continue in charge of the dispensary. RG 4, series B, box 9, folder 21, Alan Mason Chesney Medical Archives, The Johns Hopkins Medical Institutions, Baltimore, MD, hereafter referred to as the AMC.

4. The problem of isolating the child with infectious disease was solved to some extent by the "isolation" wing located off the corridor joining the Harriet Lane Home with the Henry Phipps Psychiatric Clinic. Fever was the principal criterion for isolation. The corridor, lined with benches, provided a waiting area. The afebrile child was shunted into the main waiting room leading down to Observation I where children were seen who were presumed to be without infection.

5. D. M. Young and K. B. Kinkle, "The Growth of the Dispensary in the Harriet Lane Home," *The Johns Hopkins Nurses' Alumnae Magazine* 31 (1932): 218.

6. Draft memoranda, RG 4, series C box 17, folder 30, HLH-AMC.

7. This was brought home to me when I went into private practice in 1953. I [HMS] was startled on my first day in that role by a parent's simple question: "Is it ok if my three-year old daughter sees me and my husband naked?"

8. Edwards Park to Mrs. Manly, April 11, 1928. Letter attached as an addendum to the minutes of the Board of Managers of the Harriet Lane Home, May 10, 1928, in Volume I series A, RG 2, HLH-AMC.

9. Alexander Schaffer curriculum vita. Biographical file, "Alexander Schaffer," HLH-AMC. After a year as head of the dispensary, Schaffer went into private practice. In 1964, when Schaffer retired from private practice and assumed the role of director of the Johns Hopkins Community Pediatric Program, Park noted and seemed to validate the demeaning distinction that those who wore the "gown" made about those who chose careers in "town." "I regret greatly that Alexander did not enter full time medicine earlier," Park said. "It was there that with his scholarly make-up he deserved to be from the very beginning." Edwards A. Park, "Tribute to Alexander Schaffer," 1967.

10. This was evident in the frequent arrival in the clinic of infants, still terribly ill, who had been treated for diarrhea with the suggestion that there be oral feedings of salt and sugar water: a teaspoon of salt and a tablespoon of sugar to a quart of water. Too often, the children were given a mixture made with a tablespoon of salt and a teaspoon of sugar. In time, the correct instructions were mimeographed, but even then the treatment error was occasionally made.

11. Edwards Park to Mrs. Manly, April 11, 1928.

12. Helen B. Taussig, "Dr. Edwards A. Park, Physician, Teacher, Investigator, Friend," comments made at the dedication of the Edwards A. Park Building at the Johns Hopkins Hospital, February 23, 1973, *Johns Hopkins Medical Journal* 132 (1973): 374.

13. Robert H. Dombro, "Helen Schnetzer Child Life Program," *The Johns Hopkins Nurses Alumnae Magazine* 63 (March 1964): 7 and 10. The School of Nursing viewed the program as a "laboratory" and each student spent two weeks there during her study of pediatric nursing. See also the Johns Hopkins Children's Center site on the World Wide Web http://www .hopkinschildrens.org/specialties/aboutus.cfm?specialtyID=44.

14. R. H. Dombro and B. S. Haas, "The Helen Schnetzer Child Life Program," in *The Hospitalized Child and his Family*, ed. J. A. Haller Jr. (Baltimore: The Johns Hopkins University Press, 1967), 79.

15. Gerald F. Powell, "A Child Life Program within a Department of Pediatrics," *The Johns Hopkins Nurses Alumnae Magazine* 63 (March 1964): 12.

16. Jerriann Wilson, conversation with John Littlefield, Lawrence Wissow, and author, August 17, 2001.

17. Ibid.

18. L. E. Holt Jr., "The Department of Pediatrics, Johns Hopkins University," *Journal of Pediatrics* 4 (1934): 812.

19. Edwards A. Park, "The Social Aspects of Medicine," *Journal of Pediatrics* 28 (1946): 106.

20. Edwards Park to Mrs. Manly, April 11, 1928.

21. Helen B. Taussig, "Dr. Edwards A. Park, Physician, Teacher, Investigator, Friend," 374.

22. A. McGehee Harvey, "Helen Brooke Taussig," *Johns Hopkins Medical Journal* 140 (1977): 138.

23. Catherine Neill, conversation with author, February 26, 2002.

24. A. McGehee Harvey, "Helen Brooke Taussig," 138.

25. Ibid.

26. Walter Cannon to Dean Lewis Weed, June 4, 1924. Student file, "Helen B. Taussig," AMC.

27. Helen Brooke Taussig, "Tetralogy of Fallot: Early History and Late Results." *American Journal of Roentgenology* 133 (1979): 426.

28. Ibid.

29. Ibid., 427.

30. Catherine Neill conversation.

31. Mary Allen Engle, "Helen Brooke Taussig: The Mother of Pediatric Cardiology," *Pediatric Annals* 11 (1982): 630.

32. Helen Brooke Taussig, "Tetralogy of Fallot: Early History and Late Results," 427.

33. A. McGehee Harvey, "Helen Brooke Taussig," 139.

34. Helen Brooke Taussig, "Tetralogy of Fallot: Early History and Late Results," 428.

35. A. McGehee Harvey, "Helen Brooke Taussig," 140; Helen Brooke Taussig, "Tetralogy of Fallot: Early History and Late Results," 428.

36. Helen Brooke Taussig, "Tetralogy of Fallot: Early History and Late Results," 428.

37. Mary Allen Engle, "Dr. Helen B. Taussig, the Tetralogy of Fallot and the Growth of Pediatric Cardiac Services in the United States," *Johns Hopkins Medical Journal* 140 (1977): 149.

38. Ibid.

39. This conductive hearing loss was repaired by a stapes fenestration operation in the 1960s.

40. Helen Brooke Taussig, *Congenital Malformations of the Heart* (New York: Commonwealth Fund, 1947).

41. Helen Brooke Taussig, "Tetralogy of Fallot: Early History and Late Results," 427.

42. H. J. Dietrich Jr., "Helen Brooke Taussig, 1898-1986," *Transactions and Studies of the College of Physicians of Philadelphia* 8 (1986): 270.

43. Taussig was persistent in her protests against this drug, testifying in Annapolis and elsewhere until the use of thalidomide was banned in the United States and the drug was prevented from doing the damage here that she had seen in Germany, where children exposed to thalidomide in utero often were born with malformations of the upper extremities.

44. In 1976 the Johns Hopkins University awarded Helen Brooke Taussig the Milton Stover Eisenhower Medal for Distinguished Service. The citation concluded, "The astounding progress of cardiac surgery in the last thirty years began with Taussig and Blalock." At the same ceremony, the university honored Vivien Thomas with a doctor of laws degree. Mame Warren, *Johns Hopkins: Knowledge for the World* (Baltimore: The Johns Hopkins University, 2000), 70 and 267.

45. A. McGehee Harvey, "Helen Brooke Taussig," 140; H. J. Dietrich Jr., "Helen Brooke Taussig, 1898–1986," 269.

46. Lawson Wilkins, "Epilepsy in Childhood: I. A Statistical Study of Clinical Types; II. The Incidence of Remissions; III. Results with the Ketogenic Diet," *Journal of Pediatrics* 10 (1937): 317.

47. A. McGehee Harvey, "The First Full-Time Academic Department

of Pediatrics: The Story of the Harriet Lane Home," *Johns Hopkins Medical Journal* 137 (1975): 42–43.

48. Lawson Wilkins, "Acceptance of the Howland Award," *Journal of Pediatrics* 63 (1963): 809.

49. A. McGehee Harvey, *Science at the Bedside* (Baltimore: Johns Hopkins University Press, 1981), 254–57 and 375–80.

50. A. McGehee Harvey, *Science at the Bedside;* Samuel P. Asper Jr, "Lawson Wilkins (1894–1963)," *Transactions of the Association of American Physicians* 76 (1964): 33; A. M. Bongiovanni, "Introduction of Lawson Wilkins for the John Howland Award" *Journal of Pediatrics* 63 (1963): 803; A. M. Bongiovanni, "Lawson Wilkins: Memorial (1894–1963)," *Journal of Clinical Endocrinology and Metabolism* 24 (1964): 1; Edwards A. Park, "Lawson Wilkins," *Journal of Pediatrics* 57 (1960): 317; Alexander J. Schaffer, "Lawson Wilkins, 1894–1963," *Pediatrics* 33 (1964): 10.

51. Walter Fleischmann worked in the Harriet Lane Home from 1938 to 1952, when he moved to Johnson City, Tennessee, to become chief of laboratory services at the Mountain Home Veteran's Administration Hospital. Born in Vienna, Austria, he had received his MD degree at the University of Vienna in 1922 and a PhD in 1934 before coming to Baltimore. "Walter Fleishmann Dies; Was Retired Pathologist," *Baltimore Sun*, April 8, 1979, A18.

52. Claude Migeon, originally a fellow with Wilkins, was much involved with the studies of the adrenal gland and eventually became the chief of the division of pediatric endocrinology at the Harriet Lane.

53. A. McGehee Harvey, "The First Full-Time Academic Department of Pediatrics: The Story of the Harriet Lane Home," 44. The university had by this time given up its rule that there could be but one full professor in a department.

54. Lawson Wilkins, *The Diagnosis and Treatment of Endocrine Disorders in Childhood and Adolescence* (Springfield, Illinois, Charles C. Thomas, 1950).

55. L. E. Eisenberg, "In Memoriam," *American Journal of Psychiatry* 138 (1981): 1124.

56. Edwards A. Park, "A Child Psychiatric Clinic in a Paediatric Department," *The Canadian Medical Association Journal* 38 (January 1938): 74.

57. E. Schopler, S. Chess, and L. Eisenberg, "Our Memorial to Leo Kanner," *Journal of Autism and Developmental Disorders* 11 (1981): 260.

58. Edwards A. Park, "A Child Psychiatric Clinic in a Paediatric Department," 74–75.

59. Clifford Beers, *A Mind That Found Itself* (Pittsburgh: University of Pittsburgh Press, 1981); Leo Kanner, *The Canadian Medical Association Journal* 38 (1938): 71–74.

60. Kanner, ibid.

61. E. Schopler, S. Chess, and L. Eisenberg, "Our Memorial to Leo Kanner," 264.

62. Ibid.

63. Ibid., 265.

64. Leo Kanner, *Child Psychiatry* (Springfield, Illinois: Charles C. Thomas, 1935).

65. E. Schopler, S. Chess, and L. Eisenberg, "Our Memorial to Leo Kanner," 266.

66. Leo Kanner, *In Defense of Mothers* (New York : Dodd, Mead and Company, 1944).

67. Leo Kanner, "Autistic Disturbances of Affective Contact," *Nervous Child* 2 (1943): 217–50.

68. E. Schopler, S. Chess, and L. Eisenberg, "Our Memorial to Leo Kanner," 267.

69. Leo Kanner, "Habeas Corpus Releases of Feebleminded Persons and their Consequences," *American Journal of Psychiatry* 94 (1938): 1013–33.

70. Leo Kanner, "Exoneration of the Feebleminded," *American Journal of Psychiatry* 99 (1942): 17–22. "Mr. Shiklgruber" almost certainly refers to Adolf Hitler, whose father was the illegitimate son of Maria Anna Shiklgruber.

71. E. Schopler, S. Chess, and L. Eisenberg, "Our Memorial to Leo Kanner," 268.

72. "Bull neck" is an enlargement of the cervical nodes or severe pharyngitis and associated edema, which give the swollen neck an appearance suggestive of a bull.

73. J. H. Jones, M. Rapoport, Horace L. Hodes," Source of Excess Calcium in Hypercalcemia Induced by Irradiated Ergosterol," *Journal of Biological Chemistry* 89 (1930): 647; J. H. Jones, M. Rapoport, Horace L. Hodes, "Effect of Irradiated Ergosterol on Thyroparathroidectomized Dogs" *Journal of Biological Chemistry* 86 (1930): 267.

74. "Horace Hodes, a Pediatrician, 81," obituary in the *New York Times*, April 25, 1989.

75. Horace L. Hodes , G. I. Lavin, L. T. Webster, "Antirabic Immunization with Culture Virus Rendered Avirulent by Ultraviolet Light," *Science* 86 (1937): 447; Horace L. Hodes and L. T. Webster, "Relation between Degree of Immunity of Mice Following Vaccination with St. Louis Encephalitis Virus and the Titre of the Protective Antibodies of the Serum," *Journal of Experimental Medicine* 68 (1938): 263.

76. Biographical file, "Horace Hodes," AMC; Jacob S. Light and Horace L. Hodes, "Studies on Epidemic Diarrhea of Two Newborn: Isolation of a Filtrable Virus Agent Causing Diarrhea in Calves," *American Journal of Public Health* 33 (1943): 1451–55.

77. L. R. Chandler to Alan Chesney, January 27, 1949. Biographical file, "Horace Hodes."

78. Alan Chesney to L. R. Chandler, January 31, 1949 Biographical file, "Horace Hodes."

79. "Horace Hodes, a Pediatrician, 81." Biographical file, "Horace Hodes."

80. "Baltimore's Sydenham Service for Hospital Care of Communicable Diseases," *Baltimore Health News* 26 (1949): 151–52.

81. Samuel Livingston, "Medical Treatment of Epilepsy: Part l," *Southern Medical Journal* 71 (1978): 298.

82. Edwards Park to Mrs. Manly, April 11, 1928; biographical file, "Edward Bridge," AMC.

83. Samuel Livingston, "Medical Treatment of Epilepsy: Part l," 298.

84. Edwards Park to Mrs. Manly, April 11, 1928.

85. "Dr. Edward Bridge named Pediatrics Head at Children's," *Buffalo News*, December 3, 1943.

86. Wilburt C. Davison to Dean Lewis Weed, June 4, 1926. Biographical file, "Laslo Kajdi," AMC.

87. Wilburt C. Davison was called to Durham, North Carolina, where he played a major role in the establishment of the Duke University School of Medicine. He was also the author of several editions of a popular pediatric textbook, *The COMPLEAT Pediatrician, a precursor in a way to the Harriet Lane Handbook.*

88. Wilburt Davison to Lawrence R. Baker, executive secretary, the Johns Hopkins School of Medicine, June 23, 1926. Biographical file, "Laslo Kajdi."

89. Robert E. Cooke, "Sam Livingston Testimonial Breakfast Address," February 15, 1970, 2–3. Biographical file, "Samuel Livingston," AMC.

90. Ibid., 4. Robert Cooke, in his 1970 testimonial to Livingston stated, "I am here today to apologize for the mistake Johns Hopkins made 40 years ago, and to conclude my theme—Johns Hopkins has come a long, long way in getting rid of its prejudices as well as improving its science. Students now come from Catholic universities. There is no quota: forty, fifty, sixty per cent, or more, of classes may be Jewish, Irish, or Black, for that matter, if we have adequate applicants. The Dean of Academic Affairs is Jewish, as are at least five department chairmen. Yes, Sam, we have all come a long, long way, thanks to examples from people like yourself."

91. Samuel Livingston and Edward M. Bridge, "Tests of Carbohydrate Metabolism," *Journal of the American Medical Association* 119 (1942): 117.

92. Samuel Livingston curriculum vita to 1967. Biographical file, "Samuel Livingston."

93. Robert E. Cooke, "Sam Livingston Testimonial Breakfast Address," 5–6; Livingston curriculum vita.

94. Livingston obituary, *Baltimore Sun*, August 24, 1984.

95. Samuel Livingston, "Medical Treatment of Epilepsy: Part l," 298.

96. Charlotte F. Gerczak, "The Courage of Her Convictions: The Story of Miriam Brailey," 1999, unpublished manuscript, 3. Our profile of Miriam Brailey was heavily dependent on Charlotte Gerczak's work. Dr. Janet Hardy inscribed the copy she shared with us as follows: "Charlotte Gerczak said that I might share her unpublished manuscript with you [Larry Wissow], John and Henry" We are deeply indebted to Ms. Gerczak. A copy of her manuscript is available in Miriam Brailey's biographical file in the AMC.

97. Ibid., 4.

98. Ibid., 5.

99. Janet and Paul Hardy interview.

100. Charlotte F. Gerczak, "The Courage of Her Convictions: The Story of Miriam Brailey," 8. Health Commissioner Huntington Williams apparently did not resist the intimidation of those he saw as superiors. Paul Hardy, one of Francis Schwentker's chief residents in Harriet Lane at the time, recalled an episode during his time at Sydenham Hospital: "One Saturday night I got a call from the guy who was the head of infectious disease in the city health department.... 'There is a prominent man in the city here whose youngster

Edwards Park's Legacy

has chicken pox and he doesn't want him at home. Send your ambulance in and pick him up and take him out there.'" Hardy refused, saying that the disease did not require hospitalization and that he had no beds. Two days later, Horace Hodes, Sydenham's director, told Hardy that Williams had requested an audience with Hardy. Williams confronted Hardy about his presumed misdeed but Hardy remained adamant and, in effect, invited Williams to come to the hospital himself and displace a child who needed a bed there in order to give it to a child who did not really need it. Williams, Hardy remembered, "shut up. He never gave me any more guff." Over the years, Williams was the man who confronted Park, Schwentker, and others at Harriet Lane in their negotiations with Baltimore City. Janet and Paul Hardy interview.

101. Miriam Brailey and Janet Hardy, *Tuberculosis in White and Negro Children*, two volumes (Cambridge: Harvard University Press, 1958).

102. Charlotte F. Gerczak, "The Courage of Her Convictions: The Story of Miriam Brailey," 9.

103. Miriam Brailey to Dr. Charlotte Silverman and Dr. Carol Chandler, November 24, 1958. Biographical file, "Miriam Brailey."

104. Charlotte F. Gerczak, "The Courage of Her Convictions: The Story of Miriam Brailey," 12–13.

105. Curriculum vita for Janet Hardy in the author's personal archive.

106. Janet and Paul Hardy, interview with author, March 24, 1999. Nicholson J. Eastman was chief of the department of obstetrics from 1945 to 1960.

107. Ibid.

108. Ibid.; Hardy curriculum vita.

109. Janet and Paul Hardy interview.

110. Helen Schnetzer, B. Moulton, and Margaretta Biddle, "The Harriet Lane Premature Nursery," *The Johns Hopkins Nurses' Alumnae Magazine* 45 (1946), 152.

111. Ibid., 154.

112. Michael Smart, "Mother's Age Contributes to Child's Success," *Brigham Young Magazine* 52 (summer 1998): 14–15.

113. "Baltimore Embraces School Clinic that Gives School Children Contraceptives, Counseling," *U.S.A. Today*, September 28, 1982; "Teen-Age Birth Control Test," *New York Times*, November 24, 1985.

114. "Baltimore Embraces School Clinic That Gives School Children Contraceptives, Counseling."

115. "Teen-Age Birth Control Test."

116. "Shortchanging Children," *Baltimore Sun*, August 28, 1984.

117. Janet Hardy to Henry Seidel, July 8, 2004, in the author's personal archive.

118. C. M. McCarthy, "Hugh W. Josephs, M.D. Visiting Professorship," delivered at the Hugh W. Josephs memorial ceremony, May 17, 1982. Biographical file, "Hugh Josephs," AMC.

119. "Hugh Wilson Josephs," *Harvard Class of 1914, 25th Reunion Class Report*, [1939], 427. Biographical file, "Hugh Josephs."

120. Ibid., 426.

121. Ibid., 427.

122. Werner Heisenberg (1901–1976), a German physicist and a founder of quantum mechanics, postulated that the increased accuracy of one observable quantity increases the uncertainty with which other quantities may be known. A rough translation into lay terms suggests that no experiment or observation can be "pure" because of the unique variables unwittingly introduced by the experimenters. In patient care and in interpretation of the literature, this suggests that the caregiver and the interpreter introduce the variables unique to them that modify the interpretation of the patient or of the scientific article.

123. "Hugh Wilson Josephs," *Harvard Class of 1914, 25th Reunion Class Report*, 430.

124. Peter Colt Josephs [a nephew], "Hugh W. Josephs—A Remembrance," May 17, 1982, unpublished, 2. Biographical file, "Hugh Josephs."

125. C. M. McCarthy, "Hugh W. Josephs, M.D. Visiting Professorship," delivered at the Hugh W. Josephs memorial ceremony, May 17, 1982.

126. Harriet Guild to Mary Ellen Avery, January 16, 1982. Avery was a 1952 Hopkins graduate distinguished for her discovery of pulmonary surfactant during her tenure on the Harriet Lane faculty. Later she became chairperson of the department of pediatrics at McGill University and then at the Boston Children's Hospital.

127. "Dr.Guild, After 40 Years, Is Retiring to Private Practice," *Baltimore Sun*, June 25, 1965.

128. We know that Park paid attention to class rank. He recommended a student for a house staff position at Baltimore City Hospitals in 1945, indicating "… we would have taken [him] as an intern in the Harriet Lane if we had not found him to be so low in his class. He was seventy-seventh in a class of seventy-nine." Edwards Park to Harold Harrison, July 9, 1945.

129. "Gentle Woman Doctor Leads Dedicated Life," *Baltimore Sun*, June 25, 1965.

130. "Dr.Guild, After 40 Years, Is Retiring to Private Practice."

131. Edwards Park to Harold Harrison, July 12, 1945.

132. Barton Childs, conversation with author, March 23, 2004.

133. Memorandum by Samuel Asper concerning a meeting with Harriet G. Guild, March 2, 1965. Biographical file, "Harriet Guild," AMC.

134. Harriet Guild, conversation with author, date uncertain.

135. L. Finberg, "Presentation of the Howland Award, May, 1983," *Pediatric Research* 17 (1983): 844.

136. Ibid., 843.

137. Edwards Park to Harold Harrison, April 12, 1938. Correspondence between Edwards Park and the Harrisons was given to the author by Stephen Harrison. They remain in the author's files.

138. L. Finberg, "Presentation of the Howland Award, May, 1983," 843.

139. Edwards Park to Harold Harrison, December 5, 1944. Money, it seems, had never been a long suit at Harriet Lane. Howland had set the pattern of fiscal frugality. A note written by Park tells of the bare remnants of records from the Howland era. Apparently, admonished by his secretary about the overflow of paper, Howland told her to throw them out rather than to buy new file cabinets. There is little evidence, apart from some research funds,

that the chiefs had devoted a great deal of time to the pursuit of financial support. This was as true for Park in his personal life as it was in his professional life.

140. Edwards Park to Harold Harrison, December 5, 1944.

141. Ibid.

142. Ibid.

143. Ibid.

144. Edwards Park to Harold Harrison, February 5, 1945, and June 29, 1945.

145. L. Finberg, "Presentation of the Howland Award, May, 1983," 845.

146. Edwards Park to Daniel Darrow, copy to Harold Harrison, August 4, 1945. This study, accomplished with the help of the then chief resident, Clifton Govan, confirmed the importance of potassium repair in severe diarrhea. Darrow and Harrison understood before others the need for and the practicality of the oral administration of electrolytes, and used Baltimore City Hospitals and Yale as trial sites for the first rationally developed oral glucose-electrolyte solutions. It "seemed so simple and automatic to them that little was published, necessitating rediscovery 25 years later." L. Finberg, "Presentation of the Howland Award, May, 1983," 846. One of the many physicians trained at City Hospitals, Mathuram Santosham, was central to that rediscovery. The composition of Harrison's first glucose/electrolyte solution, the Special Rx used at the Baltimore City Hospitals: BCH #1, a liquid: Na, 62 meq/L; K, 20 meq/L; Cl, 52 meq/L; Lactate, 30 meq/L; Glucose, 33 gm/L.

147. L. Finberg, "Presentation of the Howland Award, May, 1983," 847.

148. Edwards Park to the Harold and Helen Harrison, January 6, 1956.

A Litany of Frustrations

Francis F. Schwentker, 1946–1954

By Henry M. Seidel

WHEN IT CAME time to select his successor, Edwards Park "ventured the opinion that the committee should include among its candidates a few able young internists, since 'such a person could soon familiarize himself with the problems of infant feeding.'"[1] The potential of a candidate with an open-minded intelligence and sensitivity to the human condition meant more to him than the parochial pediatric paranoia of those who might take exception to the appointment of an internist. Park almost certainly had in mind Charles Janeway, then chief at the Boston Children's Hospital. Janeway's father had been Park's mentor in New York, and the Janeway and Park families had remained close through the years.

The selection committee decided differently. No pediatrician was on the committee, a habit of the time presumably to avoid the risk of self-interest. Instead, there was the dean, Alan Chesney; the chief of the department of obstetrics, Nicholson Eastman; an adult endocrinologist, John Eager Howard; a pharmacologist, E. K. Marshall; and the director of the hospital, Winford Smith. Their preference was for a competent clinician, still young, who "gave promise of advancing the field."[2] They canvassed the faculties of what they considered the strong medical schools in the United States and Canada and were rigorous in requiring that a candidate be a member of either of the prestigious research societies, the American Pediatric Society (for older pediatricians) or the Society for Pediatric Research (for younger pediatricians). Each society required nomination, seconding, and election by its membership. Proven research expertise was the common denominator in members of both organizations but proposal for admission also reflected the influence of academic politics.

The original list of candidates contained eighty-six names. The penultimate included just nine, many at Park's suggestion, and it was quickly narrowed down to three: Allan Butler at Harvard, Daniel C. Darrow at Yale, and Francis F. Schwentker at the Rockefeller Institute.[3] Butler was the successful chief of pediatrics at the Massachusetts General Hospital, and Darrow, while not the head of a department, had an established research reputation. He came to Baltimore in the final years of Park's tenure to study diarrhea and dehydration. Along with Clifton Govan (then the chief resident) he established the importance of potassium in the restitution of electrolyte balance in the dehydrated child.

The committee learned a great deal from outside comments about Butler and Darrow but not much about Schwentker. In addition, the comments that were available were conspicuously less enthusiastic about him than his two rivals. The committee's first vote, nevertheless, opted for him four to one. The decision was then made unanimous and referred to the Advisory Board of the School of Medicine and the Medical Board of the hospital. Age appeared to be a factor in the decision as the two "losers" were over the age of fifty. The committee's final memo of recommendation to Johns Hopkins University President Isaiah Bowman on January 5, 1946, indicated that one of them "appears to be much older than his chronological age."[4] This seemed to seal the decision. The boards approved the selection of Francis F. Schwentker in January of 1946, when he was almost forty-two years old.

An Inquiring Mind and a Tinkerer

Schwentker was Hopkins bred. He was born in Schenectady, New York, on February 13, 1904, and graduated from Union College there. He originally intended to become an engineer but a Christmas vacation spent chauffeuring for a pediatrician in Schenectady and having long talks about medicine and patients with him changed his mind.[5] Schwentker graduated from the Johns Hopkins School of Medicine in 1929 and served his internship and residency at Harriet Lane. Three years at the Rockefeller Institute for Medical Research in New York solidified Schwentker's reputation as an investigator. Thomas M. Rivers, a Hopkins and Harriet Lane alumnus, was his mentor there. A study of psittacosis preoccupied him intellectually and physically, since he was severely ill with the disease for a time.

EDWARDS PARK SHAKING HANDS WITH FRANCIS SCHWENTKER. Schwentker, right, the
Harriet Lane Home's fourth chief, was the first to have received his medical education at
Johns Hopkins and to have trained as an intern in the Harriet Lane.

Recovered and academically successful, Schwentker returned in
1934 to Harriet Lane as resident pediatrician (the position we now call
chief resident) specializing in infectious disease. Park noted that while
Schwentker was resident pediatrician, "His clinics were remarkable
for their clarity, conciseness, and completeness and were some of the
finest presentations of infectious diseases, in particular from the im-
munological point of view, that I have ever listened to."[6]

Schwentker was appointed director of medical research at the
Sydenham Hospital in Baltimore in 1935, an infectious disease institution under the control of the Baltimore City Health Department.
He assumed responsibility for medical care of all patients in the hospital, for research work in communicable diseases, and for teaching

programs for residents and medical students. Park played a direct role in setting up the position and picking the director.[7] Schwentker thrived at Sydenham. He had an inquiring mind and he was a tinkerer, always working to adapt instruments and equipment to better fit their purpose and always willing to explore. At one point, his colleague Perrin Long, chairman of the new department of preventive medicine at Johns Hopkins, obtained the new medication sulfanilamide in England.[8] Together, Long and Schwentker treated patients who were desperately ill with streptococcal disease with the new medication and the patients recovered. This was the first use of sulfa drugs in the United States.[9]

An opportunity to participate in an epidemiological study in Romania sponsored by the Rockefeller Foundation attracted Schwentker in 1938. His goal was to gain a better understanding of the origins of scarlet fever and develop steps for its prevention.[10] He was fully involved in this when a letter from Lowell Reed, Dean of the Johns Hopkins School of Hygiene and Public Health, arrived in 1939. The chair in the department of bacteriology was vacant. Reed offered the post to Schwentker: "In asking you to accept the professorship, we had in mind the interest that you have in the bacteriology of disease, the special work that you have been doing in the field of the bacteriology of streptococcal infection, and your general interest in communicable disease as evidenced in your work at Sydenham Hospital." Long's hand in this was obvious. Reed continued: "We realize you are now engaged in a project which you might not want to drop in an incomplete state, and although we are anxious to have you come to the School as soon as possible, in case you do accept our offer, we are entirely willing to hold the position open for you through a part or the whole of the next academic year, if that amount of time is necessary for the completion of your present assignment."[11] Despite Reed's generous offer, Schwentker declined and stayed in Romania until the start of World War II in Europe, which ended all but the writing phase of his effort for the Rockefeller Foundation.

During the war, Schwentker's mentor Thomas Rivers took command of a naval unit set up by the Rockefeller Institute. The unit's original mission was to solve epidemiological problems in the United States. But given the demands imposed by the uncertainties of war, the unit ended up in Guam. Schwentker served under Rivers as the unit's executive officer and was commended for his performance in that secondary role. Schwentker was a commander in the navy at the time of his discharge in 1946.[12] It was then that he succeeded Park as director of the Harriet Lane Home and chair of the department of pediatrics.

A Litany of Frustrations

Schwentker's tenure began on July 1, 1946 and lasted eight years. They were not particularly happy years and, in a sense, were but a transition to the era of Robert Cooke. Still, Schwentker began with a vision for the future of Harriet Lane with research and development of new knowledge at its core.

Time magazine[13] and the *New York Herald Tribune* heralded Schwentker's return to Baltimore. The *Tribune* described at some length "a long-term, full-scale, coordinated study" of rheumatic fever initiated on the first day of Schwentker's tenure. He was quoted extensively in that article and presented as lead character in the drama to "stalk relentlessly the mysterious mechanism" that enabled the disease "and has, up to this point, successfully covered its tracks."[14] Schwentker was assisted in this crusade by Helen Taussig, Ruth Whittemore,[15] and, in particular, Lewis Thomas, then a young assistant professor.

Thomas' essential supporting role was evident in Schwentker's letter to Dean Alan Chesney asking for more money to increase Thomas's salary: "As you know, it is my plan to organize the department around two or three key men. [Lawson] Wilkins is one of these in the chemical field, and Thomas is one in microbiology. I propose to pay these men the substantial salaries they are worth, and to make every reasonable effort to have the continuity of their work unbroken by calls elsewhere." He asked for a raise in Thomas' salary from $5,500 a year to $6,500: "Should there be any question concerning the advisability of a salary of $6,500 for an assistant professor, I may explain that Dr. Thomas is definitely associate professor calibre. He was started as assistant professor because he had not had previous training in Pediatrics, but his basic science and clinical ability over-balance this. Just as soon as he has obtained the necessary Pediatric experience, I shall request an appointment as associate professor."[16] The tone of the letter betrayed a genuine concern that this potential star would leave.

Taussig, Wilkins, and Helen and Harold Harrison, among others, were of the Park era at Harriet Lane. Thomas, the key to establishing Schwentker's imprint on the department, was given laboratory space on the fifth floor of the Harriet Lane. I pursued a modest research project under Thomas's guidance and observed his eager approach and great vitality during those few months. He reveled in the discovery of something new, once proclaiming with joy that a complement fixation test he was studying could "be performed with ease during a ballgame at Yankee Stadium between the innings." Schwentker was profoundly disappointed that Thomas' stay in Baltimore was brief. Schwentker, deeply frustrated when the administration rebuffed his salary request for Thomas, had to watch as his hopes for Thomas' impressive career were confirmed elsewhere.[17]

It was also evident that Schwentker considered the physical environment of Harriet Lane wanting. A February 4, 1946, letter from President Bowman confirmed Schwentker's request for "a service bacteriological laboratory to be built and equipped by July 1, 1946, according to plans to be designed and approved by [Schwentker]." The new facility was to be housed on the fifth floor and complemented Schwentker's wish for a department of bacteriology separate from the department of pathology, one that would be useful to both the departments of medicine and pediatrics. Bowman also acknowledged the need for "the ultimate extension of Harriet Lane, "possibly in the form of a wing with a separate entrance on Jefferson Street," which would house fifty beds with approximately thirty "in separate rooms for infants and infectious disease patients, the division of use to correspond with changing demands," and twenty on a ward for children over two years of age.[18] Moreover, in addition to those fifty beds, Schwentker asked for twenty-five private and semi-private beds.

Bowman gave assurances that these plans would be kept "steadily in view" and that they would be part of a master plan, which had the purpose of putting "all departments, as rapidly as possible, in first class working condition."[19] There is nothing to suggest that the plans for the Harriet Lane Home ever approached fruition during Schwentker's tenure or that the void left by Thomas's departure was ever filled to his satisfaction. These frustrations lingered and they may have contributed to his distance from day-to-day clinical and teaching responsibilities. Schwentker did not have Park's charismatic presence. It did not occur to me, the chief resident in 1952–53, to ask Schwentker to make attending rounds. He had not taken on that task in his first years as chief and he was not often at conferences. Thinking back, I recall very little consistent interaction with him through that year.

Schwentker was also frustrated by his inability to add a significantly increased pediatric content to the School of Medicine's curriculum although he was able to introduce an elective second-year course in history taking and physical diagnosis in children.[20] At least two of the ten students who took the course went on to be pediatricians and another, George Zuidema, ultimately became the chief of surgery at Hopkins. Schwentker asked Chesney to relieve students who participated in this class of other responsibilities to make their participation easier, but there is no indication that the request was ever acknowledged. One letter from Chesney in response to one of Schwentker's requests suggested a reluctance to be helpful. A quirk of scheduling by the Curriculum Committee resulted in an odd circumstance: "the unreasonable arrangement that the pediatric clinics are required work for half the class and not for the other half." Schwentker wondered if the problem might exceed Chesney's authority[21] and Chesney, presumably responsible for education of medical students, agreed. A curt two-sentence letter Chesney wrote from Deer Isle, Maine, said, "I really do not believe that your request comes within the scope of my authority as Dean and I must therefore refer you to the Curriculum Committee."[22]

There is nothing to suggest that another Schwentker proposal—this time for a profound change in medical education—received much attention. A letter to Dr. John Whitehorn, the psychiatrist-in-chief and chairman of the Curriculum Committee relayed Schwentker's thoughtful concerns:

> Medical education originally began with three departments concerned—Medicine, Surgery and Obstetrics. Eventually, gynecology split off from obstetrics. Various surgical sub-specialties were formed; ophthalmology came into being and pediatrics became a department separate from medicine. In each instance the teaching in these newly formed departments was grafted on the old structure in which medicine and surgery were the primary teaching units.
>
> I believe that we should consider a different concept of teaching. I suggest that pediatrics is the logical area about which to centralize the early teaching of medicine. The student could begin his medical training in pediatrics and learn the development of a human being psychologically and physiologically up to adult age. He would then be in a better position to evaluate these factors, which have determined the character of the adult individual with whom he will deal later. Under the present system we present him first with a formed individual and then try to teach him how that individual came into being.

In such a plan of teaching there would have to be a great deal of cooperation with the Department of Medicine. It would, however, assume a lesser role in the major teaching than at present. There would also need to be a great deal of cooperation with Psychiatry which would from the very beginning point out the various factors which cause a patient to develop into the individual he becomes. In our institution where an average of 90% of the graduates go into specialties, I would assign surgery, the obstetrical divisions and ophthalmology to a lesser role. I believe that knowledge in these fields will be obtained by later post-graduate training.

I hope that your committee will also consider the possibility of accepting students after two years of college and assuming the responsibility for part of their pre-medical education, but more specifically to have a final year of student training in which all students will have, in effect, a rotating internship with us. This year would be kept free of formal lectures but the students would attend the staff conferences and other activities which are held in the department to which he is currently assigned. In any event, I hope that it will not be necessary to lengthen the total period of training required to qualify a man as a physician.

In summary, I believe that in a training program pediatrics and psychiatry are the two major subjects and should together bear the load of teaching especially in the earlier years. Then should come medicine together with psychiatry and finally brief courses in the surgical specialties, followed by a period of what amounts to a rotating internship.[23]

Schwentker closed his letter with the rather humble concession that these were "merely subjects for consideration" and indicated his availability for further discussion if the committee wished it. The letter was no more than summarily acknowledged. In hindsight, it seems naïve and it did not take into account the political power of the departments of medicine and surgery at Hopkins or, for that matter, at any medical school.

The lack of a response to this letter, written in the last year of Schwentker's life, was but one more in the litany of frustrations that dogged his efforts at the Harriet Lane. The opportune time for dramatic innovation was at a pause. While Schwentker was certainly bright and able, at the time he assumed his position at the Harriet Lane he had not yet demonstrated an ability to command, and his lack of charisma hindered his efforts. During his tenure as the HLH director he gave little indication that he knew the game of politics or how to play it, a necessary skill if he was ever to overcome the institutional inertia that stood as a barrier to the realization of his ideas.[24]

Crystallizing Competence

Still, the department of pediatrics sustained itself during Schwentker's eight years. Taussig and Wilkins were well into their pioneering work and were attracting young physicians who would go on to seed many other divisions of cardiology and endocrinology. The house staff continued its key role in patient care. The presence of subspecialty fellows with significant funding from the National Institutes of Health was just beginning to be felt but did not undercut the primacy of the residents.

Schwentker did not play a major role in the life of the house staff and he did not become an attending physician on the wards. He emphasized research and the optimization of physical space but, oddly in a clinical department, not clinical effort.[25] I do not remember his constant presence at conferences, formal or informal, and, unlike other faculty members, he did not go to the parties that Wilkins gave for house officers.

The chief resident ran the inpatient service on Harriet Lane 3 and 4 and arranged the various house officer, attending, and conference schedules. The outpatient department was similarly under the day-to-day care of senior residents and a chief resident. Harriet Guild's private patient service on Harriet Lane 2, under her strict control, carried on with a great degree of autonomy. The house officers were the source of departmental unity.

It is unfair to suggest that Schwentker was completely detached. He envisioned a future for the department built on two or three people, and with that purpose in mind he acted almost immediately to change Wilkins' status to full time. Taussig's cardiac clinic, an appendage to the Harriet Lane outpatient department, was promptly built. And he paid at least some attention to the young physicians in his department. Barton Childs, then recently out of the chief residency, began to study congenital anomalies and lectured about children who signaled their anomalies with abnormal heads and faces. Childs asked Schwentker for advice about the next best steps in his career since there were very few places in the United States at that time that might provide nourishment in pediatric genetics. Schwentker's response was a phone call to

BARTON CHILDS CONSULTING WITH A NURSE IN WAITING ROOM. The dispensary was often the first place where sick children and their parents met staff members. Sometimes they endured long delays on uncomfortable wooden benches in the waiting room. Childs, seen here consulting with pediatric nurse Jeanne Dougherty, c.1962, found Francis Schwentker to be very supportive as Childs began a career specializing in medical genetics.

the Commonwealth Fund, which got Childs on his way to a formative experience in England and a major role in the development of medical genetics in this country. In Childs' view, Schwentker "helped people to crystallize their competence."[26]

And Schwentker was not without sensitivity to social imperatives. An October 22, 1951, memorandum from him to Chesney and hospital director Edwin L. Crosby noted that Taussig had as an applicant for a fellowship in her division a Dr. Effie O'Neal Ellis.

> My purpose in writing at this date is to get this matter clarified since Dr. Ellis is a Negro. She graduated from the University of Illinois in 1950 ranking near the top of her class and was elected to AOA.[27] She had nine

months in the Research and Educational Hospital in Chicago as an intern and is now on a pediatric residency with Allan Butler at Massachusetts General. She is highly recommended not only for her medical ability but also for the way in which she has handled the social problems, which would necessarily arise, in her case.

Dr. Taussig is anxious to have her and believes that the potential problems concerning her seeing white patients can be solved without difficulty.

Since this will bring up various questions which must be answered, I am writing immediately to ask that this matter be laid before the Board for consideration."[28]

Schwentker's support in this instance derived from Taussig's absolute commitment to Ellis and, considering Taussig's major contributions and fame, it would have been difficult to deny the appointment. Still, the response was not rapid in coming. Chesney met with Schwentker and wrote in a memorandum on November 15, 1951, "It was agreed between us that the matter would not be brought before the Advisory Board of the Medical Faculty until after the Medical Board of the Hospital had acted on the question of appointing her to the staff of the Hospital."[29] The major issue was the possible reaction of patients. There had been but one appointment of a black physician to the staff to that point and his was but a part-time appointment in the department of medicine. In the end, the hospital determined that Taussig could not be denied. Ellis came to Harriet Lane in July of 1952 and the sky did not fall. She went on to a distinguished career, working in several capacities as a health officer in Maryland and Ohio, as a frequent consultant for the federal government, and as a special assistant for health services at the American Medical Association. Her constant concerns were the poor and socially disenfranchised.[30]

The house staff managed well during Schwentker's tenure. In 1946 the house staff consisted of a combination of war veterans and recent medical school graduates. Some of the older men were the chief residents in the mid-1940s. Most—Jack Peck, Barton Childs, and Frank Kibbe among them—were splendid teachers and role models. A very few were indifferent to the needs of the recent graduates. By the early 1950s, however, there were many fewer war veterans and the majority of residents were no longer tempered by combat experience.

The vitality of the Harriet Lane experience was sustained by the

A Litany
of Frustrations

responsibility invested in the residents, the constancy of the advice and counsel from the readily available faculty in the relatively small space of the Harriet Lane, and the abundant needs of the children of East Baltimore. The official policy of The Johns Hopkins Hospital reinforced this. The "House Staff Manual" had as its first mandate that the members of the house staff "are responsible, in the diagnosis and treatment of patients, to the chief of the given service," and that the chief resident "on each service has direct authority over all members of the House Staff on that service." The manual was just as firm in its emphasis on the real meaning of "resident": "The Hospital Administration and all chiefs of services expect a full House Staff to be on call 24 hours a day, every day, unless expressly excused from duty by Chief of Service or Chief Resident. Availability of the House Staff at all times is essential not only for the proper care of patients but because a major catastrophe may occur without warning."[31]

The chief resident in 1952, as in the past, made rounds every day on every patient on the ward service. Each house officer was on duty on Monday, Wednesday, and the weekend in alternate weeks with Tuesday, Thursday, and Friday. The chief resident set the schedule and, respecting the manual, "expressly excused" each person for each day off. Each house officer had a room in the hospital (often shared) and white uniforms and board were provided, but there was little in the way of salary.

To be successful as a primary counseling resource, the chief resident needed sensitivity and an alert presence. I was no longer an intern when I returned home from two years in the army in 1950, and I felt inadequate for the more supervisory role of assistant resident. Harrison Spencer, my chief and the father of the *Harriet Lane Handbook*, realized this and sat me down in a cubicle just off the dispensary waiting room to pull the fear out of me. He listened to me, and said the words that provided the bridge to an appropriate confidence.

The house staff really did take primary care of the patients except, of course, for those on the private floor. The few subspecialty fellows were hardly intrusive and the faculty, when approached, was willing to advise but was not overbearing. Final decisions about admissions, therapy, and management orders were made most often by the intern in close consultation with the assistant resident, and the chief resident— truly the hospital's resident pediatrician—was constantly at hand. He (it was generally a "he" in those days) also served as a consultant for the

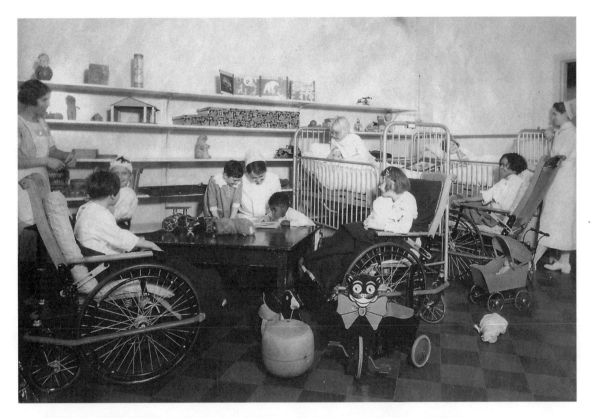

NURSES WITH CHILDREN IN BEDS AND WHEELCHAIRS. Nurses provided hour-by-hour care in the wards, and they closely monitored the condition of patients. By late 1946 the hospital was hiring and training nurses' aides (most were young women—one of whom is seen here at the far left) to take on many routine tasks so that nurses could focus on more professional responsibilities. Both nurses and nurses' aides understood the importance of play for their patients and they frequently took the time to get down to their patients' level to encourage them.

other services in the hospital. It was always a pleasure to be called to place an intravenous line in the tiny vein of an infant surgical patient, a skill many young surgeons had apparently not mastered.

The nurses were intimately involved in the support of house officers. I recall the time when infants with the tetralogy of Fallot were cared for on Harriet Lane 4, both pre- and post-operatively. It was hard to fall asleep because of the tense expectation of the inevitable phone call. That often happened at two or so in the morning and the night supervisor on Harriet Lane 4, Eileen McCarthy, would most likely be on the calling end. "Dr. Seidel, Baby Doe is having a cyanotic spell. Until you get to the floor, would you suggest that I—" and she would go on to list the necessary measures. "Yes, Miss McCarthy, I would, and I'll be right there." And usually, by the time I arrived, the baby was on the way to improvement. The orders, however, needed to be written and signed.

Admission work-ups were up to the intern, beginning with a full history and physical examination, urinalysis and basic blood work. The STS [the serologic test] for syphilis and an intra-dermal tuberculin test were routine on every patient. The house staff did it all, without the assistance of bloodletting teams. Most often, the assistant resident wrote a brief admission note that explained the reasons for admission and outlined the approach to diagnosis and management. The intern wrote the complete history and physical examination, subsequent progress notes, and discharge summary. There was no consistency in assuring that referring physicians received any follow-up or a copy of that summary. Often, they had sent the patient to the dispensary with a note written on a prescription blank describing the problem and ending with a terse "please see."

Acute infectious disease was just one of many concerns on the wards but the advent of more readily available penicillin to complement well-established sulfadiazine assured a significant change from the relative helplessness often felt in the pre-war period. Patients with contagious disease, most often diphtheria, measles, poliomyelitis, scarlet fever, and pertussis, were transferred to Sydenham. Prior to the ready availability of penicillin, many children with acute rheumatic fever were treated with aspirin and hospitalized at Happy Hills or St. Gabriel's, institutions specific for that purpose, when their hearts were seriously compromised.

Epidemic diarrhea in the summer months was a potential killer but the lessons taught by Darrow concerning the need to replace potassium loss were taking hold.[32] We treated diarrheal dehydration differently in those days. Babies were put on nothing by mouth, a "therapeutic starvation" long since out of mode. Mild dehydration was often repaired with a subcutaneous clysis. The babies looked as if they were sprouting wings from their scapulae.

Cancer in all its forms had always been resistant to cure. The average life expectancy of a child with leukemia was three to three-and-a-half months from the time of diagnosis in the 1940s. The uses of drugs such as alpha-methopterin, 6-mercaptopurine, nitrogen mustard, and steroids were just beginning to be included with surgery and radiation therapy to treat, for example, neuroblastoma. Physicians experienced repeated frustration fighting cancer and this encouraged some to take matters into their own hands. Often, their efforts did not have the benefit of organized study or protocols, and there were no ethics committees or institutional review boards in the 1950s. For example, we had some success with nitrogen mustard in the treatment of neuroblastoma. Schwentker heard from Alan Woods, the chief of the Wilmer Institute, about a teenager with one eye already lost to retinoblastoma and a tumor in the second eye. Aware of the pathologic similarity of the two tumors, Schwentker suggested that nitrogen mustard be tried and told the Harriet Lane chief resident to give mustard to the patient. That was done immediately with the help of Carl Kupfer of the Wilmer house staff—without a formal study, protocol, or informed consent. The tumor melted beautifully over the next two weeks. That was 1952. Mustard was more formally studied after that, particularly at the College of Physicians and Surgeons in New York City.

The house staff was imbued with respect for the privilege and responsibility given them and with a genuine sense of inquiry. Constructive communication with children and parents, sensitive care for the more subjective needs of the terribly ill and dying, the relief of pain, behavioral issues, the ethical underpinnings of medical decision making, a sense of the business aspects of practice, and many other areas of concern in primary care were generally given inadequate attention. Greater emphasis on these and similar areas, based on a sound body of knowledge, is more evident in recent decades. Still, it was only in 2001 that Residency Review Committees began to mandate formal attention to such matters.[33]

Inadequacy in training was universal in the United States at the midpoint of the twentieth century. Park gave training a strong push in the right direction, but the totality of care and patient need was not often fully addressed. The relationship of the house staff to their patients and the children's parents was in large part governed by policies dictated by the hospital. A mimeographed sheet handed out to parents on the admission of a child firmly stated that the visiting hours were limited to one hour on two days of the week (later on, every day) unless "the child is seriously ill," and that only parents could visit because of the limitations of space. Additionally, the best time to call the house officer for information was 4:30 to 5:00 p.m. The rules clearly favored the needs of the hospital and the push of daily duties often overwhelmed the wish to give parents the time, information, and assurance they needed. But there were ways to break the administrative hold. There was always the possibility and often the probability of a loose definition of "seriously ill," particularly with the agreement of the nurses.[34]

After Schwentker

Francis Schwentker died, a suicide, on November 8, 1954. He had been given a leave of absence several months earlier because of an unspecified illness.[35] The promise of this intensely committed and productive investigator, blessed with "an intellect of great power and clarity," was not fulfilled, primarily because Schwentker did not possess the skills required to be an effective administrator.[36] Also, the university and hospital clearly had not afforded the department of pediatrics a high priority during Schwentker's time. There was a suggestion of something better to come in a letter Schwentker wrote to Park early in 1954 about the uses of various funds available to the chief. Schwentker assured Park that any funds used to ease his retirement would not "hamper the work of the Harriet Lane Home" and indicated that "the principal of the Van der Berg Fund" would go "into the construction of the new building."[37] There was no further mention of such a building and, in fact, Schwentker never got a substantial portion of the funds he requested. His only memorials at Johns Hopkins are his portrait, which hangs with those of his fellow pediatric chairmen, and a yearly Francis F. Schwentker Award.[38]

The challenges inherent in so sudden a death were assumed by Wilkins, already named interim chief. Money was the major problem. The total annual budget for the department was less than one hundred and seventy thousand dollars. Professional fees remained relatively constant while expenses increased so that a surplus of about twenty-five thousand dollars in 1949–50 had converted to a deficit of more than twenty-six thousand dollars by 1954–55. The cause was the pediatric psychiatric clinic. Schwentker had agreed to take over its expenses from the department of psychiatry and it was from the start a heavy money loser. Moreover, Schwentker had authorized the construction of a steroid chemistry laboratory and the private outpatient service needed reorganization.[39] The physical setting of the Harriet Lane was constraining and getting old, and salaries were reminiscent of the Howland days. Indeed, Schwentker's ultimate salary of fifteen thousand dollars a year was not much beyond that of Howland, and

Lewis Thomas had left because he could not get the sixty-five hundred dollars he needed for life in Baltimore.

Wilkins requested the psychiatric clinic's immediate return to the department of psychiatry, instant approval for the funds essential to his own chemistry laboratory, and a reorganization of the private outpatient service to begin on July 1, 1955. He wanted "a young but well-qualified *full-time pediatrician* with good clinical and administrative ability" to invigorate that service and he proposed to pay that person a salary of six thousand dollars. He hoped that "the income from professional fees can be increased by more efficient service but aside from this the good will and improvement in relations with the public demand corrections in our Private Patient Service."[40] The limited vision implicit in Wilkins' letter to Dean Philip Bard suggested that Wilkins considered himself truly temporary in the chief's role and that his primary interest remained in his division.

Still, the department's essential strength remained. William Zinkham, a graduate of the School of Medicine, a chief resident, and ultimately a distinguished chief of the division of hematology, reflected: "There were always people who prodded you, who made you think....There will always be questions to be asked and answers to be found, always discovery as the result of asking questions. It was most important to know how to identify a problem and pursue it. Even as interns [there was] the feeling that 'I'm going to start finding out'—the inquisitive mind over the years—and the humility to say, 'I don't know.'"[41]

Schwentker had been frustrated in his effort to reorganize the department as he saw fit and he was unable to counteract the sluggish responses of the university and hospital administrations. Ironically, Park had foretold this in a confidential 1938 letter to Maurice Pincoffs at the University of Maryland School of Medicine. Pincoffs had offered Schwentker a leadership position in pediatrics. Park wrote,

> I am as fond of Schwentker and ambitious for him as if he belonged to me.... [ellipsis inserted by Park] I doubt, however, if he will accept your post. He is headed, I think, toward epidemiology. I do not believe he would be satisfied with the kind of position which the head of a pediatric clinic offers. However, I may be mistaken. I might suggest to you that an opportunity be created for him by which he would be your professor of pediatrics and at the same time would have special facilities at Syden-

ham for carrying out further studies in scarlet fever. The opportunity at Sydenham might neutralize in his mind the drudgery of a headship of a department.

> Schwentker is not by nature a physician. He is primarily interested in disease, not in the individual.... [ellipsis by Park] Schwentker is the ablest man scientifically I have ever had and has had quite a remarkable experience.[42]

Schwentker seemed to understand his limitations. His daughter remembered that her father "told my mother that he never measured up to Park. He couldn't fill those shoes."[43]

Park's Private Recruitment Effort

By this time, the department of pediatrics suffered both as a result of the School of Medicine's indifference to it and by Schwentker's deteriorating leadership and sudden death. So Johns Hopkins turned to Park for help in finding a new chief. Park had not imposed himself on Schwentker and deliberately chose an office in the department of pathology physically distant from the Harriet Lane Home. Now, with Schwentker gone, the new circumstances demanded Park's involvement. Once again, Park wanted Charles Janeway, the chief at the Boston Children's Hospital, to take over the reins of the Harriet Lane.

In 1947 Park had offered counsel to Janeway about the pleasure and pain of chairmanship. When Janeway revealed that he was uncertain about his ability to fulfill the responsibilities of the chair at the Boston Children's Hospital because he was an internist and had doubts about his clinical abilities, Park assured him that he had no doubts about Janeway's abilities. Park made his point very carefully in a letter, noting first his dismay at administrative demands and suggesting a solution to Charles's problem:

> I was very glad to hear that you had gotten off the heaviest part of the burden of administration. Looking back on my past, I would have been enormously helped to have had a second string man, who loved administration and who could have relieved me of most of it. But I never had just the right person for it in a high enough departmental position. I would have secured [Sidney] Gellis for that job if I could have persuaded him to return to the Harriet Lane. I wonder if you ought not right away to bring in some young man to act as your assistant in administration, not expecting much else from him.[44]

On one occasion, Park brought Janeway to the wards at the Harriet Lane to reassure Janeway of his clinical abilities. Afterward, Janeway wrote to Park's wife, Agnes: "Please tell Punk that my brief period of instruction at his hands in Baltimore served me in very good stead and that I picked up a case of congenital syphilis on the wards my first day back in which the eye grounds exactly duplicated those of the child he showed me at Harriet Lane. My stock as a diagnostician has risen considerably as a result of this experience and I think I probably ought to charge the batteries in Baltimore more frequently than I have."[45]

The relationship these two men shared ran deep and Park decided to use it in his effort to get Janeway installed as chief in Baltimore. His "confidential" letter of April 6, 1955, to "My dear Charlie" began innocently enough with a comment that W. Barry Wood, a graduate of the School of Medicine who trained at Hopkins as an internist and was a great friend and sometime confidant of both men, had agreed to return to Baltimore as vice president for the Johns Hopkins Medical Institutions. Park then went on to discuss a proposal to bring Janeway to the Harriet Lane, eating at the start perhaps a bit too much humble pie:

> I have been thinking over your problem. No one can say that the honor of being professor here is greater than that of being professor at Harvard. Very likely it is not so great. No one can maintain that your opportunity at Johns Hopkins is greater than your opportunity at Harvard and no medical school or university can possibly offer more than Harvard Medical School and University. In fact Johns Hopkins University is small potatoes compared to Harvard. I have always thought that I would far rather live in Boston than in Baltimore although Baltimore is an exceedingly pleasant place to spend one's life in.

Park then listed "reasons why you might be attracted to Baltimore in preference to Boston." In particular, he emphasized that at the Harriet Lane, Janeway "would have opportunity to devote yourself more effectively than I think is possible at the Children's Hospital to scholarship. The pediatric department here is much smaller and the load of administration far less than I fancy is the case at the Children's Hospital in Boston." In fact, Park felt that there was a fundamental difference between the two institutions that should not be overlooked.

One more point which seems to me of considerable importance is this, I believe that the Children's Hospital is founded on incorrect principles. In my humble opinion, to make pediatrics complete and independent and to make it stand out as an entity is an error. Here [A. McGehee] Harvey is all prepared to integrate pediatrics with internal medicine on a parity with a view to making the study of the human being from birth to death continuous.[46] In other words pediatrics will not be regarded, as has been the case in the past, as a specialty but as an integral part of internal medicine. This is made easier here because the departments are housed under the same roof. Here your contact is not with children's surgery, children's ophthalmology, or children's otolaryngology and neurology but with those subjects in their universal aspects. I, personally, do not believe that the great progress in pediatrics is going to come from children's hospitals organized as yours is in progress of being at Harvard but rather in the pediatric departments that are integrated in the closest possible fashion with all the other departments of a great medical institution. I believe that you have the chance here to develop a different kind of pediatric department than exists anywhere in the country.[47]

These thoughts were not new for Park. Years before he had suggested that an internist could easily be his immediate successor.[48] Obviously unconcerned that Janeway had not trained as a pediatrician, Park probably had him in mind even then.

In closing, Park invoked Wood's return to Baltimore as a lure and then: "Nothing would give me more delight than to have you come and be my successor and to carry the department to heights which I was never capable of attaining. I should get great satisfaction in the thought that a son of your father, to whom I owe my start in life and whom I have venerated as almost no other man, were to take my place here." But he acknowledged that this would not be an easy decision and that Janeway and his wife, Betty, were "probably exclaiming, 'Why could they not have left us alone?'"[49] Signed "Affectionately, Punk" this letter was an enticing but ultimately unsuccessful coda to all of Park's effort for the Harriet Lane Home.

There is, of course, considerable and durable dispute over the position Park took about the freestanding children's hospital, and Janeway may well have disagreed with him. Park's inclusion of such a vigorous, forthright opinion may not have served his recruitment endeavor. It is possible, perhaps probable, however, that Janeway's refusal had more to do with his wife Betty's reluctance to leave Boston.[50]

Park finally gave up his hope that Janeway would come to Baltimore. Instead, the Harriet Lane Home entered the Robert Cooke era. In retrospect, the Schwentker period was often painful but it proved to be a sustaining bridge to Cooke's time. It was then that burgeoning federal funding and a growing nationwide research establishment fed by that funding resulted in the exponential increase in knowledge that would dramatically improve medical and health care. Lamentably, Schwentker may have been on the cusp of that time but he was no longer at the helm when it arrived.

Notes

1. Thomas B. Turner, *Heritage of Excellence: The Johns Hopkins Medical Institutions, 1914–1947* (Baltimore: The Johns Hopkins University Press, 1974), 523. Interestingly, the suggestion that an internist might be suitable as the chief for Harriet Lane had been made and rejected in 1926, when Edwards Park was selected.

2. Ibid.

3. Memorandum from Alan Chesney to President Isaiah Bowman, January 5, 1946. Office of the Dean Correspondence Files, "Pediatrics," Alan Mason Chesney Medical Archives, The Johns Hopkins Medical Institutions, Baltimore MD, hereafter referred to as AMC.

4. Ibid.

5. "A Medical Explorer Returns to the Children," *Baltimore Sun*, July 14, 1946, biographical file, "Francis F. Schwentker"; Ann Phillips (Francis Schwentker's daughter), conversation with author, May 14, 2002.

6. Thomas B. Turner, *Heritage of Excellence*, 525. It continues to be a practice in the Johns Hopkins Children's Center to have a resident do something more after the first three years of training to gain a greater experience before assuming the chief residency. As Schwentker demonstrated, this pays dividends.

7. "Baltimore's Sydenham Service for Hospital Care of Communicable Disease," *Baltimore Health News* 26 (1949): 149–50.

8. A. McGehee Harvey, Gert H. Brieger, Susan L. Abrams, and Victor A. McKusick, *A Model of Its Kind, Volume I: A Centennial History of Medicine at Johns Hopkins* (Baltimore: The Johns Hopkins University Press, 1989), 277–79. Perrin Long later became head of the department of medicine at the newly organized State University of New York, Downstate Medical Center in Brooklyn.

9. "A Medical Explorer Returns to the Children," *Baltimore Sun*.

10. Ibid.

11. Lowell Reed to Francis Schwentker, February 15, 1939, biographical file, "Francis F. Schwentker."

12. Memorandum from Alan Chesney to President Bowman, January 5, 1946.

13. "Crippled Hearts," *Time*, July 26, 1946.

14. "New Search On for Rheumatic Fever's Cause," *New York Herald Tribune*, July 19, 1946.

15. Ruth Whittemore was a member of Taussig's pediatric cardiology group. One evening, Whittemore and I were writing notes at a desk on a hushed Harriet Lane 3 West. Whittemore wondered aloud if it were permissible to describe a patient's breathing "as if he were holding a hot potato in his mouth." I have used that line ever since. Whittemore went from Hopkins to Yale and spent the rest of her long, fruitful career there.

16. Francis Schwentker to Alan Chesney, February 6, 1947. Office of the Dean Correspondence Files, "Pediatrics," AMC.

17. Lewis Thomas, of course, went on to a distinguished career that culminated in leadership of the Sloan-Kettering Institute in New York. He was particularly lauded for his perceptive commentary and essays about medicine and, more generally, life.

18. Johns Hopkins University President Isaiah Bowman to Francis Schwentker, February 4, 1946. Office of the Dean Correspondence Files, "Pediatrics," AMC.

19. Ibid.

20. Francis Schwentker to Alan Chesney, March 9, 1951. Office of the Dean Correspondence Files, "Pediatrics," AMC.

21. Francis Schwentker to Alan Chesney, July 15, 1952. Office of the Dean Correspondence Files, "Pediatrics," AMC.

22. Alan Chesney to Francis Schwentker, August 15, 1952. Office of the Dean Correspondence Files, "Pediatrics," AMC.

23. Francis Schwentker to John Whitehorn, February 25, 1954. Office of the Dean Correspondence Files, "Pediatrics," AMC.

24. Barton Childs, conversation with author, March 1, 2002.

25. Barton Childs, conversation with author, February 12, 2002.

26. Barton Childs, conversation with author, March 1, 2002.

27. Alpha Omega Alpha is the honor society in medical schools.

28. Francis Schwentker to Alan Chesney and Edwin Crosby, October 22, 1951.

29. Memorandum by Alan Chesney concerning interview with Schwentker, November 15, 1951. Office of the Dean Correspondence Files, "Pediatrics," AMC.

30. Biographical file, "Effie Ellis," AMC.

31. "House Staff Manual of The Johns Hopkins Hospital, 1952–53," author's files.

32. Daniel Darrow, a colleague of Park's at Yale, came to Baltimore during the war years to explore better approaches to hydration in response to the severe wasting that was often the result of epidemic diarrhea and the importance of replenishment with potassium as treatment. He also taught the need to assure a competent kidney when hydration was undertaken.

33. Residency Review Committees constitute the formal mechanism set up by national organizations such as the Association of American Medical

Colleges and the American Medical Association to provide oversight and certification of residency programs. It is not clear even today that residency training—really an apprenticeship with varying supervision, originally established to serve the in-hospital care of the seriously ill as well as educational ends—can adapt to the demand of the twenty-first century for a physician completely at ease in the care of the so-called whole patient. Today's doctor is expected to be intimately familiar with objective and subjective aspects of care, sensitive to cross-cultural issues, a comfortable and complete communicator, and, of course, to have absolute competence blended with unreserved compassion. The pragmatic demands of hospital care, the limited number of years available to the residency, the explosion in the base of knowledge and technical competency, the advent of managed care and control by insurance companies, and the frequent fatigue that is common to the years spent in training mitigate the possibility of complete success.

34. "Policies of the Harriet Lane Home, 1952–1953," author's files.

35. *The Annual Report of the Dean of the Medical Faculty, 1954–1955.* Biographical file, "Francis F. Schwentker."

36. "Francis F. Schwentker, 1904–1954," *Pediatrics* 16 (1955): 134.

37. Francis Schwentker to Edwards Park, January 21, 1954.

38. By May 20, 1955, 227 individuals had contributed a total of more than three thousand dollars to the Schwentker Memorial Fund. The money was used to commission Schwentker's portrait and to establish the Francis F. Schwentker Award. The award was established at the direction of the Medical Board of the hospital but the major impetus came from Thomas Reichelderfer, chief resident from 1953 to 1954, and Victor Najjar and Lawson Wilkins among others. The award recognized the member of the Hopkins house staff who had submitted the best scientific paper during the preceding year. The first award, a check for one hundred dollars and a bronze medal, went to Gerald Holman for a paper titled "Studies on Physiologic Hyperbilirubinemia of Negro and White Premature Infants." Department of Pediatrics, Francis F. Schwentker Research Award Collection, "Schwentker Award 1955–1967" file, Chesney Medical Archives. For some time there were a variety of formats for the award and house officers other than pediatricians were involved. In 1992 the competition was limited to pediatric house officers and fellows. The annual presentation is made at Grand Rounds in Hurd Hall and the sense of special promise that had been evident in 1946 is evoked again when William Zinkham speaks about Francis Schwentker.

39. Lawson Wilkins to Philip Bard [then dean of the Johns Hopkins School of Medicine], November 22, 1954.

40. Ibid.

41. William Zinkham, conversation with author, spring 1999.

42. Edwards Park to Maurice Pincoffs, November 9, 1938. Edwards Park Letters, box 4339233335, folder P-17, AMC.

43. Ann Phillips (Francis Schwentker's daughter), conversation with author, May 14, 2002.

44. Edwards A. Park to Charles Janeway, May 28, 1947. Robert Haggerty, who is writing a biography of Janeway, provided copies of correspondence between Edwards and Agnes Park and Charles Janeway to the author.

245

A Litany of Frustrations

Sidney Gellis had been on the Harriet Lane house staff under Park and the chief resident in 1941–42. He went on to Boston and a very successful career. Thomas B. Turner *Heritage of Excellence*, 573. There was nothing to suggest that Gellis might have considered such a secondary, administrative role even as an academic steppingstone.

45. Charles Janeway to Agnes Park, August 23, 1945. Robert Haggerty.

46. A. McGehee Harvey succeeded Warfield Longcope as chief in the department of medicine in 1946. There is no evidence among Schwentker's papers that he and Harvey had had any discussion in this regard. Park, not known to speak or write without justification, might have had informal talks in this regard with any number of people.

47. Edwards Park to Charles Janeway, April 6, 1955. Robert Haggerty.

48. Thomas B. Turner, *Heritage of Excellence*, 523.

49. Edwards Park to Charles Janeway, April 6, 1955. Robert Haggerty.

50. Personal communication between Robert Haggerty (Charles Janeway's biographer) and the author, May 21, 2003.

A Champion of Children

Robert Cooke 1956–1973

BY LAWRENCE S. WISSOW   247

ROBERT COOKE'S CHAIRMANSHIP of the Harriet Lane Home from 1956–1973 spanned years that witnessed revolutions in both science and society. He came of age during the global wave of scientific activity stimulated by World War II. In the United States, that growth was spurred by Vannevar Bush's 1945 report to President Franklin D. Roosevelt, "Science—The Endless Frontier," which proposed a massive peacetime government investment in scientific research to continue and expand on research accomplishments during the war. This growth was also spurred by the Servicemen's Readjustment Act of 1944, better known as the "GI Bill of Rights," which flooded universities with millions of new students before its expiration in 1956.[1] Cooke became chair barely three years after Watson and Crick published their findings about the double-helix structure of DNA, and four years before Nirenberg showed how the DNA code was translated into proteins.[2] Two years before Cooke's term began, the U.S. Supreme Court decided *Brown v. the Board of Education*, beginning a civil rights movement that had vast implications for segregated cities like Baltimore.[3]

Enormous Changes

Robert Cooke's pediatric training coincided with the heyday of McCarthyism, and his chairmanship took place as the cold war evolved into a national preoccupation with scientific competition between the United States and the Soviet Union. Cooke shared in the optimism of the Kennedy years and Lyndon Johnson's Great Society, and weathered the disillusionment of Vietnam, Watergate, and the country's swing back toward a more conservative social agenda. He became chair in the middle of the presidency of Dwight Eisenhower (1953–1961), and stepped down just nine months before Richard Nixon resigned.

Bob (as he was known) Cooke became a champion of children at a time when youth was part of the national consciousness. It was a time of "fashionable pessimism," he said at the dedication of the new Johns Hopkins Children's Medical and Surgical Center (CMSC) in May 1964. "Delinquency, race riots, assassinations, are the 'Big Stories,'" Cooke observed, but he was "proud to be called a Pollyanna" and recognized that "the opportunity for the improvement of man is a pediatric fact." The "real significance" of the CMSC, he said, was that it demonstrated the importance of the child for the development of man. He proposed that building the CMSC was "the first step in the eventual organization of a laboratory complex for the study of the acceleration of human development," and predicted that "the rewards will be staggering and the race to the moon or the conquest of poverty will seem pale in comparison."[4]

During Cooke's tenure there were enormous changes in the practice of medicine. The National Research Act of 1974[5] set in motion a mechanism that would rewrite the ethics of medical care and medical experimentation, bringing previously undisclosed medical practices into the light of day. Medicare and Medicaid, signed into law in 1965 by President Johnson[6] redefined the relationship between urban health-care institutions and the poor, marking the beginning of the end of charity care and bringing with it federal standards for the quality and availability of medical services. A similar redefinition took place in the world of medical research, as the National Institutes of Health (NIH) took over from private foundations as the dominant source of research funding, which increased oversight and review and provided vastly larger resources. Before World War II the National Cancer Institute (NCI) had a successful program that awarded research and training support to scientists and clinicians who were not part of the NCI. In 1944 the Public Health Service Act[7] expanded this program to the entire NIH. In the ten-year period from 1947 to 1957, available NIH "extramural" research funding grew from about $4 million to over $100 million, reaching $1 billion in 1974.[8] NIH funding became the engine that drove growth at departments like the Harriet Lane, but that growth also helped transform them from intimate, almost club-like communities into much larger, more impersonal research and clinical institutions. Cooke predicted that this would happen, though

ROBERT COOKE AT THE DEDICATION OF THE CHILDREN'S MEDICAL AND SURGICAL CEN-
TER (CMSC) IN 1964. Cooke declared that he was "proud to be called a Pollyanna" at the
dedication of the new CMSC in 1964. During his tenure at Johns Hopkins, Cooke earned
a reputation as a champion of children, especially the underprivileged and the mentally
retarded.

he hoped it would not. In his 1964 CMSC speech, he warned that the
department faced the danger of "bigness," and that "as the building
grows big, the spirit thins out."[9]

Other clinical changes were subtler but just as far reaching. Cooke's
leadership began as the antibiotic era was exploding. Mainstays of pediatric care—vancomycin, methicillin, ampicillin, gentamycin, and the
cephalosporins—were discovered or introduced between 1956 and
1964.[10] In the early 1950s children's hospitals had their own labora-

tories where infant formula was prepared.[11] By the time Cooke left, the formula industry was firmly established and breast-feeding rates were in marked decline.[12] Standards for how children and families were treated in the hospital, including isolation from parents, changed radically. Publication of C. Henry Kempe and his colleagues' influential paper on the battered child spurred a national wave of child-abuse laws and gave a new set of roles to pediatricians.[13]

Doctors not much younger than Cooke underwent enormously different experiences during their training. Paul Hardy, for example, described his first year on the Harriet Lane house staff in 1945, doing emergency tracheotomies without anesthesia for children with diphtheria at Sydenham Hospital for infectious diseases in Baltimore. "These people would come in and they would be absolutely black and blue. You would throw them on the table and tie them down and you didn't bother [with anesthesia], you just took a scalpel and cut right down below the cricoid and stick a thing in it and stuff would come flying out all over you."[14] World War II also had a permanent impact on the composition of residency programs around the United States. Prior to the war, chief residents often worked several years in the community prior to taking up their positions, and interns in pediatrics frequently completed a year of internal medicine before coming to pediatrics. With the war came accelerated training schedules, and it became more common for interns to come directly to pediatrics and for chief residents to take over immediately or only shortly after their senior "assistant" resident year.[15] The Harriet Lane service in Cooke's time rode out these changes and prospered under them, becoming one of the premier incubators for other pediatric departments. Writing in 1991, when Cooke received the John Howland Award, Hopkins faculty member Saul Brusilow calculated that twenty-two pediatric residents from Cooke's era had gone on to become department chairs, and 104 held positions in academic medicine.[16]

"Let's Go to Baltimore"

It took a search committee, chaired by A. McGehee Harvey, about a year to find a replacement for Francis Schwentker.[17] The committee was composed of a surgeon (Alfred Blalock), an internist (Russell Nelson), a neurophysiologist (Philip Bard), and a radiologist (Russell Morgan). Though the committee formally lacked a pediatric representative, Blalock and Harvey had pediatric connections. Blalock was the long-time collaborator of Helen Taussig, the pediatric cardiologist with whom he developed the field of pediatric cardiac surgery in the 1940s. Harvey had also worked with Taussig while he was a medical resident in the 1930s.[18] Perhaps more importantly, during his residency Harvey worked with Charles Janeway, who was at Hopkins at the time and who later became pediatrician-in-chief of the Boston Children's Hospital. In early 1955 the Johns Hopkins Hospital Medical Board heard a presentation from Harvey about the search committee's deliberations and offered Janeway the job of pediatrician-in-chief at Hopkins.[19] When Janeway turned them down, the committee next proposed a young pediatrician at Yale, Robert Cooke.[20]

In 1955 Cooke was thirty-five and had not yet held any leadership position, though he had been promoted to associate professor. Cooke's profile of youth and scientific promise, minus prior administrative responsibility, fit a pattern established by members of the search committee themselves. Bard had come to Hopkins from Harvard at age 34, moving from assistant professor at Harvard to full professor and chair of the department of physiology at Hopkins.[21] Morgan had come to Hopkins in 1947, also in his mid-thirties, to become a professor and founding chair of the department of radiology. Harvey was just turning thirty-five when he became chair of the department of medicine. Nelson, an internist who was primarily interested in administrative issues, had risen to the post of assistant director of the Johns Hopkins Hospital (the post he held during the pediatric chair search) at age thirty-nine.[22] Blalock was the only late bloomer among the committee members; he had not become chair of surgery at Hopkins until 1941, when he was at the advanced age of forty-two.[23]

Six months or so after an interview with the search committee, at which Cooke thought he had shown "no spark," he received a plain card ("cheap looking" he called it in an interview), easily overlooked in a stack of mail. Nearly disguised by the offhand trappings of the note was an offer Cooke found hard to resist. Over the university president's signature, he was offered the appointment as chairman of pediatrics at a salary of twenty thousand dollars a year, more than four times what he earned at Yale. "I gotta go," he said to himself.[24] Though he loved Yale, the financial offer was compelling for a married man who by this time had two developmentally disabled children aged five and eight and was looking for a chance to "stand on [his] own two feet."[25]

It is not clear that Cooke ever wanted to be a doctor or a pediatrician. He was born in 1920 in Attleboro, Massachusetts, a small city south of Boston whose motto is "the birthplace of the jewelry industry in America." Cooke's father, Ronald, was a New Englander who traced his ancestry to Sir Francis Cooke, who had landed at Plymouth, Massachusetts, in 1620.[26] Bob Cooke's mother, Renee, was Swiss. Ronald Cooke had wanted to be a doctor but lacked the money to go to college. He ended up in the insurance business and his wife had left school at fourteen to work in a factory.[27] The family was not well off, and Ronald Cooke leaned hard on his two sons to go into medicine. In an interview in 2000, Bob Cooke said of his father, "He paid the bills and he tended to call the tune. In my time parents did a lot of deciding for their children."[28]

Although Ronald Cooke may not have had money for his own education, he saw to it that his sons attended elite New England institutions. Bob was sent to the Loomis School, in Windsor, Connecticut, then to Yale's Sheffield Scientific School for his undergraduate degree, and to Yale medical school.[29] He graduated Yale's Sheffield School with high honors in physiological chemistry and bacteriology and took courses in Latin, German, French literature, and philosophy. As a junior he was elected to Phi Beta Kappa and to Sigma Xi, the science honor society, and in his senior year he lettered in baseball. In medical school he won no fewer than four prizes, ranging from recognition for having the best record in the basic sciences to being the student with the best qualifications for becoming a successful general practitioner.[30] Ronald Cooke wrote to his son on September 16, 1944, to congratulate him on graduating from medical school and succeeding despite the "many personal problems which were with you at all times." He predicted that his son would "come to like to be in many people's company and to respect their point of view as well as your own." Ronald noted that this was "the only problem you have left" and that it was "getting less and less."[31]

Cooke's record as a medical student earned him eighteen months of internship and residency at New Haven Hospital under Grover Powers, who was pediatrician-in-chief and a professor at Yale. Powers was seventeen years into what would be his twenty-five-year tenure as chairman of pediatrics at Yale, having taken over from Edwards A. Park when Park returned to Johns Hopkins.[32] Powers was probably one of the most influential figures in pediatrics at the time, and many of those who trained under him—"Grover's boys"—went on to prominent careers. But perhaps more significant for Cooke's influence on the Harriet Lane, Powers was known as a humanist who was keenly interested in the emotional and developmental impact of illness on children. Powers was also known for his work with mentally retarded children, and in 1952 he became the first chair of the Research Advisory Committee of the National Association of Retarded Children (NARC).[33] Powers continued to advise Cooke after Cooke's move to Baltimore and may have helped him secure some of his early research funding from the NARC. In 1958 Cooke, as chair of pediatrics at Hopkins, wrote curt, frank letters to many correspondents, but he still addressed his former chief "Dear Dr. Powers."[34]

Cooke's initial position at Yale, separated from his residency by two years in the army, was as a fellow in physiology, working with John Brobeck. His work in Brobeck's lab involved trying to understand the mechanisms that led to obesity in brain-lesioned rats. Cooke said this work was "a wash" and he recalled feeling as if he was being treated like a clinician rather than as a scientist.[35] When he worked with Yale professor Daniel Darrow, however, Cooke's career was launched. Darrow was a leading researcher on problems of fluid and electrolyte metabolism in infants. Between 1948 and 1956, when he left for Baltimore, Cooke was a lead or co-author on some twenty medical journal articles about fluid metabolism, and half that many on subjects ranging from hypothyroidism to teaching in pediatric clerkships.[36] While a pediatric resident at Yale, Saul Brusilow worked in Darrow's lab alongside Cooke. Brusilow said that Cooke himself did relatively little work in the lab, but rather was "marked" from the beginning as someone who would have an important career. Cooke was not only smart but his enthusiasm and intellectual open-mindedness attracted others. Brusilow had been expecting to finish his third year of residency at Yale until the day when Cooke came into the lab and said to him, "Let's go to Baltimore."[37]

Great Work in Terrible Circumstances

At the time of Cooke's arrival in Baltimore, the Harriet Lane service may have lacked a chairman but it was populated by solidly established senior faculty and many junior faculty members who would subsequently make important contributions to pediatrics. Perhaps the best known were Helen Taussig, the pioneering pediatric cardiologist mentioned earlier, Lawson Wilkins, the founder of pediatric endocri-

HARRIET LANE STAFF ON STEPS C.1960. By the time the photographer composed this portrait, c.1960, the department of pediatrics was so large that its members spilled off the front entrance steps of the Harriet Lane Home. With the encouragement of longtime staff, Robert Cooke began to press for a new building as soon as he arrived in 1956. Cooke was a political master who achieved many goals for children's health and well-being within Johns Hopkins and beyond, particularly in Washington, D.C.

nology, biochemist Victor Najjar, and Leo Kanner, one of the pioneers of modern child psychiatry and care of the mentally retarded. Younger faculty included the hematologist William Zinkham (the single senior "resident" in Cooke's first year), geneticist Barton Childs (who was interviewing for a chairmanship at the University of Colorado when Cooke arrived), Julian Chisolm (who became one of the world's leaders in the diagnosis and treatment of lead poisoning), child psychiatrist Leon Eisenberg, and Harold Harrison, who was the pediatrician-in-chief at Baltimore City Hospitals.[38] A year after Cooke's arrival, Mary Ellen Avery, then a resident in pediatrics, began working with Peter Gruenwald, a Hopkins pathologist, and Johns Clements, a physiologist at the Army Chemical Center in Edgewood, Maryland. Together, they identified the role of pulmonary surfactants in the prevention of atelectasis (a condition in which portions of the lungs collapse and no longer support the exchange of oxygen with the blood). They also demonstrated that a lack of surfactant was the cause of hyaline membrane disease, a condition that frequently caused the death of premature infants. These observations eventually led to the development of surfactant replacement therapy, now widely used around the world, and to a marked reduction in the deaths of newborns.[39]

One of Cooke's talents, according to cardiologist Catherine Neill (who was a fellow with Dr. Taussig from 1951 to 1954, and who remains on the Harriet Lane faculty now as professor emeritus of pediatrics), was his level of comfort talking to and making deals with bright people, including many who were considerably older and better known.[40] Lawson Wilkins was Cooke's host and guide during the transition from Yale to Hopkins. Wilkins had been acting chair of pediatrics since the fall of 1954 when Francis Schwentker took a leave of absence (two months before his death). According to Cooke, Wilkins was a connoisseur of bourbon, and the orientation visits to Baltimore took the form of days of meetings at the hospital and the Harriet Lane Home, followed by late nights of talking and drinking.[41]

The Harriet Lane's role in teaching, however, may have fallen behind its scientific prominence by 1956. In a 1957 letter, Cooke wrote that he felt that pediatrics at Hopkins had fallen on hard times. "In the last several years," he wrote to Julian Price, a South Carolina physician and former Harriet Lane resident, "Harriet Lane has meant little to the students and the rest of the faculty of the Johns Hopkins, despite the presence of remarkable people in the department." Cooke felt that the pediatric residency program had also lost its appeal to the best medical school graduates. He told Price that he had to spend his first year rebuilding the teaching to "instill active interest in the student." But Cooke had a broader agenda. He told Price that he was undertaking "a complete readjustment of the residency training program... in accordance with my views on the need in training for greater emphasis on the humanistic aspects of pediatric practice, without neglecting the role of physical disease."[42]

Cooke also believed that the medical school faculty as a whole saw pediatrics as an uninteresting and low-prestige area of medicine. In an interview, he quoted then-NIH Director James Shannon as saying, that "there are no major death-dealing problems with children and any grandmother can take care of them."[43] In contrast, as Cooke wrote to Price, his goal was to "make the rest of the faculty aware of the fact that pediatrics represents the broadest area in medical education and that it should someday be the foundation for clinical medicine and the ideal transition from basic science to clinical work."[44]

Perhaps his thinking was the influence of one of Cooke's teachers at the Loomis School, whom he recalled having said that one should call a spade a spade, "and not an agricultural implement or a goddamned shovel."[45] It may also have been that he believed that pediatrics enjoyed second-rank status among the medical specialties at Hopkins. Whatever the influence, from the beginning Cooke earned a reputation for not mincing words. Early on he complained to Blalock (the influential chief of surgery and a member of the search committee that had chosen him) that only an intern had been sent in response to a request for an urgent surgical consultation about an ill infant. In reply, Cooke was summoned to a meeting with Barry Wood, a professor of microbiology and a vice president of the university and hospital, who suggested that Cooke had been too "aggressive" with Blalock[46] It might have been wise of Cooke to listen to Wood, who was widely respected as a tolerant influence at Hopkins. Among other things, Wood was a pioneer in recruiting and promoting Jewish faculty members at a time when Hopkins had a reputation as an anti-Semitic institution.[47] But Cooke already saw himself as an equal to the members of Hopkins' inner circle. After moving to Baltimore, he bought a home on Gibson Island on the Chesapeake Bay. Gibson Island was home to several Hopkins faculty members, including Tommy Turner, who would later become dean of the School of Medicine. The community excluded Catholics, blacks, and Jews, and such was its concern for propriety, reported Cooke's friend Brusilow, that as a requirement for buying his home, Cooke had to agree to put up a fence to shield neighbors from the sight of his two handicapped daughters.[48] Cooke ultimately became comfortable in much higher social circles than his Gibson Island neighbors could ever have imagined, but he seemed never to have been completely accepted by the most powerful leaders of the Hopkins faculty and administration.

Early on, there was also some tension between what Cooke referred to as his "Yale Mafia" and the "Hopkins people."[49] His "Mafia" included former residents and fellows from Yale whom Cooke recruited to Hopkins, sometimes with the aid of additional funding that he secured from outside sources. Its members included Brusilow, Gerry Odell, Bill Nyhan, Guy McKann, and several others. Cooke's main interest at Yale was in fluid and electrolyte metabolism and his work included studies of cystic fibrosis. In Baltimore Brusilow, who studied how sweat glands regulate their excretion of salt and fluids, developed a test that demonstrated abnormally high salt content in the sweat of children with cystic fibrosis.[50] The test allowed doctors to make a diagnosis of cystic fibrosis in children who might have few other symptoms of the disease. For many years Harriet Lane house staff went to Brusilow's laboratory to pick up the "sweat test machine" (formally, a device for carrying out pilocarpine iontophoresis) for use at a patent's bedside, carefully following instructions in the *Harriet Lane Handbook*. The homemade device consisted of a power supply, a pair of electrodes borrowed from an electrocardiogram machine, and several pieces of precisely weighed filter paper. Instructions in the *Handbook* noted that the electrodes had to be applied carefully "to prevent electrical burns" and that the current from the power supply could be adjusted based on "patient discomfort."[51] Later in an interview, Cooke lamented that the procedure had never been patented, depriving the department of "a fortune" in royalties. He added, however, that the business instinct was one of his "great disappointments" with modern medicine. He observed, "every time somebody's got an idea they run out and patent it and get a company going."[52]

Cooke said that when he arrived in Baltimore the Harriet Lane building was in a bad state of repair. "The waste of space in the building was just extreme."[53] Harriet Lane legend had it that the corridors had been designed to be wide enough so that Clemens von Pirquet, the first chair of the department (who never worked in the completed building), could parade through them with his retinue on either side of him when he made rounds. The elevator was said to be so slow it "held up science more than any other invention," and in the summer the top-floor labs were so hot "stuff would boil on the counters" and faculty put aluminum foil over the windowpanes to keep out the sun, Cooke recalled. Brusilow told a story that, at one point, Sidney Farber, the pioneering pediatric oncologist, came to Baltimore for a site visit and came up to Harriet Lane 5, where the laboratories were housed. Farber reportedly asked if this was where Wilkins, Najjar, Childs, and other prominent people in pediatrics at Hopkins were working. Told that this was true, he reportedly asked that a photo be taken, to document "what great work can be done in such terrible circumstances."[54] The inhabitants of the fifth floor didn't necessarily see things the same way. A few years

PARENTS AND CHILDREN WAITING IN THE DISPENSARY. Facilities in the Harriet Lane Home were becoming antiquated by the time Robert Cooke took over in 1956. The reception area of the dispensary was often so cold that patients had to wear their coats while awaiting treatment. Parents often brought their sick children an hour before the registration desk opened in an attempt to avoid long delays. Photo by the Barton Gillet Company of Baltimore.

earlier, in the June 1950 issue of a newsletter called *The Harriet Laner*, Hugh Josephs had written, "The Fifth Floor is more than a place, a group of laboratories and offices built on what used to be a sort of roof-garden where sometimes on summer evenings internes used to relax in a deck chair and wish they had some beer. [It] is also in the nature of a club—open to all who could find an answer to the question, 'What are you interested in?'"[55]

In Cooke's first week on the job, he visited Leo Kanner, whose office ceiling had a big patch of paint "hanging there ready to fall down on his desk" and whose first question for the new chairman was, "Is the new children's medical center (in planning at that point for over ten years) on time?" Cooke recalled telling Kanner that he hoped to start construction within the next year. Kanner reportedly replied, "That's what they told me in 1929."[56] Though Cooke would eventually preside at the opening of the new children's center in 1964, the old Harriet Lane provided many opportunities for him to engage the hospital's central administration over what he perceived as its attitude toward pediatrics. One winter, he recalled, it was so cold in the outpatient area that the residents rented a torpedo-shaped, gas-fired space heater, normally used outdoors, to heat the waiting area. Cooke then fought with the central administration for a month to get reimbursed for the twenty-eight-dollar rental fee.[57]

The Harriet Lane wards were also very different from those at Yale. Saul Brusilow described the Yale service at the time as made up of "boutiques," small wards of fifteen to twenty patients, often not full, covered by two interns at the most. In contrast, in the early 1950s Harriet Lane 4 had thirty-seven patients cared for by four interns and was nearly always full. On any given night, three or four children might be admitted; most were very sick with conditions such as lead poisoning, tuberculosis, or bacterial meningitis. The infant floor was the same size and also filled with extremely ill children. The x-ray department consisted of two rooms for taking images, a developing room, and a viewing box adjacent to the elevator, on which wet films were posted for the house staff to come by and read. It was easy to practice reading films since the elevator was slow and residents who didn't want to climb the stairs could look at films while they waited. The x-ray rooms also doubled as procedure rooms. Brusilow recalled one day standing outside the x-ray area, flirting with passing nurses, while surgeon Gunter Schultze performed a bronchoscopy.[58]

Brain abscesses were another relatively common problem, and had to be approached with a small armamentarium of antibiotics and imaging tools. The standard technique, after obtaining a skull film and EEG, was to ask the neurosurgeons to create a "burr hole" in the skull and then to probe for the abscess using a long needle with a stylette. Brusilow remembered neurologist David Clark repeatedly pushing a needle through the hole into a child's brain, coming up dry, and pushing again, trying to locate abscesses to be drained and cultured.[59]

Strained Relationships

Cooke personally assumed the task of increasing student and resident interest in pediatrics. He invited rotating students to his home to "discuss the shortcomings of the department program" and invited a handpicked group to become part of his first cohort of house staff, including Brusilow, Frank Gruskay, Gerry Odell, Genevieve Matanoski, and Guy McKhann.[60] Cooke rapidly became an imposing but charismatic figure for the interns and residents. He and other senior faculty were fixtures at rounds and conferences, and at the house staff picnic Cooke took part along with other faculty playing football or baseball against the residents. A visit to his office in the new Children's Medical and Surgical Center (CMSC), however, could be intimidating. Ken Roberts recalled that the office seemed large, and the first things one saw were pictures of Cooke with John Kennedy, Sargent and Eunice Shriver, and Lyndon Johnson, along with a model of the frigate USS *Harriet Lane*.[61] Cooke would sit behind his desk looking like a figure from *Gentlemen's Quarterly*, dressed impeccably in a shirt and carrying a stethoscope that seemed to match the color of his eyes.[62]

Cooke had a reputation among the house staff for encouraging young people to develop new ideas and perspectives.[63] Despite identifying himself as a bench scientist and only a "medium" clinician, Cooke encouraged his house staff to embark on a wide variety of scientific, clinical, and public-health career paths. Despite his low regard for the business aspects of science, one of Cooke's most visible steps as a champion of the house staff involved his role in the dissemination of the *Harriet Lane Handbook*. Today, the Handbook is perhaps the most visible symbol of Hopkins' influence on pediatric practice. Revised every three years by successive cohorts of Harriet Lane residents, its most recent (sixteenth) edition has grown to over a thousand pages with two hundred illustrations. The handbook was conceived by Harrison Spencer to help pediatric house staff remember the correct way to perform procedures, administer fluids, and calculate medication doses. It was first distributed during the chief residency of Henry Seidel in 1953 as a set of typewritten notes. Cooke recalled that when he arrived he recognized its utility, and "thought it was a shame that just a few residents carried it around." He persuaded a publisher to issue the next edition in a pocket-sized format. Profits flowed to a discretionary account in the Harriet Lane Fund.[64]

The handbook royalties got Cooke into one of his many scraps with Russell Nelson, who by this time was director of the Johns Hopkins Hospital. Cooke used the money, he recalled, for "something that was probably a little illegitimate." At the height of the Vietnam War, Cooke circulated a letter to American pediatricians urging them to "speak out" to their patients. The letter introduced a pamphlet that

GIRL PLAYING PIANO. Some conditions required long hospital stays and not all patients could expect a positive outcome. Efforts were made to give pleasure to patients in whatever form might be possible. This young girl found at least temporary contentment playing a piano in the hospital as her companion listened.

Cooke had written, and copies were available in bulk for distribution. Under the title of "A message to parents from your pediatrician," the pamphlet suggested that it was understandable that children might be angry and frustrated when some of the nation's "most powerful leaders" could not affect the course of the war, and when the government showed that it could not be trusted by invading Cambodia at the same time as it claimed to be "winding down" the war effort. "Our sons and daughters," Cooke wrote, "are torn by the thought of soldiers ordered to execute women and children and by guardsmen that fire at their own friends." The pamphlet included a tear-off sheet that parents could send to the president asking him to end the war.[65]

Cooke's antiwar efforts became part of an Internal Revenue Service decision to audit Johns Hopkins Hospital's accounts and tax-exempt status. In 1970 Nelson wrote Cooke a personal and confidential letter that gave the "very bad news" that the IRS was "displeased" with the use of hospital postage meters for the mailing, and that it was "unacceptable" to charge the mailing to the *Handbook* fund. Nelson also told Cooke that he couldn't spend *Handbook* money on house staff activities or entertainment, either.[66] The IRS had previously been involved with Hopkins over the question of whether resident stipends were subject to federal income tax. One of the skits at the 1961 turtle derby (the annual house staff party held on the first Friday before the Preakness horse race, now a fund-raising event for the CMSC), starred the "arch criminal Baby Face" Nelson visiting his two hundred dependents (former Hopkins house officers) in a federal penitentiary where they were being held for tax evasion.[67]

Cooke's tense relationship with Nelson was public knowledge. Ken Roberts, while he was a Harriet Lane resident, threw a "dessert party," for which his wife made a cake in the shape of the hospital. Roberts, not expecting a response, had extended Cooke an invitation. Cooke arrived, however, and sighting the untouched cake is said to have asked where Nelson's office might be represented. Cooke reportedly took a knife, cut out that part, and put it on a plate, saying something to the effect that what remained was now a much better cake.[68]

The Harriet Lane service answered to several "communities" outside its doors. It served a local neighborhood, largely poor and working class, composed of many ethnic groups, including many black families who had migrated from the Southeast to work in Baltimore's heavy industries. Though the area around Johns Hopkins had once been a thriving immigrant and manufacturing area, by the beginning of the twentieth century it was on the decline.[69] Racial and economic divisions were reflected within the hospital by the presence of economically and racially demarcated wards in many departments. Although racial segregation in the pediatric department had been formally ended during Park's tenure, it persisted well into the late 1960s in other departments including the newborn nursery in the Women's Clinic.[70]

Cooke's first summer in Baltimore was marked by a particularly bad outbreak of lead poisoning among local children. It was a condition that he knew of but had not encountered at Yale. Children in Baltimore were exposed to lead from paint inside the neighborhood's deteriorating row homes and from the city's soil, where it had been deposited by

RESIDENTS DRESSED AS "CONVICTS" AT A 1961 TURTLE DERBY. Robert Cooke had a prickly relationship with Russell Nelson, director of the Johns Hopkins Hospital. For example, in 1970 Cooke got into trouble by distributing an antiwar message to American pediatricians. Nelson was incensed, and not only because the Internal Revenue Service questioned the use of hospital postage meters for the mailing. Nelson was not pleased to be reminded of his 1961 run-in with the IRS about whether residents' stipends were subject to federal income tax, a situation that was spoofed by the house staff at that year's turtle derby, photographed here by William Hamilton. Photo courtesy of the Ferdinand Hamburger Jr. Archives in the Milton S. Eisenhower Library of the Johns Hopkins University, Baltimore, Maryland.

car exhaust and soot from industrial plants.[71] In an interview, Cooke recalled that several children died that summer from massive brain swelling caused by lead.[72] By the time Cooke left Hopkins in 1973, Hopkins faculty member Julian Chisolm had developed methods of testing for lead in children's blood, removing lead from children's bodies, and was working on methods to prevent lead absorption.[73]

Most interns, residents, and many nurses lived in the area immediately around the hospital. The relatively few married house staff lived in "the compound," a fenced group of low-rise brick apartments between Broadway and Caroline Street that closely resembled the nearby Perkins, Latrobe, and Frederick Douglass low-income housing projects a few blocks away. Jerry Winkelstein, a Harriet Lane resident from July 1965 to June 1968 (he returned in 1971 to serve a year as chief resident, and subsequently became a faculty member), remembered the neighborhood as segregated: black families lived west of Broadway and white families lived to the east.[74] Marilyn Winkelstein, a Harriet Lane nurse in the mid- 1960s, remembered needing a lawyer's help when her landlord balked at letting an African-American roommate sign their lease. She also recalled being horrified when she later learned that Testani's, a neighborhood bar and restaurant that was a favorite among hospital personnel, would not admit blacks and was alarmed that she hadn't noticed that it had only a white clientele.[75]

Although house staff and nurses entered and left the hospital at all hours (an advantage of living close-by was being able to eat dinner at home when on call), the area was not always considered secure. Ken Roberts recalled that his apartment in the compound was twice burglarized. Roberts said he tried to get an appointment with hospital director Nelson to talk about his and other residents' concerns about security. According to Roberts, he was told that Nelson's schedule was too tight to accommodate a meeting. At that point Roberts said he asked to have a question relayed to Nelson via the director's secretary. Roberts asked whether the administration would pay for damages to an adjacent church should house officers arm themselves and "miss" while trying to frighten off intruders. Roberts recalled that an appointment materialized that day, at which Nelson reportedly said that he made a habit of never staying in the neighborhood past five in the evening.[76]

Jerry Winkelstein observed that relationships with neighborhood residents were often strained. It was not unusual for parents to come to the walk-in or emergency clinic, have their child seen, but then refuse the suggested treatment, saying that doctors at the hospital were racist, didn't care, and did experiments on their children.[77] At least one source of such attitudes may have been parents' experiences in what was known as the walk-in clinic. Parents could bring children to the clinic without an appointment, and most did literally walk to the hospital from where they lived. In winter the clinic was notoriously backed up, with two residents assigned to see an unwieldy number of patients, most of who had arrived early in the morning but would not be seen until late in the afternoon. Parents often brought their children by seven o'clock in the morning so as to be first, even though registration did not begin until eight. Nurses' aides circulated through the waiting area checking for children they thought too sick for the wait. Winkelstein recalled that he would sometimes evaluate a particularly ill child in the clinic and be tempted to ask the parent why they had waited so long to bring the child for care. At that point he would realize that, considering the possibly day-long wait and the need to care for other children at home, he would not have come in any sooner himself had it been his child.[78]

Johns Hopkins Hospital also struggled in its relationships with community physicians. In 1959 the hospital's Medical Staff Conference Committee established a subcommittee on professional relations, composed of surgeon William E. Grose, orthopedist Moses Gellman, and Harry Klinefelter from internal medicine. Their report to the committee was very critical of how the hospital related to both patients and referring physicians. The subcommittee concluded "activity of Hopkins doctors in the affairs of local medical groups has fallen off to a point where recovery of influence will require serious, organized, protracted, and generalized effort." The report noted "Recurring self-descriptive words like 'smug,' 'self-satisfied,' 'condescending,' and 'aloof' indicate internal sources for some of the antagonism that they feel against us. Add poor performance in dealing with referring physicians to a 'holier than thou' attitude and a recipe for unpopularity is at hand." Continuing on, the report conceded, "The medical profession and Hospital authorities have lost a measure of popular confidence... Utterly dependent on each other, they have become disputatious.... The public is confused and alarmed by squabbles, charges, and counter-charges...." The report went on to describe problems that remain chronic: the difficulties outside doctors endured to get their patients admitted, a culture within the hospital that looked down on community-based doctors, poor communication with referring physicians, and a hospital that was not friendly to visitors.[79] Former Harriet Lane residents in practice in the community were not immune to such treatment. Henry Seidel remembered that after he completed his training in 1953 and set up a private practice in Baltimore, he sometimes had difficulty getting his patients admitted through the emergency room at Hopkins.[80]

Such was the backdrop for Cooke's first major interaction with the Baltimore area pediatric community: a dispute over whether he should be allowed to join the American Academy of Pediatrics without having taken the board examination in pediatrics. When Cooke came to

Baltimore, the local chapter of the AAP proposed that Cooke be made a member without taking the board exam, based on the principle, per Cooke, that someone appointed to a position such as his "had been scrutinized very severely from many standpoints" and required no further evaluations. During his six years on the faculty (in the department of physiology) at Yale, Cooke had never taken the boards, and had never joined the academy (for which the board exam was required). In a 1957 letter explaining this, he wrote that he "never had any intention of practicing pediatrics nor for that matter any very serious notion that I would ever be a Professor of Pediatrics."[81]

At the end of the 1940s and early 1950s, Cooke's position was not unusual. Edwards Park himself had initially been against taking the pediatric board exam, and many felt that pediatricians with "good reputations" need not take it.[82] Cooke's supporters cited the case of Lawson Wilkins who, they said, had also been admitted to the AAP without being board certified.[83] This thinking was also emblematic of the way in which academic pediatricians saw themselves as different from pediatricians in practice. Dr. Julian Price wrote Cooke in 1957 saying that the academy needed Cooke as a member to inspire other Hopkins graduates, who had been slow to join. But Price wanted Cooke to take the exam rather than "demand special favors."[84] Cooke wrote back saying that he supported the efforts of residents "going out into pediatric practice" to be board certified, but noted that his efforts at Hopkins included turning out "people who have more contributions to make than simply 'general practitioners for children.'" In his opinion, the boards were for people who would be in practice, not for academic leaders.

Cooke's main ally in the dispute was John Askin, a pediatrician in the Baltimore suburb of Pikesville. Askin defended Cooke as a "brilliant" man very devoted to pediatrics who lacked the time to take the board exam during the period when he was developing programs in his new job. Askin argued that it was "preposterous" to insist that someone in such a "high academic position" take a qualifying examination.[85] Ultimately, Cooke was made a member of the AAP in April 1962.

Johns Hopkins was not the only hospital in Baltimore that cared for children. On the eastern edge of the city, Baltimore City Hospitals had a pediatric service chaired by Harold Harrison, with whom Cooke developed a "friendly competition" over clinical or research-related observations at conferences and rounds.[86] Across the street from Hopkins, Sinai Hospital had a pediatric service chaired by Harry Gordon.[87]

Both City and Sinai had their own residency programs, functioned independently, and gained Cooke's respect.[88] Hopkins had ties to two other general pediatric services, at Union Memorial and Greater Baltimore Medical Center (GBMC), where Cooke made rounds periodically. The epidemiology of children's illness, however, was shifting rapidly in the late 1950s and early 1960s. The increased availability of antibiotics and immunizations plus improvements in sanitation had drastically reduced the number of children who needed hospital admission and some pediatric services, recalled Cooke, had "more residents than patients."[89] There was a brief attempt made to have Hopkins administer a joint community-based residency program with Union Memorial and GBMC, but these efforts were short-lived.

Advocating for the Mentally Retarded

At the testimonial dinner held to mark his stepping down as chair in 1973, Cooke gave a talk called "The Gorks are Gone."[90] It was printed as a brochure and distributed to emphasize that he wanted his "heritage" to be that the term "gork" would no longer be applied to the mentally retarded. Instead, the retarded would be treated as individuals with potential, who deserved comprehensive, quality care. Cooke's interest in the retarded was fueled by many things: teaching and advice from his mentor, Grover Powers; Cooke's experience with his own children; the interests of his most powerful benefactors; the cold war; and the civil rights movement. Care for the developmentally disabled and the prevention of developmental disabilities became central themes of his chairmanship and of his activities in the larger world of child health-care policy and research.

Cooke recalled that Herman Yannet, a faculty member he met in 1944 during his internship at New Haven Hospital, was one of those who had sparked his initial interest in the care of the retarded. Yannet had "an air of optimism, and a feeling of interest, no matter how serious, no matter how hopeless" might be a child's situation.[91] Four years later, while Cooke was doing postdoctoral research at Yale, his daughter Robyn was born with obvious dysmorphic features. She proved to be severely developmentally delayed, though at the time the cause of her condition was unknown. In 1951 Cooke's second daughter was born with the same, as yet unnamed condition. It was not until 1963 that both girls were given the diagnosis of cri du chat syndrome, a then newly described condition that resulted from a heritable chromosomal abnormality.

Cooke and his wife cared for the girls for many years, sometimes bringing them to Hopkins where residents also took part in their care. Brusilow recalled Cooke leaving the hospital abruptly—with intravenous lines, needles, and bottles of fluids—to make the hour or so trip to Gibson Island if the girls were ill and dehydrated.[92] Eventually the girls were placed at a residential institution in Connecticut, but not before caring for them had a profound influence on Cooke's approach to life.[93] He referred to his daughter Robyn, who died in 1967, as having become immortal through her influence on his work.[94] Though it seems that Cooke had a driven, impatient side to him long before he became a parent of disabled children, this experience clearly contributed to his conception of justice and his impatience with those who put up bureaucratic roadblocks to his ideas. In a 1972 exchange of letters with Bill Bartholome, who had been a resident at Hopkins and was at the time a military physician during the Vietnam War, Cooke wrote, "I believe that suffering can strengthen the individual and society." Bartholome wrote back, saying that Cooke was "one of the few men of conviction" with "an obsession for responsiveness to the needs of the less fortunate."[95]

Although Cooke already had a strong academic record and intimate connections with Grover Powers, Daniel Darrow, and the elite of academic pediatrics, the turning point in his career—and for the Harriet Lane service under Cooke—came in the late 1950s with his association with the Kennedy family. The Joseph P. Kennedy, Jr. Foundation was founded in 1946 by Ambassador Joseph Kennedy and his wife, and named for their son who was killed in World War II. The foundation gave money to advance the prevention and treatment of mental retardation. By the mid-1950s, the foundation was looking for ways to leverage its investments. The foundation turned to Richard Maslin, then director of the National Institute of Neurologic Disorders and Stroke, part of the NIH. Maslin advised the foundation to solicit proposals from major academic institutions. Cooke was one of those invited to submit a proposal, partly because he was at Hopkins, but likely, also, because he was known as a pediatrician with personal experience in caring for the retarded.[96] Cooke's innovative pitch to the foundation proposed that rather than funding research only in pediatrics, he would coordinate the distribution of money across the university and thus be able to address issues related to retardation from a wider range of perspectives. In letters back and forth with Sargent

Shriver, the husband of Kennedy daughter Eunice and the point man for the project, Cooke argued that retardation was not a "solitary disease" like so many other pediatric problems, and that it required a broad-based effort across many departments rather than a single institute devoted to research on its causes.[97]

Cooke says he was "tipped off" that Sargent and Eunice Shriver, who were to visit Hopkins to assess its candidacy for the grant, liked "young, vigorous people." So he assembled four young researchers—Don Medearis from pediatrics, Henry Vanderloos and John Menkes from neurology, and Andre Hellegers from obstetrics (who would later go on to found the Kennedy Institute of Ethics at Georgetown University)—and asked for a million dollars to fund their work, build new research laboratories, and provide seed money for new research efforts. This last idea for a "fluid research fund" that could be disbursed at the discretion of an internal committee rather than the outside foundation came from his former mentor at Yale, Daniel Darrow.[98] It had the potential to alter the equilibrium at Hopkins, elevating the chair of pediatrics by giving him money to dispense not just to his own department but also to others in the institution.

On the day of the Shrivers' visit, Cooke gathered the group in his office in the old Harriet Lane building. An additional guest was a representative of the Children's Rehabilitation Institute, a facility for children with cerebral palsy located in Cockeysville just outside Baltimore. Cooke had persuaded the institute to affiliate with Hopkins and to contribute to building the long-planned children's medical center. "Everything was going beautifully," recalled Cooke, "and Mrs. Shriver was sitting next to the institute representative and asked him, 'how many retarded children do you have?' He said, 'we don't have any, we wouldn't have retarded children there for anything.'" Cooke thought, "Oh my God, I just saw the million bucks flying out the window." But Cooke broke up the discussion by getting lunch and the institute's man discreetly disappeared.[99] There must have been other disagreements and close calls during the conversation because in a follow-up letter Cooke thanked the Shrivers for their visit and said that he enjoyed the "running debate" similar to when "two bulldogs" face each other with different points of view."[100]

In the end the foundation was convinced of Cooke's plan. The Shrivers began negotiations with Thomas "Tommy" Turner, then dean of the Johns Hopkins School of Medicine, for a $1.275 million grant, to be spread over ten years, for laboratories and new hospital facilities for the retarded, for support for a group of senior scholars, and for discretionary research funds. Shriver insisted that Cooke not only be the director of the program, but that this should be prominently noted in the Johns Hopkins catalog and other literature. Shriver pointed out to Turner that the foundation's motivation for giving the grant resided as much or more in Cooke's "personal enthusiasm" for the work as it did in Hopkins' prestige as a research institution.[101] This evidently rankled Russell Nelson, who told Cooke that he worried that Cooke's interest might stray from the subject and that the conditions of the Kennedy grant might prove restrictive to Hopkins in the future. Cooke wrote back, "It is impossible to imagine that in the next fifty years interest in a problem as common as mental retardation would be absent in any progressive department of pediatrics."[102]

One place where Cooke's vision of care for the retarded may have hurt, rather than helped the Harriet Lane was in his vision of the role of psychiatry. Cooke saw pediatricians as those who had the most to offer in the comprehensive care of the developmentally disabled. He saw psychiatry as having a limited, though important, contribution to helping the disabled adapt to their handicaps. Cooke wrote to Eunice Shriver in 1964 that psychiatrists could make important contributions to the care of the retarded if they would be willing to study their emotional problems rather than "everything else but this."[103] Cooke's position not only brought him into conflict with state authorities but also with one of the most prominent members of his department, Leo Kanner, and with Kanner's successor as chief of child psychiatry, Leon Eisenberg. In 1930 Kanner was selected by Edwards Park and Adolf Meyer, chief of psychiatry at Hopkins, to start—as a one-man operation—the first child psychiatry service based in a pediatric hospital. Kanner achieved international fame for describing and naming infantile autism, and for writing the first U.S. textbook on child psychiatry. Before that, he had gained fame in Baltimore as a champion of the rights of retarded children. Kanner had led a successful campaign to expose and end the common practice of removing children from the Maryland Training School so that they could work as unpaid help in the homes of the wealthy. He also was a vocal opponent of proposals to euthanize the retarded.[104]

Eisenberg was a child psychiatry fellow with Kanner from 1952 through 1954, and in 1961 became chief of child psychiatry (he left

270

THE
HARRIET LANE
HOME

Hopkins for Harvard in 1967). Though Eisenberg ultimately became well known for a variety of accomplishments, at the time of Cooke's arrival at Hopkins he was one of the few child psychiatrists doing research in psychopharmacology.[105] In a 1957 report to the federal Children's Bureau about pediatric research at Johns Hopkins, Eisenberg is listed as having two grants from pharmaceutical companies to study ataractic (or "calming") medications for children.[106] But Cooke may have pegged Eisenberg, who did his psychiatric training at the analytically oriented Sheppard and Enoch Pratt Hospital in Baltimore, as a psychiatrist of the "old school." The two engaged in a somewhat public debate (through articles and letters to the editor of the *Baltimore Sun*) over who should run Maryland's facilities for the retarded.[107] Eventually, after Cooke's departure from Hopkins, the Harriet Lane division of child psychiatry left pediatrics and became, instead, a part of the department of psychiatry. A vestige of the old relationship remains: the current director of child psychiatry answers to two "bosses"—the chair of psychiatry and the pediatrician-in-chief of the Children's Center (the chair of pediatrics), where child psychiatry is housed.

One last area in which the Cooke-era Harriet Lane may be best remembered is human genetics and its relationship to developmental disabilities. Barton Childs was one of the first geneticists to point out the centrality of genetics to human diseases and its near absence from American medical education. Michael Kaback conducted some of the first community outreach screenings for Tay-Sachs disease, going to Baltimore area synagogues to teach about the illness and the possibility of genetic testing. Tony Holtzman, initially a resident at Harriet Lane, had a key role in setting up Maryland's neonatal genetic screening program.[108]

A Sense of Community

At the same time that Cooke could be extremely critical of house staff and faculty, he presided over a department that many described as competitive but communal. The sense of community may have had two major sources. One was that Cooke and other senior faculty were regulars at conferences and rounds, often arguing over diagnoses or treatment plans but feeling that being present was part of their role. With perhaps the exception of endocrinology, faculty were not divided into divisions, and senior faculty associated with different specialties— William Zinkham, Saul Brusilow, Gerry Odell, Bill Blizzard and Sidney Levin among them—had offices close to one another, seeing and speaking with each other regularly. Faculty members helped establish the hallmark ethos of the Harriet Lane service during the second half of the twentieth century: near total absorption in the clinical, teaching, and research activities associated with the department; almost fanatical attention to clinical detail; and immense pride in being independent clinical thinkers. In the 1960s and on into the '70s and '80s, the person who may have most embodied this ethos was hematologist William Zinkham. Jerry Winkelstein described Zinkham as "the heart and soul of the department" during those years, and "probably the most dedicated teacher" the pediatrics department had ever known.[109] While Zinkham had a well-earned reputation outside the department for his research in biochemistry, to the house staff he was the consummate clinician-teacher. "Time would stop cold when he sat with you about a patient," said Winkelstein, whether "it was an hour or it was ten minutes."

Zinkham established a clinical routine and bedside manner that was widely emulated by residents. When a child suspected of having leukemia was admitted, Zinkham would review the microscope slides of the child's blood with the admitting intern and resident, suggest a few preliminary orders, and tell the residents and family that he would be back at eight o'clock that evening when the ward was quiet. When he returned he would patiently sit with the family and explain the condition, the tests, and the rationale for treatment. At that time the mortality rate from childhood leukemia was quite high; Winkelstein remembered that Zinkham would always tell parents that though he could not promise to cure the leukemia, he could make sure that their child felt better. These admissions were also often the beginning of a long-term relationship among the family, the intern, and Zinkham. Prior to the child's discharge from the hospital, Zinkham would ask the intern, "So when do you want to see him in clinic?" When the child did return to clinic, Zinkham would not see the child or family without the intern present. These families all knew Zinkham and recognized him as the chief doctor overseeing their child's treatment, but the intern or resident became the child's main doctor, the one they would call at any time for questions or problems and the one they expected to see at the time of clinic visits and admissions. Residents were expected to act the part, calling ahead or coming in themselves if the child had to be seen in the emergency room, and writing a background note in the chart—just as a community or faculty physician might—if the child had to be admitted to the hospital. Other faculty physicians also left their mark on trainees. Dave Carver, at one point in charge of the pediatric infectious disease group, was a stickler for clinical detail; and Bob Blizzard, said Winkelstein, "knew his patients better than anyone I have ever seen."

Although faculty physicians typically had three months per year of "attending" duty (time spent as the physician in charge of a particular hospital ward), they had widely varying amounts of involvement with running the clinical services on a day-to-day basis. Care of endocrine and hematology patients tended to be closely overseen by faculty, but the house staff might manage children with other problems. The in-patient services had attending rounds three times a week, but most teaching took place in rounds run by residents—in the chief resident's daily evening rounds on the two main inpatient floors (5 to 6 p.m. on infants, 6 to 7 p.m. on children's) and on the senior resident's late-night rounds where each patient was reviewed, usually while walking around the wards prior to the house staff going to sleep. One prominent exception was x-ray rounds, held each weekday morning. These conferences involved a review of all the studies ordered the day before. Interns were expected to give a one-minute or less synopsis of the case, after which one of the two faculty radiologists, John Dorst and David Heller, would talk about the diagnostic possibilities. Dorst and Heller were known as master clinicians with an uncanny ability to make accurate and useful comments after having only seen x-ray films and heard brief snippets of information about a patient.

If there was an overarching culture to the residency program, it was, in Winkelstein's words, that one was supposed to be independent and individual and never do anything as a "knee-jerk" response. Residents were expected to know their limits and ask faculty for advice, but house officers sometimes then developed their own plans and the faculty often did not insist on a review of them. Sometimes the house officers turned out to be right, and at other times wrong. Patients seen as more routine might have most of their care delivered without faculty input, and the majority of patients, in fact, were officially on the chief resident's service. Brusilow remembered one case, in particular, that illustrated the house staff's degree of independence. One night a child, obviously ill, was referred for treatment of what was probably pneumonia. Brusilow and his intern did fluoroscopy themselves and, seeing a pleural effusion in the child's chest, did an x-ray as well. They put a needle in the effusion to drain it, set up the cultures themselves, and started antibiotics. In the morning they told their attending what they had done and how the child was doing. This level of autonomy, unheard of now, was common at the time. The extensive system of chief and senior resident rounds was supplemented in the outpatient areas by chart review. Senior residents were expected to look over and approve write-ups of cases seen by the "walk-in" and "overnight" residents. Winkelstein remembered that this mechanism uncovered that one resident, having read about the benefits of acidifying urine, was prescribing cranberry juice instead of antibiotics to children with urinary tract infections.[110]

House staff independence was fostered by the fact that many key services in the children's center were run virtually without direct faculty involvement, including the infant special care unit, the pediatric intensive care unit, and the pediatric emergency room. Care in these areas relied on the expertise of the house officers themselves, supervised and advised by one of the two (inpatient and outpatient) chief residents.

Interns and residents during Cooke's era spent most of their waking hours in the hospital or nearby.[111] The first and last years of the three-year training were particularly intense, composed mostly of month-long inpatient rotations where the on-call schedule was thirty-six hours of service followed by twelve hours off in a two-week cycle, with everyone coming on Saturday morning for the department's grand rounds at eight o'clock. The routine was a bit lighter in the second year, when rotations consisted more of outpatient clinics, specialty consultation services, and stints on the pediatric wards of other Baltimore hospitals. Senior residents, however, were mostly back on the wards and followed the first-year schedule.

Interns were expected to arrive on the ward between seven and seven thirty in the morning to draw blood from their patients and get ready for the day. For Winkelstein and others this might also be an opportunity for breakfast— grabbing leftovers from children's trays as they visited each of their patients to see what had happened during the night. X-ray rounds were at eight thirty; they lasted an hour and were followed briefly by coffee and work until attending rounds at eleven. Much of that work involved trying to get results from the hospital laboratories. Until the late 1970s printed results reached the wards by hospital messenger several days after the tests had been run. To get them sooner, interns had to telephone or go to the labs themselves to look through logbooks and copy the results by hand. Simply gathering results for one's six or so patients could take an hour or more.

For all interns and residents on the inpatient floors the day lasted until seven thirty at night. The chief resident made rounds from five until seven, and then there was the process of signing out to the interns and residents who would work the night. If the floors were quiet and no admissions were in the offing, it was possible for some of those on call to leave the hospital for dinner at their apartments, in the compound, or at one of the neighborhood bars, where one could have a "quarter salad" and a piece of lasagna (and sometimes a beer). Testani's was one of the favorites among the pediatric house staff. The hospital paging operators knew that if they could not find an intern or resident by calling over the hospital public-address system, they could call Frank Testani, who might yell out, "Is Winkelstein here?" Nights on call were long but often not sleepless. The senior resident's job was, in part, to protect his or her intern from late-night admissions. When a child who might need admission was seen in the emergency room, it was the senior resident's responsibility to see the child and make a decision. Senior residents were required to have a certain sense of altruism—admitting the child would give the intern work, but sending the child home frequently resulted in the child becoming the long-term responsibility of the senior resident him or herself. These decisions could become tests of the residents' willingness to follow the advice of attendings, to accede to the wishes of community doctors who had sent their patients to Hopkins for admission, or to risk the appearance that they were not tough, independent "walls" who allowed no admissions on their watch.

Nights might also be the time when residents wrote papers for medical journals. It was not unusual for residents to have published one or more papers prior to finishing their training, despite the fact that the residency schedule contained little or no elective time. Jerry Winkelstein said that there were two things that made this possible. The first was the work culture: the residency experience was all-consuming, taking up nearly all of one's waking moments during the intern and senior resident years, and the overriding themes of the residency were teaching and learning. Chief and senior residents prided themselves on being able to ask and answer pithy questions, and many faculty had the time to mentor residents through the writing process. The second factor, said Winkelstein, was that the state of medical technology meant that residents were probably less busy than now. "You got a child then and you could not do an MRI, you could not do a CT scan, there were no central [intravenous] lines. The nature of the beast was that there was less to do. Life was less complicated—not as good for the patients, but you might have two hours in the evening when you were first up to take the next admission, you would only have patients of your own, and you had been on the whole day and might have gotten all your work done."[112]

Despite the fact that Winkelstein remembered only a single night during his internship when he did not sleep, the fatigue associated with working thirty-six out of every forty-eight hours took its toll. "Ask me how many dates I went on as an intern," suggested Winkelstein. The answer was six. "Ask me if I fell asleep on any of them—every one. I finally learned after the fourth time not to go to the movies. I routinely fell asleep in the barbershop on Saturday afternoon."

By the end of Cooke's tenure there were several forces prompting change in the residency program. House staff autonomy was being challenged on a number of fronts. The first community-based comprehensive care organizations were requiring more accountability for their patients and wanted faculty supervision of their care. The bioethics movement, still relatively in its infancy, was focusing on the rights of patients (and parents) to participate in medical decision making. There was also a growing awareness of a degree of contradiction in the Harriet Lane educational philosophy. On the one hand it was rooted in the basic laboratory science work of many of its faculty members, and in the rigorous clinical scholarship and thinking espoused on rounds and in patient care. House staff autonomy, however, sometimes seemed to leave too much in thoughtful but inexperienced hands. The system was a good one for many residents, especially the more conscientious ones, but not always the best for patients and families.[113] It also contributed to a clinical oral tradition that was not always based on the best thinking. For example, clinical wisdom that persisted into the 1980s had it that children from the hospital's surrounding neighborhood with common bacterial infections of the ear or throat should be treated with injectable (and uncomfortable) antibiotics instead of being given prescriptions for oral medication. The underlying rationale was that "these people" could not be trusted to follow through with a course of medication.[114] When the community health plans began insisting on attending physician input for their patients, Winkelstein said that we all thought, "This would be the death of the training program as we know it—and we were right... but that wasn't necessarily all bad."

One of Cooke's major battles on behalf of the faculty—and one that he ultimately lost—was against the administration's requirements that faculty document their use of time. This request had come in large part because the federal government was asking universities to account for the spending of research grant support coming from the NIH. Documentation, however, set off a flurry of arguments between the department and the administration over just what faculty members were expected to do.[115] David Clark outlined his typical week in 1963 as totaling over seventy hours:

> twelve hours with private patients, but along with fellows
>
> twelve hours on the Cerebral Palsy Project
>
> ten hours in outpatient clinics, also with fellows
>
> six to ten hours providing consultation on the inpatient wards
>
> six hours preparing a pathology conference
>
> twenty to twenty-four hours "in administrative duties... and a losing effort to keep abreast of the literature and do some effective research."[116]

At the time, however, many doctors much preferred such an academic schedule to the alternative of private practice. Brusilow said that when he finished his residency he was first offered the option to be the second pediatrician in a two-person practice in White Plains, New York. Trying to decide what to do, he asked his wife to speak with the wife of the other pediatrician in the practice. She told Brusilow's wife, "Don't do it, you'll never see him. It's a two-man practice and he will be working every other night and the night he's not working he'll be asleep."[117]

In the debate over reporting at Hopkins, Janet Hardy wrote medical school dean Tommy Turner saying that she challenged the right of the NIH or even the university to question how she spent her time over and above the usual forty-hour work week, so long as she fulfilled her responsibilities. Turner replied that "time spent on writing papers, books, etc." was "in no way required by the University" and therefore did not need to be subtracted from time that was paid for by federal research grants. Cooke, obtaining a copy of Turner's letter, marked at the bottom, "Circulate as a guide to principal investigators in the department."[118]

Notes

1. Vannevar Bush, "Science—The Endless Frontier, A Report to the President," (Washington: United States Government Printing Office, 1945). http://www.nsf.gov/od/lpa/nsf50/vbush1945.htm.

2. J. D. Watson and Francis H. Crick, "Molecular Structure of Nucleic Acids: A Structure for Deoxyribose Nucleic Acid," *Nature* 171 (4356) (1953): 737–38. J. Heinrich Matthaei and Marshall W. Nirenberg, "The Dependence of Cell-Free Protein Synthesis in E. coli upon RNA Prepared from Ribosomes," *Biochemical and Biophysical Research Communications* 4, no. 6 (1961): 404–08.

3. *Brown v. Board of Education*, 347 U.S. 483 (1954).

4. Robert E. Cooke, "The Biological Advantage of Man," in *A Symposium on the Child*, ed. John A. Askin, Robert E. Cooke, and J. Alex Haller (Baltimore: The Johns Hopkins University Press, 1967), 3–13.

5. *The National Research Act of 1974*, Public Law 93–348.

6. *The Social Security Act of 1965*, Public Law 89–97.

7. *Public Health Service Act*, Public Law 78–410.

8. "A Short History of the National Institutes of Health," on the World Wide Web, http://history.nih.gov/exhibits/history.

9. Robert E. Cooke, "The Biological Advantage of Man," 12.

10. Stuart B. Levy, "The Antibiotic Paradox." (New York: Plenum Press, 1992), 47.

11. Polly Hesterberg (pediatric nurse at Johns Hopkins Children's Medical and Surgical Center), interview with John Littlefield and Henry Seidel, April 16, 1999.

12. E. H. Starbird "Comparison of Influences on Breastfeeding Initiation of Firstborn Children, 1960–69 vs 1970–79," *Social Science and Medicine* 33 (1991): 627–34.

13. C. H. Kempe, F. N. Silverman, B. F. Steele, W. Droegmueller, H. K. Silver, "The Battered Child Syndrome," *Journal of the American Medical Association* 181 (1962): 17–24.

14. New doctors at Sydenham in the 1940s might see more than two hundred cases a month at the height of diphtheria epidemics. Sydenham also cared for children who were victims of one of the other great epidemics of the era. It had a major ward on its bottom floor devoted entirely to iron lung machines for polio patients. Paul Hardy and Janet Hardy interview with John Littlefield, Henry Seidel, and author, March 24, 1999.

15. Barton Childs conversation with Henry Seidel, May 2004.

16. Saul W. Brusilow, "Howland Award Presentation to Robert. E. Cooke." *Pediatric Research* 30 (1991): 622–25.

17. Minutes of the Medical Board, December 21, 1954. Medical Board Minute Book no. 6, 162–64, Alan Mason Chesney Medical Archives, The

Johns Hopkins Medical Institutions, Baltimore, MD, hereafter referred to as AMC.

18. Victor A. McKusick, biographical memoir of Abner McGehee Harvey, 1911–1998. Association of American Physicians, 1999. World Wide Web, http://www.aap-online.org/In_memoriam/InMemHarvey.htm.

19. Minutes of the Board of Trustees, Johns Hopkins Hospital, no. 9, March 31, 1955, 116; April 5, 1955, 119–20. Minutes of the Medical Planning and Development Committee, 226th Meeting, March 30, 1955, AMC.

20. Joint Committee of the Trustees of The Johns Hopkins University and Hospital, minutes of the eighty-fifth meeting, November 3, 1955, 167, AMC.

21. T. S. Harrison, biographical memoir of Archibald Philip Bard, October 25, 1898–April 5, 1977. National Academy of Sciences, World Wide Web, http://stills.nap.edu/html/biomems/pbard.html.

22. G. Stephenson, Johns Hopkins Medical Institutions, Office of Communications and Public Affairs, "Russell Nelson, former Hopkins Hospital President, dies at 88," news release, May 21, 2001.

23. Guide to the Alfred Blalock Personal Papers Collection, AMC, World Wide Web, http://www.medicalarchives.jhmi.edu/sgml/blalock.html.

24. Robert Cooke, interview with Henry Seidel and John Littlefield, May 18, 1999.

25. Robert Cooke to Dr. Vernon W. Lippard, November 14, 1955, Robert E. Cooke Papers, file L, box 11JF, AMC.

26. Robert Cooke to Mrs. Jesse W. Norman, July 19, 1962, file J, box 8JF, AMC; Robert Cooke interview with author, May 16, 2000.

27. Undated speech by Robert Cooke, addressed to "Mrs. Johnson, Mrs. Shriver, distinguished ladies." Robert E. Cooke Papers, file: "Head Start – Speeches, box 23JF, AMC.

28. Robert Cooke, interview with Henry Seidel and John Littlefield, May 18, 1999.

29. Curriculum vitae, Robert E. Cooke, Undated. Author's files.

30. Dr. C. N. H. Long to John M. Russell, John and Mary R. Markle Foundation, [1950]. Robert E. Cooke Papers, folder "souvenirs," box 40JF, AMC.

31. Ronald Cooke to Robert Cooke, September 16, 1944, Robert E. Cooke Papers, unmarked brown envelope, box 39JF, AMC.

32. Department of Pediatrics, Yale University School of Medicine, World Wide Web, http://info.med.yale.edu/pediat/history.html.

33. M. A. Wessel, A Bit of History of Behavioral Pediatrics, World Wide Web, http://www.dbpeds.org/section/history/wessel.cfm; The National Association for Retarded Citizens, http://www.thearc.org/history/segal.htm.

34. Robert Cooke to Grover Powers, June 2, 1958, Robert E. Cooke Papers, folder "National Association for Retarded Children," box 13JF, AMC.

35. Robert E. Cooke, interview with Robert Grayson, September 8, 1996, Vero Beach, Florida, Oral History Project, Pediatric History Center, American Academy of Pediatrics, Elk Grove Village, Illinois (2003), 5, 48–50.

36. Curriculum vitae, Robert E. Cooke.

37. Saul Brusilow, interview with Henry Seidel and author, March 28, 2000.

38. The list of locally and nationally well known figures, (and of those destined to become so) who were present when Cooke arrived is quite long: Lawson Wilkins was acting chair; Hugh Josephs, Helen Taussig, Harold Harrison, Leo Kanner, Victor Najjar, Alexander "Buck" Schaffer, Harry Gordon, and Paul Harper were associate professors; Miriam Brailey, Sam Livingston, Janet Hardy, Barton Childs (who was also a John and Mary R. Markel Foundation Scholar in Medical Science), Charlotte Ferencz, David B. Clark, Claude Migeon, Leon Eisenberg, and Milton Markowitz were all assistant professors; Laurence Finberg, Henry Seidel, Thomas Reichelderfer, Marvin Cornblath, Julian Chisolm, William Zinkham, and Helen Harrison were instructors; Anthony Perlman, Mary Ellen Avery, and James Gamble Jr. were assistants; Robert M. Blizzard, James Sidbury, and David W. Smith were instructors. The Johns Hopkins University Circular, October 1955. School of Medicine, Catalogue for 1955–1956. New Series 1955, Number 9, Whole number 637, Baltimore, MD, (1955) 118–19.

39. Mary Ellen Avery, interview with John Littlefield, and author, November 9, 1999.

40. Catherine Neill, interview with author, May 15, 2001.

41. Robert Cooke, interview with Henry Seidel and John Littlefield, May 18, 1999.

42. Robert E. Cooke to Dr. Julian P. Price, July 30, 1957. Robert E. Cooke Papers, folder "American Academy of Pediatrics," box 1JF, AMC.

43. Robert Cooke, interview with Henry Seidel and John Littlefield, May 18, 1999.

44. Robert E. Cooke to Dr. Julian P. Price, July 30, 1957.

45. Robert Cooke interview with John Littlefield and author, May 16, 2000.

46. Ibid.

47. A. Kornberg. *Arthur Kornberg.* Regional Oral History Office, University of California, Berkeley, 1977. Available from the Online Archive of California, http://ark.cdlib.org/ark:/13030/kt6q2nb1tg.

48. Saul Brusilow, interview with Henry Seidel and author, March 28, 2000.

49. Robert Cooke, interview with Henry Seidel and John Littlefield, May 18, 1999. The competition between Yale and Hopkins—and one suspects among other university's departments of pediatrics—was quite intense. After Cooke's move to Hopkins, Yale's chair of pediatrics Milton Senn wrote an angry letter accusing Cooke of betraying loyalty that he had pledged to Senn and the Yale department. Cooke had evidently waited until after the fact to let Senn know that he was recruiting Yale faculty members William Nyhan and Ira Brandt to Baltimore. Senn told Cooke that he was "selfishly interested in Hopkins" and "personally, I would rather have a second rate department than to develop one of first rate quality by methods which my colleagues in education would consider tinged with unfairness." Milton J. E. Senn to Robert Cooke, September 16, 1957, Robert E. Cooke Papers, box JF, folder "S," AMC.

50. Saul W. Brusilow, E. H. Gordes, "Solute and Water Secretion in Sweat," *Journal of Clinical Investigation.* 43 (1964): 477–84.

51. K. C. Schuberth and B. J. Zitelli, editors. *The Harriet Lane Handbook, 8th edition.* (Chicago: Year Book Medical Publishers, 1978), 12–13.

52. Robert Cooke interview with John Littlefield and author, May 16, 2000.

53. Ibid. Though Cooke may have been being dramatic in his description of the old building, he was not alone. A 1960 article in the *Baltimore Sun* noted that the Harriet Lane Home hallways were "wide and somber" and took up forty-nine percent of the space in the building, whereas the new pediatric building's halls would take up only ten percent of its space. F. Henry, "Revolutionary New Children's Hospital," *Baltimore Sun*, September 18, 1960, A1.

54. Brusilow interview with Seidel and author, March 28, 2000.

55. *The Harriet Laner,* Issue 6, June, 1950. RG4, Ser C, Box 17, folder 4. AMC.

56. Robert Cooke interview with John Littlefield and author, May 16, 2000.

57. Robert Cooke interview with Henry Seidel and John Littlefield, May 18, 1999.

58. Saul Brusilow, interview with Henry Seidel and author, March 28, 2000.

59. Ibid.

60. Robert E. Cooke to Dr. Julian P. Price, July 30, 1957, Robert E. Cooke Papers, folder "American Academy of Pediatrics," box 1JF, AMC. *The Johns Hopkins University Circular,* October 1956 (School of Medicine Catalog for 1956–57), 42–43.

61. The vessel named for the Harriet Lane's benefactor, when she was First Lady of the United States in 1857, by virtue of being President James Buchanan's niece. See the foreword.

62. Kenneth Roberts, interview with author, May 2, 2004.

63. Neil (Tony) Holtzman, interview with author, January 18, 2002.

64. Robert Cooke, interview with Henry Seidel and John Littlefield, May 18, 1999.

65. Robert Cooke, interview with Robert Grayson, 23. Draft letters, undated, Robert E. Cooke Papers, folder "Robert E. Cooke–Peace Pamphlet," box 40JF, AMC.

66. Letter from Russell Nelson to Robert Cooke, September 8, 1970. Robert E. Cooke Papers, folder "N," box 13JF, AMC.

67. "The Untaxables," audiotape excerpt of 1961 turtle derby skits, provided by Tony Holtzman.

68. Ken Roberts, interview with author, May 2, 2004.

69. Elizabeth Fee, Linda Shopes, and Linda Zeidman, editors. *The Baltimore Book: New Views of Local History,* (Philadelphia: Temple University Press, 1991).

70. Marilyn Winkelstein (a nurse in Harriet Lane in the 1960s), conversation with author, August 2, 2004.

71. Baltimore's first highway tunnel was opened in the fall of 1957. Prior to that time, two of the East Coast's main highways, US Routes 1 and 40, brought vehicles burning leaded fuel through East Baltimore and the heart

of the city. Johns Hopkins Hospital sits two blocks north of US 40 (Orleans Street) and not far south of US 1 (which runs along Belair Road and North Avenue). The Baltimore beltway (Interstate 695) was begun in 1954, but it was not complete until around 1980. World Wide Web, http://www.kurumi. com/roads/3di/i695.html.

72. Robert Cooke interview with Henry Seidel and John Littlefield, May 18, 1999.

73. Julian J. Chisolm Jr., "Evolution of the Management and Prevention of Childhood Lead Poisoning: Dependence of Advances in Public Health on Technological Advances in the Determination of Lead and Related Biochemical Indicators of its Toxicity." *Environmental Research* 86 (2001): 111–21.

74. Jerry Winkelstein, interview with author, July 19, 2004.

75. Marilyn Winkelstein, conversation with author, August 2, 2004.

76. Ken Roberts, interview with author May 2, 2004.

77. Jerry Winkelstein, interview with author, July 19, 2004.

78. Ibid.

79. Report of the subcommittee on professional relations of the staff conference committee, 1959–1960, presented to the Medical Board April 26, 1960. Medical Board minute book #7, 141–47.

80. Henry Seidel, interview with John Littlefield and author, February 17, 1999.

81. Robert E. Cooke to Dr. Julian P. Price, July 30, 1957. Robert E. Cooke Papers, folder "American Academy of Pediatrics," box 1JF, AMC.

82. Janet Hardy and Paul Hardy, interview with John Littlefield, Henry Seidel, and author, March 24, 1999.

83. Dr. John Askin to Dr. E. H. Christopherson, American Academy of Pediatrics. May 6, 1957. Robert E. Cooke Papers, folder "Askin, John," box 1JF, AMC.

84. Dr. Julian P. Price to Robert Cooke, July 18, 1957. Robert E. Cooke Papers, folder "American Academy of Pediatrics," box 1JF, AMC.

85. Dr. John Askin to Dr. E. H. Christopherson, American Academy of Pediatrics.

86. Tony Holtzman, interview with author, January 18, 2002.

87. Sinai was located on the north side of Monument Street, on the present site of the Kennedy Krieger Institute, until 1960 when it moved to its new location in Northwest Baltimore.

88. Robert Cooke interview with Henry Seidel and author, May 18, 1999.

89. Ibid.

90. Robert E. Cooke, "The Gorks are Gone," an eight-page pamphlet, reprinted from a speech given by Cooke May 8, 1973, published by the Joseph P. Kennedy Jr. Foundation. Not dated, author's files.

91. Robert E. Cooke to Herman Yannet, Robert E. Cooke Papers, folder "Y," box 5JF, AMC.

92. Saul Brusilow, interview with Henry Seidel and author, March 28, 2000.

93. Robert E. Cooke to Frank R. Gilliberty, Superintendent, Southbury

State Training School, Southbury, Connecticut. July 27, 1964. Robert E. Cooke Papers, folder "S," box 18JF, AMC.

94. Robert E. Cooke to Rev. Hollis Huston (First Congregational Church, Windsor, Connecticut). March 22, 1967, Robert E. Cooke Papers, folder "H," box 6JF, AMC.

95. William G. Bartholome to Robert E. Cooke, October 19, 1971, and Cooke to Bartholome, September 7, 1972, Robert E. Cooke Papers, folder "B," box 2JF, AMC.

96. Robert E. Cooke to Robert Sargent Shriver, November 11, 1959. Robert E. Cooke Papers, folder "General 1959–1970," box 9JF, AMC. Robert Cooke interview with Henry Seidel and John Littlefield, May 18, 1999.

97. Robert E. Cooke to Robert Sargent Shriver, December 18, 1959. Robert E. Cooke Papers, file "General 1959–1970," Box 9JF, AMC.

98. Robert Cooke, interview with Robert Grayson, 12.

99. Robert Cooke, interview with Henry Seidel and John Littlefield, May 18, 1999.

100. Robert E. Cooke to Robert Sargent Shriver, November 11, 1959, Robert E. Cooke Papers, folder "General 1959–1970," box 9JF, AMC.

101. Robert Sargent Shriver to Thomas B. Turner, December 23, 1959. Robert E. Cooke Papers, folder "General 1959–1970," box 9JF, AMC.

102. Robert E. Cooke to Russell A. Nelson, December 23, 1959. Robert E. Cooke Papers, folder "General 1959–1970," box 9JF, AMC.

103. Robert E. Cooke to Mrs. R. Sargent Shriver, September 21, 1964. Robert E. Cooke Papers, folder "Shriver, Mrs. Eunice K.," box 19JF, AMC.

104. Leo Kanner (1894–1981) Papers finding aid, Melvin Sabshin Library & Archives, American Psychiatric Association, Arlington, VA, November 12, 1985. Leo Kanner, *Child Psychiatry*, with prefaces by Adolf Meyer and Edwards A. Park (Springfield, Ill., Baltimore, Md., C. C. Thomas, 1935).

105. Faculty profile, Leon Eisenberg, Harvard Medical School. http://www.hms.harvard.edu/dsm/WorkFiles/html/people/faculty/LeonEisenberg.html

106. Robert E. Cooke to Madeline E. Morcy, regional medical director, Children's Bureau, October 14, 1957, with attached list of JHU School of Medicine, Department of Pediatrics research projects, 1957–58. Robert E. Cooke Papers, folder "Children's Bureau," box 3JF, AMC.

107. Robert E. Cooke to the editor, *Baltimore Sun*, November 4, 1963. Robert E. Cooke Papers, folder "Mental Retardation: Maryland Facilities for," Box 12JF, AMC.

108. M. M. Kayback, "Editorial: Heterozygote Screening—A Social Challenge," *New England Journal of Medicine* 289 (1973): 1090–91; B. Childs, L. Gordis, M. M. Kaback, H. H. Kazazian Jr., "Tay-Sachs Screening: Motives for Participating and Knowledge of Genetics and Probability," *American Journal of Human Genetics* 28 (1976): 537:49. N. A. Holtzman, A. G. Meek, E. D. Mellits, "Neonatal Screening for Phenylketonuria. I. Effectiveness," *Journal of the American Medical Association* 229 (1974): 667–70. B. Childs, *Genetic Medicine: A Logic of Disease* (Baltimore: The Johns Hopkins University Press, 1999).

109. Jerry Winkelstein interview with author, July 19, 2004.

110. Ibid.

111. In fact, house staff routines and working hours changed very little in the twenty-year period from the mid-1960s to the mid-1980s, with the primary difference being that the main ward services changed from every other night call schedules to every third night. The pediatric intensive care unit call schedule continued to be "thirty-six on, twelve off" for a four-week period. The adolescent ward, which was shared with internal medicine, was every-other-night during the week and then every other weekend (the pediatric and internal medicine senior residents took turns). Pediatric residents on the general pediatric surgery rotation had a call schedule of "on" five nights out of seven.

112. Jerry Winkelstein, interview with author, July 19, 2004.

113. Ibid.; Tony Holtzman, interview with author, January 18, 2002.

114. Jerry Winkelstein, interview with author, July 19, 2004. In retrospect, the error in clinical wisdom was not the underestimation of parental follow-through with prescriptions, but the assumption that only poor parents were likely to be negligent. Research suggests that non-adherence is widespread and that doctors do poorly predicting who will or will not take prescribed medication. J. W. Finney, R. J. Hook, P. C. Friman, M. A. Rapoff, and E. R. Christophersen, "The Overestimation of Adherence to Pediatric Medical Regimens," *Child Health Care* 22 (1993): 297–304. As late as 1986, the photocopied manual for residents in the Harriet Lane outpatient clinics listed oral medication for strep throat as the second choice—"for patient you know will be compliant." The first choice for total compliance was an injection. Beryl J. Rosenstein, Patricia D. Fosarelli, Rebecca E. Ribovich, M. Douglas Baker, editors. "Therapeutic Shorts" (1986), 58. There was also a long tradition at the Harriet Lane, as elsewhere, of codifying clinical conventions given a lack of other information (thus the current movement for "evidence-based medicine"). As Henry Seidel noted about the original editions of the *Harriet Lane Handbook*, "We were doing it [writing the book] for ourselves.... In fact, we made up drug dosages out of whole cloth. Who knew? We would say, 'Gee whiz, how much do we use?'" Henry Seidel, interview with author, August 1998.

115. This accounting has become a perennial issue for the School of Medicine. Most recently, new faculty requirements for "effort reporting" have rekindled the controversy. The new requirements were instituted after Johns Hopkins settled, for $2.6 million, a federal lawsuit alleging that researchers had committed themselves to more than one hundred percent of their time and received duplicate funding for the same projects. J. Bor, "JHU, Bayview Settle Federal Lawsuit for $2.6 Million; Whistle Blower Told U.S. Grant Work Was Overbilled," *Baltimore Sun*, February 27, 2004, 1A. Should they be enforced, the new requirements have the potential to profoundly transform faculty work, since they imply that many teaching and clinical activities, which until the present have been considered to be part of faculty duties that carry no specific financial compensation, will now need to be explicitly paid for by the School of Medicine.

116. David B. Clark to Thomas B. Turner, April 10, 1963 Robert E.

Cooke Papers, folder "National Institutes of Health," box 14JF, AMC.

117. Saul Brusilow, interview with Henry Seidel, John Littlefield, and author, March 28, 2000.

118. Janet Hardy (director, Cerebral Palsy Project, Johns Hopkins Hospital) to Thomas B. Turner, April 4, 1963; Thomas B. Turner to Janet Hardy, April 10, 1963. Robert E. Cooke Papers, folder "National Institutes of Health," box 1JF, AMC.

285

A Champion
of Children

A New Home

Robert Cooke's Enduring Influence

BY LAWRENCE S. WISSOW

IDEAS FOR REPLACING the Harriet Lane Home with a more substantial building went back as far as 1946, some eighteen years before the Children's Medical and Surgical Center (CMSC) finally opened on the site of the Johns Hopkins Hospital's 1895 Thayer Building near the corner of Broadway and Monument Street in East Baltimore. Originally, in 1946, the Harriet Lane and Garrett Funds agreed to build a new Robert Garrett Hospital that would focus mostly on conditions that could be cured or alleviated by surgery.[1] But by 1954 plans had shifted toward a more comprehensive children's hospital that would integrate medical and surgical care. It was at this point that the Thayer site was first proposed, with the thought that the new building might house not only children's beds but also some central services for the entire hospital, including kitchens, laundries, and a cafeteria.[2]

Humanizing the Hospital

In 1956, as Robert Cooke was in the process of moving from Yale to Hopkins, his mentor Grover Powers was asked to chair a committee (including Walsh McDermott from Cornell and Robert Gross from Harvard) to advise the four independent boards of trustees that were interested in children's hospitals: the Johns Hopkins Hospital, the Harriet Lane Home, the Garrett Fund, and the Eudowood Hospital for Consumptives of Maryland (the former children's tuberculosis hospital).[3] Cooke credited Powers with convincing the four boards to consider a joint venture that would become the CMSC, and he credited the president of the Johns Hopkins Hospital Board of Trustees, Walter F. Perkins, for being a major source of support for children's causes.[4] In June 1957 the board members signed an agreement to collaborate, starting the final phase of negotiations about what, exactly, would be included in the new building and how much of it would be devoted to children.

Cooke, Russell Nelson, Alfred Blalock, and Barry Wood at Hopkins went back and forth on a variety of plans, which at the outset involved a substantial number of beds for adult patients (the Harriet Lane service was not the only one at Hopkins pressing for room to expand). Ultimately, some of the adult beds were swapped for adolescent beds to be shared by the departments of medicine, pediatrics, and surgery, an arrangement that lasted until the 1980s. In fact, it was not easy to establish a children's hospital, integrated with a general hospital but capable of meeting children's specialized needs.

One of the main issues became administrative authority, such as the responsibility of organizing key resources, which took decisions away from what was to become the Children's Center. Johns Hopkins Hospital director Russell Nelson at one point set up a search committee to hire a new head nurse for the Harriet Lane service allegedly without including Cooke. Cooke reportedly sent Nelson a letter, "charred with fire," threatening to quit if Nelson went through with the plan.[5] Later, disputes with the main hospital administration arose over the availability of so-called microchemistry tests. Microchemistry is the science of adapting routine blood tests to the needs of children and infants, making it possible to conduct them on much smaller than normal quantities of blood, sometimes no more than a few drops. These sorts of analyses became critical to the rise of modern pediatric care, especially in neonatology as the frontier of survivability for premature infants was pushed to lower and lower birth weights. By the early 1960s microchemistries were available at Baltimore City Hospitals, where Pediatrician-in-Chief Harold Harrison practiced, but not at Johns Hopkins Hospital.[6] Hopkins faculty members Saul Brusilow and Mary Ellen Avery remembered separate discussions with either the department of pathology (which eventually took over from the department of medicine the job of running the hospital's central laboratories) or the hospital administration itself, urging the labs to make micro assays available. Avery, when she left for McGill University, packed up the machinery that she had used to make analyses of oxygen and carbon dioxide in infants' blood. She recalled going to the hospital director at the time and saying, "I'm leaving.... You have to realize how important it is to be able to make these measurements."[7]

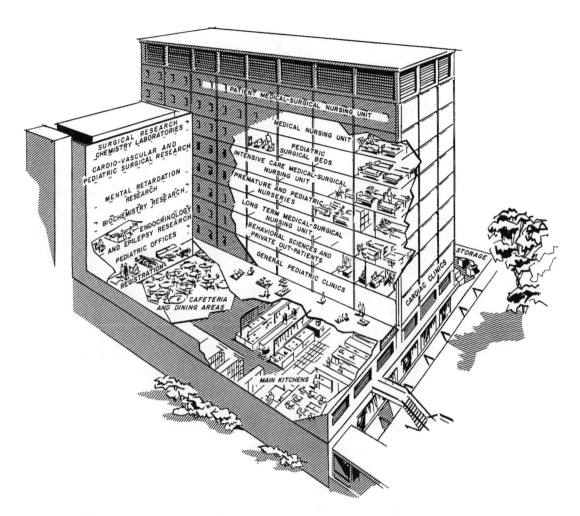

Labels within the illustration:
PATIENT MEDICAL-SURGICAL NURSING UNIT
MEDICAL NURSING UNIT
SURGICAL RESEARCH CHEMISTRY LABORATORIES
CARDIO-VASCULAR AND PEDIATRIC SURGICAL RESEARCH
PEDIATRIC SURGICAL BEDS
INTENSIVE CARE MEDICAL-SURGICAL NURSING UNIT
MENTAL RETARDATION RESEARCH
PREMATURE AND PEDIATRIC NURSERIES
BIOCHEMISTRY RESEARCH
ENDOCRINOLOGY AND EPILEPSY RESEARCH
LONG TERM MEDICAL-SURGICAL NURSING UNIT
BEHAVIORAL SCIENCES AND PRIVATE OUT-PATIENTS
PEDIATRIC OFFICES
GENERAL PEDIATRIC CLINICS
REGISTRATION
CAFETERIA AND DINING AREAS
CARDIAC CLINICS
STORAGE
MAIN KITCHENS

SCHEMATIC DRAWING OF THE PROPOSED CHILDREN'S MEDICAL AND SURGICAL CENTER. The new building more than doubled the number of pediatric beds (about half of which were for surgical patients), from 113 in the old Harriet Lane to 256 in the CMSC. There were also facilities that served the entire hospital, including kitchens and a large cafeteria on the ground floor. Despite careful planning over several years, staff soon pushed for changes of some facilities they found to be inadequate. Reproduced with permission from the *Baltimore Sun*.

The new CMSC represented a huge leap for pediatrics at Hopkins. The building, for which the initial construction budget was $11 million, would have more than double the number of beds as the old Harriet Lane, 256 compared to 113. According to J. Alex Haller, former chief of pediatric surgery, the building was also the first children's hospital in the country with an equal number of surgical and pediatric beds. Haller credited Cooke with getting Alfred Blalock, the chief of surgery, to agree to this plan; Haller also gave Cooke credit for recognizing pediatric surgeons as peers rather than technicians, and for having the first resident rotation (known as "GPS," the general pediatric surgery service) that included surgeons and pediatricians on the same care team.[8]

The new CMSC maintained the Harriet Lane philosophy of having a close relationship between laboratory and clinical space. Initial plans for the west wing of the building (paralleling Monument Street) indicated that the second through fourth floors would be reserved for outpatient facilities and its fifth through seventh floors would house laboratories. Eventually, with the help of additional Kennedy Foundation funds, all the floors above the second became laboratory space.[9] The second floor of the west wing also came to house the department's administrative offices, the office of the chair, and space for fellows and faculty. A perhaps apocryphal story told by Harriet Lane alumni is that initially Cooke wanted his office to be on an upper floor, but in negotiations during the planning phase it was seen as inappropriate for the chair of pediatrics to have an office on a higher floor than surgery or medicine.[10] Cooke indirectly gave the story some credence when he recalled that he and department of medicine chair Mac Harvey were never "on the same wavelength." Cooke felt Harvey believed that pediatrics had "grown too fast and had become, in a sense, too big."[11]

The new building allowed for several innovations in patient care. In addition to the shared adolescent ward, no room would have more than four beds. Semi-private rooms, previously reserved only for insured or paying patients, would be available to patients on the ward services as well. Cooke and the building's architect also jointly designed a special crib (the "high climber") that had sides tall enough to prevent a toddler's escape and a one-handed latch allowing nurses and doctors to lower the side with one hand while holding a baby in the other arm.[12]

Another major change from the old Harriet Lane Home was the provision for parent involvement in children's care. In the old building, children could have long separations from their parents, with only limited visiting hours or telephone contact. Polly Hesterberg, a pediatric nurse who eventually became the CMSC's coordinator for parent support, recalled that during the design of the building it was hard to convince hospital administrators that "all children had the right to have their parent be with them." Thus, while some parent facilities

290

———

THE
HARRIET LANE
HOME

MILDRED "POLLY" HESTERBERG. As the Children's Medical and Surgical Center's coordinator for parent support, pediatric nurse Polly Hesterberg lobbied hospital administrators to include accommodations for parents in the design of the new building. Facilities were planned for parents of older children, but it was not until 1969 that the hospital allowed parents of sick infants to stay overnight. Hesterberg and her colleagues helped parents to cope with the stress of their children's illnesses and encouraged them to advocate for excellent medical care.

were included on the floors for older children, none were included on the new infant floor. Hesterberg said the administrators thought that since the patients "were babies ... they won't know if their parents are there or not."[13]

By 1969, however, five years after the building opened, accommodations for the parents of infants were created. Hesterberg attributed this to several things. One may have simply been market pressure. She recalled parents who were deciding on a hospital for their child's surgery asking whether "rooming-in" facilities were available. Cooke may have lent his support because the importance of "humanizing" the hospital had been a focus of his mentor, Grover Powers, who started rooming in at Yale.[14] Other forces may have been the popularization of British psychiatrist John Bowlby's work on parent-infant separation and "hospitalism," and the work of one of Bowlby's colleagues, psychologist Mary Ainsworth. Bowlby's work, published in 1952, described the effects on infants of lengthy separations from their mothers. Ainsworth went on to describe the responses of infants to separation and reunification with their mothers, and developed the "strange situation," a method of examining infant-mother bonds. Ainsworth came to Baltimore in 1956 and was a faculty member in the department of psychology on the Johns Hopkins Homewood campus during the time her best-known work was published. Initially, her position involved clinical work and teaching through the Sheppard-Pratt psychiatric hospital. Her Baltimore years, though immensely productive in terms of writing, research, and teaching, proved to be personally difficult and she left for the University of Virginia in 1974. According to a 1983 autobiographical essay, at Hopkins she encountered a university administration that seemed unfriendly toward women faculty members. Perhaps most flagrant, she noted, was that until 1968 male and female faculty were forbidden to eat together at the Hopkins faculty club. The policy ostensibly protected women from the men's "informal garb" at lunchtime, but obviously it shielded them from participating in the intellectual and political engagement that might take place within and across departments.[15]

As was the case with gender bias, attitudes toward the involvement of parents evolved slowly and with some resistance. Like most pediatric departments around the country at the time, in the old Harriet Lane visitation was very limited. Parent protests were partly avoided by having a "pre-visiting" procedure in which nurses made sure that children's hands and faces were clean, that diapers were changed, and beds straightened before parents arrived. In the new building, visiting was still limited to short periods twice a week. As the presence of parents increased, Hesterberg recalled, many doctors, house staff, and even nurses found it inconvenient to have them at the bedside, citing increases in the time it took to provide routine care or the necessity of providing additional explanations. This reluctance pointed out how different things were at the time the CMSC opened, not just in understandings of child development but also in terms of standards for doctor-patient communication and even medical ethics. During long and sometimes repeated hospitalizations staff members became very close to children, and at times dismissive of parent involvement.[16] Even when parents' presence was encouraged, interactions with them focused on support and relaying information rather than on joint decision making.[17] Cooke himself wrote and spoke periodically about the

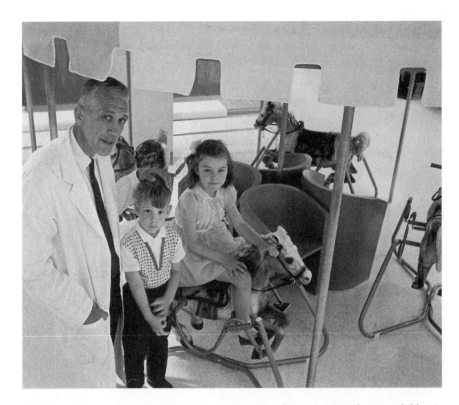

ROBERT COOKE WITH CHILDREN ON A CAROUSEL. Families arriving in the new Children's Medical and Surgical Center (CMSC) were greeted by an improvised rocking-horse carousel in the lobby and on this day in May 1964, Cooke was there to greet them. Cooke recognized the value of the Child Life Program, which became a responsibility of the department of pediatrics at the time of the move from the Harriet Lane Home to the CMSC.

need to intervene with those he labeled, "passive, uncooperative mothers," though by the early 1970s he seemed to recognize that this might relate to depression or being "worn out" rather than simple noncompliance with pediatricians' guidance.[18] By 1968 Hesterberg had been named the living-in coordinator with a broad mandate not only to help parents with the stress of their children's illnesses, but also to empower them and help them advocate for the quality of their children's care.

Closely related to efforts to improve visitation rights and increase the role of parents was the further development of a program called "Child Life." The new building was to have space in each clinical unit for children to engage in group and therapeutic activities, and it was designed so that an outdoor play area could be installed on a low roof adjacent to the third-floor patient rooms; the play deck was ultimately connected to the fourth floor ward as well by an outside staircase accessed by a door in the playroom. The program, initially called "Play

BILLINGS BUILDING WITH DOME AND THE CHILDREN'S MEDICAL AND SURGICAL CENTER (CMSC) BEHIND IT. The CMSC, built on the site of the old Thayer Building, dramatically changed the hospital's profile. This view, looking across Broadway from an upper floor of the 550 (Broadway) building in 1966, emphasizes how the CMSC loomed behind the Billings and Marburg Buildings; today it is just one of numerous high-rise structures that comprise the Johns Hopkins Hospital. Photo courtesy of the Ferdinand Hamburger Jr. Archives in the Milton S. Eisenhower Library of the Johns Hopkins University, Baltimore, Maryland.

School," got its present name in 1961. Distinct from educational programs, Child Life activities were based on developmentally appropriate mechanisms for helping children both cope and benefit emotionally from hospitalization. Child Life was well established in the old Harriet Lane Home, where it excluded infants but covered both Harriet Lane 2 and 3 (wards which housed older children with medical conditions) and Halstead 3 (where child surgical patients were cared for). With the move to the CMSC, Child Life's administrative home shifted from the School of Nursing and the hospital's nursing department and became part of the department of pediatrics. While this change allowed for the program to double the size of its staff and greatly expand its services, it created a rift with nursing that took over a decade to fully heal.[19]

Despite all the planning, some features of the CMSC building proved unworkable or were rapidly rendered obsolete. The tiny "Infant Special Care Unit" (ISCU) at the rear of the infant floor (CMSC 5) quickly proved to be too small and too far away from the hospital's obstetrical facilities. The distance from the ISCU to the delivery room had a part in insuring that several cohorts of Harriet Lane residents were both good sprinters and had good mental maps of where the building's various back stairways came out on lower floors. The elevator lobby was given extra doors for possible expansions of the building that never occurred, confusing generations of patients and staff who think there are six elevators instead of four. Innovative Venetian blinds, built into double-glazed windows of patient rooms, proved difficult to maintain in a functional status. Proximity to the hospital kitchens meant that food for children could be served on trays—an innovation at the time—but ensured that cooking smells permeated many areas of the lower floors of the building.

Cooke, through his Kennedy Foundation ties (and with the foundation's substantial contributions to Hopkins pediatrics and the new building), had received a promise that President John F. Kennedy would speak at the CMSC dedication ceremony. But in the fall of 1963 Kennedy was assassinated, making the opening a bittersweet occasion. At the 1964 ceremonies, Cooke noted that memories of the Second World War, the bombing of Hiroshima, the ongoing cold war, and racial tensions in the United States all were sobering. But he called for optimism even as he recalled "the man who was originally to have given this address." The real significance of the CMSC, he said, was in its recognition of the importance of the child for the well-being of man. Cooke called the CMSC the first step in the creation of a program that would study "the acceleration of human development" and its rewards would make the race to the moon or the "conquest of poverty" seem small in comparison. The race was on with the Soviets to accomplish this, but he felt American science would beat out the Khruschev's "doctrinaire" approach.[20]

As the department grew in terms of faculty and house staff, clinical responsibilities, and physical space, Cooke struggled with developing models of governance. He credited nursing with helping to maintain some of the communal spirit of the old Harriet Lane despite the complexity of the new building. In a 1973 letter to Isabel Kessler, the pediatric nursing supervisor for many years, he thanked her not only for her support of him when he was "a new professor" but also for her "help and tolerance" and maintenance of the spirit of the "old days."[21]

The move to the new building required big adjustments for nurses and coincided with profound changes in the delivery of pediatric nursing care and the experience of working as a nurse. The old Harriet Lane building wards were large, open rooms and teams delivered the nursing care, so that bonds between individual staff members and children took time to form. For the staff, though, these wards had their intimate side, as nursing turnover was less, and residents were on the ward much of the time and devoted more of their efforts toward bedside observation of patients—a task now largely turned over to nursing. In the Harriet Lane building, and in the early years of the CMSC, nurses themselves spent most of their time dispensing medications and caring for intravenous (IV) lines. The IVs of the time entered the bloodstream via small, easy-to-dislodge metal needles rather than the flexible catheters used today, and they were fed by gravity from bags or bottles that frequently ran dry. Nurses were responsible for counting drops to ensure that the IV fluids flowed at the right pace, and for keeping the IV site protected so that the needle would not come out. Only doctors, however, could "flush" the lines if they looked to be occluded or restart them when they failed.

In more ways than one, the foundation of the nursing staff was composed of nursing "aides," women largely from the neighborhood surrounding the hospital who trained on the job and who were responsible for feeding children and keeping them clean. Many aides were middle-aged and parents themselves, respected not only for their technical skills—knowing when a child with cardiac disease was becoming critically ill, being able to encourage a dehydrated child to drink—but also for their nurturing and advice to other staff members. One way in which aides served their fellow staff members was as sources of support when children died. Compared with today, child deaths in the hospital were very common—from untreatable cardiac disease, leukemia, and even diarrhea and dehydration. The team model of nursing seemed to work against a compassionate response to death, whether with the dead child's family or one's own response as a clinician. "The deaths may have made us a little colder, a little more aloof," recalled Marilyn Winkelstein. If you had a baby die on the night or evening shift, you had to distance yourself from it; there was still the medications and feeding of a whole other group of children. If you got too involved in it there was no one else to take your place. It was the aides who often provided the solace to young nurses, and one suspected to residents and families as well. By the 1970s, however, nursing was moving toward a "primary" rather than team model, and aides were phased out.[22]

Cooke was an early advocate of developing clinical centers and divisions, although he was opposed to narrowly defined research centers or setting up divisions that could never hope to have a critical mass of faculty. In his John Howland Award address of 1991 he lamented the disappearance of the "academic full-time system" and the increases in income of "high rolling" procedure-oriented specialty physicians. "To keep up," he said, pediatric departments had increased their dependence on practice income, while at the same time "drowning" in patients whose care was paid for by Medicaid at rates too low to support faculty salaries.[23] However, Cooke continued to attract substantial funding to the department. Philip Bard, who was dean of the Johns Hopkins School of Medicine from 1953 to 1957, helped Cooke get in touch with the Heinz family. Irene Heinz Given, daughter of H. J. Heinz, the founder of the food products company of the same name, had been a prominent medical philanthropist along with her husband, John. Bard evidently heard that the Given Foundation had become interested in developmental disabilities and he asked Cooke to help draw up a proposal. The result was the Given Foundation Professorship in Pediatrics, which has funded the chair's position in the department since 1962.[24]

Cooke did not particularly like committees or the committee process, and he did not easily accept that despite his position as chair, there were higher-ups in the hospital and university administration to whom he might have to answer. In 1963 Cooke wrote to Eunice Shriver, "I have never been employed by anyone, nor have I ever worked for anyone. The one thing I prize is independence and, for that reason, I have turned down a number of opportunities which do not offer me the chance to think, talk, and act as I feel, as compared to my present post."[25] An oft-told story about Cooke and committees involved the process of selecting new interns. A faculty committee evaluated applicants based on written materials and an interview, and met to rank those to be offered positions. Cooke, it was said, would routinely arrive early for the committee's meetings, examine the files, and rearrange them in the order that he preferred.[26]

Even those who truly liked Cooke recognized his competitiveness and ego. In a skit written for the 1962 turtle derby celebrations, the pediatric residents (among them Arnold Siegler, who practiced pediatrics in Baltimore until recently, and John Neff, now at the University of Washington) lampooned Cooke for his relationship with the Kennedy family and for finally having "his own" building (which actually would not open for another two years). In their skit, they juxtaposed Cooke with the famous painting of Welch, Osler, Halstead, and Kelly ("the big four" of the Johns Hopkins Hospital). To the tune of the song, "There is Nothing Like a Dame," they presented a Cooke impersonator singing, "What have I not, a picture frame!" Shifting tunes, "Cooke" then argued with the four, "Anything you can do, I can do better."[27]

The Kennedy Institute and the Park Building

The John F. Kennedy Institute (now the Kennedy Krieger Institute) and the Park Building represent Cooke's two other major "bricks and mortar" contributions to Hopkins pediatrics. The founding of the former owed immensely both to Cooke's vision and to his close relationship with the Kennedy family. After initially impressing Eunice and Sargent Shriver so that the Kennedy Foundation funded his plan for making Hopkins a center for research on the causes of retardation, Cooke next became a member of the health and welfare subcommittee of president-elect John F. Kennedy's incoming transition team. Ideas discussed there later led to the founding of the National Institute of Child Health and Human Development (NICHD), in which Cooke played a role along with Sinai Hospital's Harry Gordon.[28] Another of Cooke's ideas was the establishment of academically affiliated research centers to tackle the causes of retardation, based on the model that the Kennedy Foundation had funded at Hopkins. Evidently, the latter idea did not go much further until President Kennedy scheduled a speech to Congress on the joint topics of mental health and mental retardation. The Shrivers were given a draft of the speech, and reportedly finding it "dull" asked Cooke for suggestions to "make it more interesting."[29]

Cooke recalled in an interview that his opportunity to consult was, in fact, quite lucky. He happened to be playing tennis with the Shrivers when they were asked to consult on the speech. Cooke was involved in discussions with Maryland officials over the care of the retarded and had recently talked with a student who had visited the Rosewood State Hospital, a residential facility for the retarded, who found it to be "a human zoo." In contrast, Cooke pointed to the Phipps Clinic, the psychiatric wing of Hopkins, as a model for how good care could be integrated with both research and training. Cooke proposed to the Shrivers the notion of establishing academically affiliated clinical and teaching facilities for the retarded. Mrs. Shriver reportedly liked the idea and asked him to "go up to the library and write a couple of paragraphs." Those paragraphs made it into the president's speech and eventually evolved into part of the landmark Community Mental Health Centers and Mental Retardation Facilities Act of 1963.[30] The new law also funded comprehensive community mental health centers and expanded the role of the National Institute of Mental Health (NIMH) to include the translation of research into clinical and social programs. The act stipulated that the federal government would fund fifteen so-called university-affiliated facilities, or UAFs, paying for 75 percent of the costs, as well as 10 mental retardation research centers.

The task of administering the UAF program at the federal level fell to the Hill-Burton program, better known for administering funds for the construction of community hospitals in underserved areas. An advisory committee set up to select the fifteen sites was divided among physicians, psychologists, and educators. Cooke recalled making the first application, and aiming its discussion for a committee session when the educators were largely absent. "I was after something," he explained, "It was kind of self-serving." (When Cooke was absent, the sites approved had a more educational or psychological focus.)[31] With the Kennedy Institute building eventually completed—twenty-five percent of the money having come from the Children's Rehabilitation Institute, plus a loan from the Kennedy Foundation, which paid the construction overruns—the next question was how its ongoing work would be financed. Because of wrangling within the U.S. Department of Health, Education, and Welfare's (now the Department of Health and Human Service's) Administration for Children and Families, initial staff support came from the federal Children's Bureau (now the Bureau of Maternal and Child Health), assuring that the new facilities would have a child rather than adult focus.[32]

Cooke's other building project was the Edwards A. Park Building. The building's major occupant was to be a center for outpatient services, but it would also have a specialized children's trauma center, so that injured children could be cared for "away from the terrible and upsetting tragedies of an adult medical and surgical emergency room."[33] The Comprehensive Child Care Center, or CCCC as it came to be known, began its life on the second floor of the Children's Medical and

Surgical Center (in space now occupied by the neonatal intensive care unit) but it soon moved to the new Park Building.

Another idea to come out of the transition team for the Kennedy administration was increased funding for the health of pregnant women and their young children. These suggestions evolved into two major federal programs, the Maternal and Infant (M&I) Projects (funded as part of the 1963 amendments to Title V of the Social Security Act) and the Children and Youth (C&Y) Projects (1965 amendments to Title V). Ideas behind the M&I initiatives had come, in part, from work done in Baltimore in the early 1950s by Abe Lilienfeld and his colleagues in the department of epidemiology at the Johns Hopkins School of Public Health. Lilienfeld showed how various maternal factors were related to the risk of a child being born with cerebral palsy and other handicapping conditions.[34] The C&Y initiatives were built on observations that many of the serious illnesses of early childhood were strongly associated with living conditions in poor neighborhoods and with a lack of access to preventive services. As early as the 1920s, studies funded by the federal Children's Bureau had demonstrated that the death rate for black infants in Baltimore was more than twice that of white infants, and that these deaths were linked to poverty rather than ignorance or laziness, as was the common presumption at the time.[35] The C&Y monies, and the Medicaid program, also enacted by Congress in 1965, provided mechanisms for community involvement that was seen as largely lacking at institutions like Hopkins, which were under pressure to better serve residents in the neighborhoods where they were located.

In designing the CCCC as the Hopkins C&Y initiative, Cooke was influenced by having participated in the planning process for what would become Head Start, the comprehensive early childhood education and health program that is considered to be among the most important and successful social programs in U.S. history. The philosophy behind Head Start was both wide-ranging and multidisciplinary. Its objective was to promote strengths as well as remediate weakness, to work with parents and children as a unit rather than one or the other individually, and was to be tailored and responsive to local conditions. Head Start was to be not just an educational program, but was to provide medical, nutritional, social, and vocational help to children and their families.[36] Cooke incorporated these principles into the design of the CCCC. The Center's goals were to reach out to families rather than waiting for them to walk in the door, to offer continuity of care and the dignity of an ongoing, personal relationship between families and providers, and to extend a broad range of services under one roof.

The Park Building was set up to facilitate a pioneering health services research project: the attempt to compare outcomes and efficiencies between the CCCC's continuity model and a standard, clinic-based service that was housed physically in the same place.[37] A variety of studies were carried out looking at costs and personnel needs. Long before the hospital itself had computerized medical records, the CCCC had a system for inputting information from clinic paperwork to create a computerized summary of visits, problems, and immunizations. The CCCC had a catchment area of several census tracts surrounding the hospital, and may have been, in Cooke's words, one of the first experiments in capitated, managed care for children.

The evolution of the CCCC was emblematic of all that could be both right and wrong with the Harriet Lane model. The CCCC failed to integrate its staff and faculty into the teaching and academic life of the pediatrics department. Initially, residents staffed the new Center but Cooke pulled them out after they complained that the increased demands of the new system were not accompanied by adequate teaching.[38] Henry Seidel, a former Harriet Lane chief resident, returned from private practice in Baltimore to become medical director of the CCCC in 1968. He felt that he was respected as a clinician but he had the impression that in his faculty role he sometimes was seen as a "second class citizen" in a department that did not then, as a whole, value the academic potential in primary patient care.[39] Although four senior faculty members—Seidel, Robert Drachman, Jim Hudson, and Neil Sims—were dedicated to the clinical and academic goals of the effort, it was difficult to recruit qualified pediatricians to provide actual patient care. Ultimately, the services offered by the CCCC became less comprehensive as federal grants shrank and services and infrastructure could not be maintained, even with the advent of Medicaid as a source of fee-for-service payment. Despite Cooke's efforts—in a 1967 speech he said that the CCCC probably occupied more of his time than any other single activity—and a vision of complete care that continued to be highly relevant, the program gradually withered and was finally closed during the term of John Littlefield, Cooke's successor as chair.[40]

Another Baltimore "spin-off" of Cooke's national involvement was the creation of the Martin Luther King Parent and Child Center Program. The MLK Center, opened in 1969, was a multi-purpose support center for parents and young children. The center was directed by Mary Richardson, funded by the Office of Economic Opportunity (OEO),[41] and planned by parents of the Lafayette-Douglass Homes housing project adjacent to Johns Hopkins Hospital. Alejandro Rodriguez, a faculty member in child psychiatry, was also part of the team. At the time, Cooke was dissatisfied because Head Start was open only to children aged three to five years[42] and Cooke felt that efforts to support children and families had to start earlier. He also wanted to develop community sites for medical-student training, with the intention of developing "a generation of educated people who are concerned with the poor and exhibit concern by constructive action." These young people, he hoped, would be able to "guide the social revolution which has begun, to a necessary compromise."[43] Just who should receive credit for organizing the MLK Program remained a subject of discussion. In an exchange of correspondence with Richardson in 1973, Cooke faulted a report she had written to the OEO describing the Center's origins. Cooke felt that she had underplayed the department of pediatrics' role in the Center's planning.[44] Regardless, Cooke used the occasion of the Center's opening to express his views on both politics and child development. The opening was set for October 15, 1969, a day already designated as a national day of protest against the war in Vietnam. Cooke began his remarks by noting the date and saying that the Center's opening demonstrated how human energies should be used for peaceful pursuits, rather than for war. He went on to say that he hoped the Center would help children develop intelligence without diminishing their personality, and would help them develop "restraint" without "diminution in drive."[45] Cooke might well have been talking about himself.

Who Should Survive?

Until perhaps the late 1960s, medical decisions were made largely by doctors, without much involvement from patients, or in the case of children, the patients' parents. Janet Hardy recalled that when a special nursery for sick newborns and premature babies was established in the late 1940s, the residents working there made autonomous decisions about which babies could be saved and which would not be resuscitated.[46] Henry Seidel recalled a case from 1952 in which the house staff had decided to support and treat a newborn with meningomyelocele and meningitis. The next day, Lawson Wilkins, their supervising physician, came by and said, "there was no earthly reason" to treat the child. Though treatment was withdrawn, the child lived. The child's parents had not been consulted about either the initial decision to treat the baby or the decision to stop treatment.[47]

The absence of parental input and peer supervision was not limited to the nurseries. Harriet Guild, one of the senior members of the department at the time of Cooke's arrival, was said to have managed patients on the Harriet Lane's second floor "beyond anybody's touch," including Cooke's. Looking back on that time, Seidel said, "Physicians in that day were not challenged. We could do no wrong. You could get people to do what you wanted them to do.... That manipulation didn't even have to be taught. You just did it."[48]

There were many instances of this kind of decision making in both routine care and in research, which today would be considered ethically problematic. The National Research Act,[49] which created the National Commission for the Protection of Human Subjects of Biomedical and Behavioral Research, was not signed into law until 1974. Cooke was named to the commission (by that time he had left Hopkins and was vice chancellor for health sciences at the University of Wisconsin), but his membership on the commission was not supported by organized pediatrics. Robert Blizzard, then chairman of pediatrics at the University of Virginia but previously a faculty member at Hopkins who had served as acting chair while Cooke was on sabbatical, wrote Cooke saying that "a significant number" of pediatricians were concerned about Cooke's capacity to represent the field and "the well-being of unborn children." Blizzard suggested that Cooke was overly influenced by the beliefs of the Kennedy family, and asked Cooke to step aside in favor of Horace Hodes, who had been nominated by the two academic pediatric societies of the time, the Society of Pediatric Research and the American Pediatric Society.[50] Needless to say, Cooke did not step aside, and he suggested that Blizzard and his colleagues "keep [their] shirts on."

Blizzard was concerned that Cooke would take a stand against research involving fetal tissue among other things. Cooke fired back that Blizzard evidently found it difficult to think "in other than a cost-benefit mode."[51] Ultimately, the ethicists and philosophers convened by the commission issued the landmark Belmont Report, published in April 1979. It summarized the commission's philosophical stance—respect for persons, beneficence, and justice—and quickly became the central, guiding document of the bioethics movement in the United States and in much of the world.

Cooke had several motivations to involve himself in these debates over "who should survive." The cold war had prompted a sense of competition with the Soviets not only to master science in general but, in Cooke's mind, to create superior populations capable of winning the race for scientific progress. Closer to home, Cooke saw the evolving civil rights movement partially from an ethical perspective. At his farewell dinner when he left Johns Hopkins, he noted "our prior neglect of the retarded and the black residents of East Baltimore demands reparations—back payment—for what we owe them for years of neglect."[52] Undoubtedly, however, it was his experience with his own children, and his conviction that it had been right and even good to support them, that galvanized his interest in the disenfranchised. He felt strongly that society was looking for easy ways out of difficult situations that, instead, had to be faced. In a 1976 letter, Cooke wrote that he spent many years trying to interest people in the issue, but was stymied by "the preoccupation with saving society and parents from discomfort" that seemed to be "at the heart of the passive euthanasia that is presently going on."[53]

In Cooke's papers in the Alan Mason Chesney Medical Archives there is a folder marked "Speeches—mongoloids with duodenal atresia" which includes records of a baby born at Hopkins in 1963. The baby had Down's syndrome complicated by duodenal atresia, a narrowing of the intestines that, without surgery, made it impossible for the baby to eat. Notes from doctors who cared for the child (including Mary Ellen Avery, Barton Childs, and David Clark) stated that the parents did not want the baby to have surgery. One doctor wrote, after a discussion with the baby's father, "his mind was set and I was unable to change it." Another doctor noted that the surgery that would have allowed the child to eat was "dangerous and heroic," and not warranted for a child with a "severe and irreversible congenital defect." He agreed, though, that the parents' decision might have been biased because it seemed to be based on the fact that the child was "defective" rather than on the risk involved in the surgery.[54]

Eight years later a similar case arose for which Alex Haller was the surgeon consulted and Bill Bartholome was the senior resident. Again, the parents decided against surgery and the child died. This time, however, film director Werner Schumann (who worked for Charles Guggenheim, the Academy Award–winning documentary filmmaker who had produced a film about Robert Kennedy[55]) immortalized the case. *Who Should Survive?* was first shown in October 1971 at a symposium at the Kennedy Center in Washington, D.C., sponsored, as was the film, by the Kennedy Foundation.[56] The symposium was meant to generate attention. It was titled "Choices on our Conscience: an International Symposium on Human Rights, Retardation, and Research." Twelve hundred people attended, and in addition to seeing the film, they listened to a panel of twenty-one prominent scholars and media personalities.

The film started with an introduction by Eunice Kennedy, saying that the Foundation's purpose in presenting it was to help society face up to scientific progress with "knowledge and compassion... while there is still time." After a brief re-enactment of the child's birth and death (including Bartholome, Haller, and nurse Marie Parks as actors), the film featured a panel discussion led by Cooke. At one point, one of the panelists proposed that the family may have been of modest means, and thus may not have been capable of caring for a handicapped child. Cooke quickly answered back, "I guess what you're saying is 'If you're poor, your retarded children should die. If you've got an adequate amount of money, why, your retarded kids can live.'... That goes against my grain."[57]

Who Should Survive? intended to be provocative (it won four film festival awards). The audience at the symposium felt strongly that Hopkins' decision to let the parents refuse surgery was wrong, and Cooke received many letters pointing out similar cases. An article in the *Baltimore Sun* from October 21, 1971, just a few days after the Kennedy Center showing, quoted Cooke saying that the film would precipitate "drastic" changes in how such cases were handled at Hopkins, and that an "ethics unit" would be established to deal with the problem.[58] In a letter to Eunice Shriver dated March 6, 1972, Cooke wrote that since the film, he was "called upon every two or three days to give some advice on a difficult problem that borders on ethics." Prior to the movie, he said, these requests came, perhaps, "once every other year."[59] Jerry Winkelstein, a chief resident while the movie was being made, said that the filming itself went relatively unnoticed by most of the house staff, but that it seemed to have had a major influence on Bartholome and faculty member Norman Fost, both of whom went on to careers involved with medical ethics.[60]

Far from seeing him as a hero of the disadvantaged, Cooke's most articulate critics accused him of playing "God" and advocating a moral stance that society could not afford. Elaine Freeman, a freelance writer and wife of Johns Hopkins pediatric neurologist John Freeman,[61] wrote a 1972 article for the *New York Times Magazine* entitled "The God Committee."[62] In it, she posed the ethical dilemma as a choice between the "slippery slope" of deciding who should live versus the need to spend limited resources in the most productive way. She juxtaposed Cooke's views with those of British neurologist John Lorber, who proposed that societies needed to concentrate resources on those who would benefit the most from them.[63]

Cooke was furious with Freeman's article. He wrote an angry letter to the *Times* suggesting that he had been misquoted, and that Hopkins had established a "study" committee rather than one that was "playing God."[64] In fact, despite Cooke's enthusiastic letter to Eunice Shriver describing the film's impact, his attempt to establish a hospital-wide ethics committee had been only partially successful. Cooke had again stepped outside of his role as a department chair and written to the chiefs of all the other clinical departments asking for representatives interested in forming an ethics discussion group.[65] The group met regularly, but early on discarded the idea of accepting consults about active cases. Members of the group felt that active review would put their respective departments on the defensive, and the hospital's legal office reportedly gave the idea what Cooke called its "kiss of death."[66]

Cooke also struck up a correspondence with a woman who had written the *Times* to comment on the Freeman story. Her letter strongly criticized Cooke's position, saying that only "rich professionals" such as Cooke could afford to support "a child who will never be anything other than a vegetable." Cooke replied describing his experiences with his daughters, justifying the need to care for the "helpless, dependent, and less fortunate" so that "all power is not concentrated in the hands of a few." In turn, the woman wrote Cooke of her own loss of a month-old infant, twenty years prior. The pair kept writing, finally agreeing that a just solution would be the establishment of a system of universal health insurance.[67]

Cooke left Hopkins before bioethics as a clinical and scholarly endeavor had firmly taken root. In a letter to medical Dean Russell Morgan in 1972, Cooke noted that Hopkins "suffers" from a lack of law and divinity schools and "could benefit" from a "small cadre of faculty, supported out of other funds" to maintain a program in ethics.[68] Although ethics committees and ethics scholarship came to Hopkins in due course, it was not until 1995 that the university's Phoebe R. Berman Bioethics Institute was founded. Cooke was not entirely despairing, however. In his farewell talk, he noted "a profound change in the morality of the Hopkins Institutions." People, he felt, were now seen as "worthwhile in themselves, whether they bring joy or sorrow, happiness or grief, good or bad."[69]

Cooke's Enduring Influence

Cooke ultimately left Johns Hopkins for a number of reasons. By the time he resigned in 1973, he had been chair more than seventeen years and to some extent was looking for new areas in which to work. Ethics had become his major passion, and his transition out of the chairmanship began with a sabbatical during which he studied medical ethics at Harvard. Cooke also had ambitions at Hopkins that were not likely to be fulfilled. He had wanted to be named dean of the School of Medicine, but had clearly irritated too many senior members of the administration for that ever to happen. As he wrote in 1971 to Marion Fay, acting president of the Medical College of Pennsylvania, where he was being recruited, Hopkins President Milton Eisenhower had just told him that Russell Morgan, then chief of radiology, had been named dean "in response to pressure against me from the head of the hospital."[70] The "head of the hospital" was Cooke's old nemesis, Russell Nelson. The story on the street, according to Henry Seidel, was that when Eisenhower approached Nelson about the suitability of Cooke as a successor for the outgoing dean, David Rogers, Nelson replied, "over my dead body."[71] There had been overt friction over finances, interpersonal style, and turf between these two men. Clearly Cooke was not an easy man with whom to work. But there was also likely friction over politics, as Cooke became more and more vocal with his antiwar sentiments and more outspoken about the housecleaning that he thought ethics could bring both to medical practice and the role of medicine in society. Finally, Cooke's sources of influence—his ability to raise public and private money—were no longer what they had been. A conservative Republican was in the White House, and Cooke, though on the President's Commission on Ethics, was no longer intimately involved with policy for mental health and retardation. He remained active with the Joseph P. Kennedy, Jr. Foundation, but by the

1970s NIH funding was providing the lion's share of research support at Hopkins and similar institutions.

Cooke helped bring the Harriet Lane service to a new place, one where issues such as ethics, primary care, health services research, and community-oriented projects could potentially have stature and legitimacy alongside bench science and traditional inpatient medical care. He also was wise enough to let flourish a growing expertise in medical genetics, and to leave in place the pioneering program in pediatric endocrinology. But ultimately the new equilibrium between traditional and nontraditional aspects of medicine was either never really attained or, if it was briefly, could not be sustained during his tenure. Cooke's successor, John Littlefield, regained some of this ground by establishing a solid pediatric primary care clinic and, ultimately, an academic division of general pediatrics. Cooke's pediatric trauma center survived as well, eventually becoming its own division of pediatric emergency medicine and a busy pediatric intensive care unit. The Martin Luther King Center also survived but outside of research projects, the house staff's volunteer activities, and its association with the practices of Johns Hopkins Community Physicians, the department now interacts with the surrounding neighborhoods perhaps less than it should. Hopkins residents still do, however, rotate to a community hospital—now St. Agnes in West Baltimore.

Ultimately, Cooke's legacy at Hopkins may be strongest in the area that he initially championed—care of the developmentally disabled. The Kennedy Krieger Institute continues to grow and add programs and sites throughout the Baltimore region. Residents rotate through its services and graduate into its fellowship programs. Cooke perhaps did not wipe out use of the term "gork" for retarded children, nor did he make as much of a dent as he might have liked in what he called Hopkins' "moral development" as an institution, but he had the foresight to incorporate much that was new and needed into his department.

If Cooke came across in his letters and speeches as being a bit larger than life—and with an ego to match—he might be partly excused given the tone of the times and the culture of Johns Hopkins. Then as now the leaders of institutions such as Hopkins and Yale took themselves very seriously. The huge cultural shifts of the 1950s and '60s, set against the backdrop of threatened nuclear war, imbued actions and events with a special significance. And pediatrics was just emerging from an era where a relative handful of prominent men (and a few women) all knew each other and vied with each other to demonstrate their complete knowledge of the field. But Cooke also may have had his place in what seems to have been a conscious or unconscious alternation of personalities in the chairman's position. Because Francis Schwentker's eight-year chairmanship was so uneventful, in the minds of many Cooke was the heir of Edwards Park, a man thought of as a great intellect with a quiet and gentle demeanor quite unlike that of his predecessor, John Howland. Cooke was very different from Park and, in turn, Cooke's successor could not have been less like him. John Littlefield, chairman from 1974 to 1985, was (and remains) a patient scientist, who, without a background in pediatrics, set about continuing the department's transformation with a modest persistence that was the opposite of Cooke's approach to change. It became Littlefield's job to further develop and fully staff the neonatal and pediatric intensive care units, which were becoming essential parts of children's hospitals, and to create a viable and academic primary-care training program. He developed new leadership for some of the older pediatric subspecialty divisions and for new ones such as oncology, gastroenterology, pulmonology, and nephrology. Littlefield also presided over the modernization of the resident call schedule. By the mid-1970s, the Harriet Lane training program's every-other-night call schedule had become an anachronistic anomaly, and the program came perilously close to not being able to fill its ranks.[72] Littlefield's successor, Frank Oski, had more of Cooke's brash stage presence, though he lacked Cooke's intellectual pedigree and connections, and the source of his drive was more ambiguous than Cooke's focus on retardation. Which temperament best suits a department? Do healthy departments demand such an alternation of leadership styles? These are questions for which appropriate yardsticks need to be developed, and that search committees of the future may well ponder.

309

A New HomeA New Home

Notes

1. *The Johns Hopkins Nurses Alumnae Magazine* 45, no. 4 (1955): 159.1. *The Johns Hopkins Nurses Alumnae Magazine* 45, no. 4 (1955): 159.

2. Memo, Charles R. Goulet, associate director, to Russell A. Nelson, director, Johns Hopkins Hospital, about the Children's Medical Center, November 18, 1958. Russell A. Nelson, "The Children's Hospital Center Project" (typewritten manuscript), November 6, 1957. File "Medical Planning and Development Committee, minutes, 275th meeting, January 22, 1959," box "Medical Planning and Development Committee. 275–91, January 22, 1959–January 6, 1960," Alan Mason Chesney Medical Archives, The Johns Hopkins Medical Institutions, Baltimore, MD, hereafter referred to as AMC.

3. Robert E. Cooke, interview with Robert Grayson, September 8, 1996, Vero Beach. Florida, Oral History Project, Pediatric History Center, American Academy of Pediatrics, Elk Grove Village, Illinois (2003), 10.

4. Robert Cooke, interview with John Littlefield and author, May 16, 2000. The child day care center on Rutland Avenue, affiliated with Johns Hopkins and founded in 1972, was named for Walter F. Perkins. "Perkins Day Care Center provides "preparatory" education, and napkins," *Johns Hopkins Children's Center News* (Summer 2001): 6.

5. Saul Brusilow interview with Henry Seidel and author, March 28, 2000.

6. Harrison did, however, have a laboratory at the Harriet Lane Home.

7. Mary Ellen Avery, interview with John Littlefield and author, November 9, 1999.

8. J. Alex Haller Jr. to Robert E. Cooke, May 21, 1973, Robert E. Cooke Papers, box 19JF, folder "scrapbook," AMC.

9. Russell A. Nelson, "The Children's Hospital Center Project," November 6, 1957, file "Medical Planning and Development Committee, Minutes, 275th meeting, January 22, 1959." Box "Medical Planning and Development Committee 275–91, January 22, 1959–January 6, 1960," AMC; Robert Sargent Shriver to Thomas B. Turner, December 23, 1959. Robert E. Cooke Papers, file "General 1959–1970," box 9JF, AMC.

10. Larry Pakula, interview with author, February 15, 2003.

11. Robert Cooke, interview with John Littlefield and author, May 16, 2000.

12. Robert Cooke, interview with Robert Grayson, 40. Robert Cooke interview with John Littlefield and author, May 16, 2000.

13. Polly Hesterberg, interview with Henry Seidel and John Littlefield, April 16, 1999.

14. Barton Childs, undated, untitled typescript of a talk for the seventy-fifth anniversary of the Harriet Lane Home.

15. "Mary D. Salter Ainsworth," in Agnes N. O'Connell and Nancy Felipe Russo, editors, *Models of Achievement: Reflections of Eminent Women in Psychology*, (New York: Columbia University Press, 1983), 201–20.

16. Polly Hesterberg, interview with Henry Seidel and John Littlefield, April 16, 1999.

17. Jerry Winkelstein, interview with author, July 19, 2004.

18. Robert E. Cooke, "Recognizing the Uncooperative Mother," speech delivered to the Assembly of the Interstate Postgraduate Medical Association of North America, November 16, 1972. Robert E. Cooke Papers, folder I, box 6JF, AMC.

19. Jeriann Wilson (director of Child Life, Johns Hopkins Children's Center), interview with John Littlefield and Henry Seidel, May 13, 1999.

20. The version of his speech printed in the *Bulletin of the Johns Hopkins Hospital* 115 (1964): 297–305, differs from that printed in the book *A Symposium on the Child*, ed. John A. Askin, Robert E. Cooke, and J. Alex Haller (Baltimore: The Johns Hopkins University Press, 1967). In the *Bulletin* version, Cooke refers directly to Kennedy, saying that he was originally to have given the speech that Cooke himself was now making.

21. Robert E. Cooke to Miss Isabel Kessler, March 14, 1973. Robert E. Cooke Papers, folder "K," box 8JF, AMC.

22. Marilyn Winkelstein, conversation with author, August 2, 2004.

23. In the same speech, Cooke also noted that the pool of potential pediatric researchers had been reduced because many of the best and brightest residents preferred motherhood to research careers. Robert E. Cooke, "Acceptance of the Howland Award." *Pediatric Research* 30 (1991): 624–25.

24. Cooke interview with Henry Seidel and John Littlefield, May 18, 1999; World Wide Web, http://webapps.jhu.edu/namedprofessorships.

25. Robert E. Cooke to Mrs. R. Sargent Shriver, December 24, 1963. Robert E. Cooke Papers, folder "Shriver, Mrs. Eunice K," box 19JF, AMC.

26. Saul Brusilow, interview with Henry Seidel and author, March 28, 2000.

27. "The Hustler, or A Connecticut Yankee in King Alfred's Court," audiotape excerpt (made from original 33 rpm recording) of the 1962 turtle derby skit, provided by Tony Holtzman. Tony Holtzman, interview with author, January 18, 2002.

28. Robert Cooke, interview with Henry Seidel and John Littlefield, May 18, 1999. Cooke played a role in circumventing the opposition of NIH head James Shannon to the establishment of a National Institute of Child Health and Human Development (NICHD). The NIH's initial authorizing legislation had been interpreted as limiting new institutes to those that were concerned with a disease or a group of diseases. In this interview, Cooke referred to Shannon as a "son of a bitch" with whom he was determined to get even, and said that the Shrivers were instrumental in helping Cooke get in touch with Lister Hill and John Fogarty, two of the most influential members of Congress on health matters. In 1962, Public Law 87–838 was passed, authorizing establishment of a National Institute of Child Health and Human Development. Cooke served on its first National Advisory Council.

29. Robert Cooke, interview with Robert Grayson, 16. Robert Cooke interview with John Littlefield and author, May 16, 2000.

30. *Community Mental Health Centers and Mental Retardation Facilities Act of 1963*, Public Law 88–164.

31. Robert Cooke, interview with John Littlefield and author, May 16, 2000.

32. The U.S. Children's Bureau had its roots in a congressional investigation into child labor during the administration of President Theodore Roosevelt. Its original mission was to produce data about the welfare of children and to advocate for child welfare measures in federal programs. In the 1940s its authority was expanded to include making grants. In 1947 pediatrician Paul Harper became the leader of a new Division of Maternal and Child Health at the Johns Hopkins School of Hygiene and Public Health, becoming one of the first beneficiaries of the new Children's Bureau program to establish maternal and child health training programs. Harper and Cooke ended up opposing each other on the issue of creating an NIH institute for studying children's diseases (what would become the NICHD). Harper and others felt that children's health research should be based in the Children's Bureau but Cooke felt that the bureau's personnel had "neither the interest nor the

capacities to develop intensive research programs of a basic nature in the biological or behavioral aspects of human development." Robert E. Cooke to Professor Wilbur J. Cohen, assistant secretary of the Department of Health, Education, and Welfare, March 30, 1961, and July 10, 1961. Robert E. Cooke Papers, folder "NICHD: Comprehensive, General (through December 31, 1961," box 14 JF, AMC. In 1969 most of the Children's Bureau's general child health services were turned over to the Maternal and Child Health Bureau and the Children's Bureau focused on children involved with maltreatment and foster care.

33. Robert E. Cooke to Dr. Edith M. Jurka. Robert E. Cooke Papers, folder "J," box 8 JF, AMC.

34. Abraham M. Lilienfeld and B. Pasamanick, "The Association of Maternal and Fetal Factors with the Development of Cerebral Palsy and Epilepsy," *American Journal of Obstetrics and Gynecology* 70 (1955): 93–101.

35. Women at Work. The Fight for Children. World Wide Web, www. webguild.com/sentinel/women_infants.htm.

36. *Bulletin of the Johns Hopkins Hospital,* 115 (1964):297–305. Cooke had a key role in the origins of Head Start. In our interviews, Cooke told us that he put together the original planning committee for Head Start at the request of Sargent Shriver, who at that point was the head of President Johnson's War on Poverty. Interview with John Littlefield and author, May 18, 1999. Cooke attributed the basic idea to Susan Gray at Peabody College in Nashville, and said that Ed Ziegler "has been designated as the creator of HS but that's not quite right" Robert Cooke, interview with Robert Grayson, 8, 19–20.

37. Henry Seidel interview with John Littlefield and author, February 17, 1999.

38. Jerry Winkelstein interview with author, July 19, 2004.

39. Henry Seidel, interview with John Littlefield and author, February 9, 1999.

40. Robert Cooke presentation on Comprehensive Care in Baltimore, May 22, 1967. Robert E. Cooke Papers, folder "Speeches—Comprehensive Care, Minn., 1967," box 24 JF, AMC.

41. George W. Bush's secretary of defense, Donald Rumsfeld, was the head of the Office of Economic Opportunity from 1969 to 1970.

42. Now some Head Start programs offer "Early Head Start" to younger children and their parents.

43. Testimony by Robert Cooke to the Committee on Labor and Public Welfare, U.S. Senate, in support of the Head Start Child Development Act of 1969 (Mondale), August 6, 1969.

44. Robert E. Cooke to Mary E. Robinson. November 21, 1973. Robert E. Cooke Papers, folder "Martin Luther King Jr., Center," box 11 JF, AMC.

45. Robert E. Cooke's introduction at the dedication of the Martin Luther King Jr., Parent and Child Center, October 15, 1969. Robert E. Cooke Papers, folder, "Commitments—Operation Face-to-Face," box 2 JF, AMC.

46. Janet Hardy, interview with John Littlefield, Henry Seidel, and author, March 9, 1999.

47. Henry Seidel, interview with John Littlefield and author, February 17, 1999.

48. Barton Childs, interview with John Littlefield, Henry Seidel, and author, January 27, 1999. Henry Seidel, interview with John Littlefield and author, February 17, 1999.

49. National Research Act, Public Law 93–348.

50. Robert. M. Blizzard to Robert E. Cooke, October 17, 1974. Robert E. Cooke Papers, file "B," box 2JF, AMC.

51. Robert E. Cooke to Robert M. Blizzard, October 30, 1974. Robert E. Cooke Papers, file "B," box 2JF, AMC.

52. Cooke, "The Gorks are Gone," an eight-page pamphlet, reprinted from a speech given by Cooke May 8, 1973, published by the Joseph P. Kennedy, Jr. Foundation. Not dated, author's files.

53. Robert E. Cooke to Mrs. Robert K. (Pat) Nixon, Birmingham, Michigan, March 24, 1976. Robert E. Cooke Papers, file "N," box 13JF, AMC.

54. Robert E. Cooke Papers, box marked "More Cooke Papers." AMC.

55. In a 1961 telegram to Cooke, Robert Kennedy suggested that Cooke contact Ed Guthman at the Department of Justice. Telegram, Robert F. Kennedy to Robert E. Cooke, March 24, 1961. Robert E. Cooke Papers, file "K," box 8JF, AMC. Guthman was Kennedy's press secretary, but he was also known for receiving the Pulitzer Prize in 1950 while a reporter for the *Seattle Times*. (Guthman received the prize for a series of articles proving that Washington's state "Un-American Activities" committee had covered up evidence exonerating a popular university professor from charges that he was a Communist. Guthman went on to become the national editor of the *Los Angeles Times*. Later, documents from the Nixon White House, brought to light during the Ervin Committee's investigations of the Watergate break-in, showed that Guthman was number three on Nixon's prioritized list of political enemies. Sharon Boswell and Lorraine McConaghy, "Rooting out Reds," *Seattle Times*, July 28, 1996. (http://seattletimes.nwsource.com/centennial/july/reds.html). Facts on File, *Watergate and the White House*, Vol. 1, 96–97. (See also www.lehigh.edu/~ineng/mac6/mac6-NixonOnline.html.) Guthman may have been the person who linked Cooke with documentary filmmaker Charles Guggenheim. Guggenheim received an Academy Award for his 1968 film, televised nationally and at the Democratic National Convention, *Robert Kennedy Remembered*. Guggenheim Productions, Inc. http://www.gpifilms.com/filmography.html.

56. *Who Should Survive? One of the Choices on our Conscience*, Joseph P. Kennedy, Jr. Foundation, produced and directed by Werner Schumann for Guggenheim Productions, Inc. Washington, D.C., distributed by Joseph P. Kennedy, Jr. Foundation Film Services, 1972; N. S. Rovner. "Hopkins Plans Ethics Unit in Wake of Mongoloid Case," *Baltimore Sun*, October 21, 1971, 1.

57. Transcript of edited panel discussion, Joseph P. Kennedy, Jr. Foundation Film, Production #363. Not dated. Robert E. Cooke Papers, file "General 1971–1972," box 9JF, AMC.

58. N. S. Rovner. "Hopkins Plans Ethics Unit in Wake of Mongoloid Case," *Baltimore Sun*, October 21, 1971, 1.

59. Robert E. Cooke to Mrs. R. Sargent Shriver, March 6, 1972. Robert E. Cooke Papers, file "Shriver, Mrs. Eunice K.," box 19JF, AMC.

60. Jerry Winkelstein, interview with author, July 19, 2004. Bartholome became a pediatric oncologist and ethicist, working primarily at the Univer-

sity of Kansas. In 1994 he developed esophageal cancer, and he died from it 1999. He made his final contribution to medical ethics by giving several interviews in the final months of his life to the television series *On Our Own Terms: Moyers on Dying*, of which he was the central figure in one program. World Wide Web, http://www.pbs.org/wnet/onourownterms/therapy/). Fost was chief resident at the Harriet Lane service. He completed a fellowship in bioethics and is now a professor of pediatrics at the University of Wisconsin medical school in Madison.

61. Elaine Freeman would later become vice president of the Johns Hopkins University in the Office of Corporate Communications and executive director of Communications and Public Affairs for Johns Hopkins Medicine.

62. Elaine Freeman, "The God Committee," *New York Times Magazine*. May 21, 1972, 84.

63. John Lorber, "Results of Treatment of Myelomeningocele. An Analysis of 524 Unselected Cases, with Special Reference to Possible Selection for Treatment," *Developmental Medicine and Child Neurology* 13 (1971): 279–303. Interestingly, Lorber, whose specialty was the evaluation and treatment of children born with meningomyelocele, a serious malformation of the central nervous system that was also the subject of debates over neonatal treatment, later stirred debate with a 1981 paper he entitled "Is Your Brain Really Necessary?" In that paper he described the case of an apparently normal twenty-six-year-old man whose brain scan revealed that he had only the thinnest layer of functional brain tissue inside a head that was otherwise largely filled with cerebrospinal fluid. Lorber's case was subsequently cited frequently in debates about how readily doctors could predict which infants with birth defects might develop normally. John Lorber, "Is Your Brain Really Necessary?," *Nursing Mirror* 152 no. 18 (1981): 28–29.

64. Robert E. Cooke and Norm Fost to editor of the *New York Times Magazine* Lewis Bergman. Robert E. Cooke Papers, file "N," box 13JF, AMC.

65. Robert E. Cooke to Dr. A. J. Kravtin, November 7, 1974. Robert E. Cooke Papers, file "K," box 8JF, AMC.

66. Ibid.

67. Letter to the editor of the *New York Times Magazine* from Mrs. Irving Berler, June 11, 1972; letters to Mrs. Berler from Cooke; letters to Cooke from Mrs. Berler, various dates. Robert E. Cooke Papers, file "N," box 13JF, AMC.

68. Robert E. Cooke to Russell H. Morgan, March 2, 1972. Robert E. Cooke Papers, file "Me," box 11JF, AMC.

69. Cooke, "The Gorks are Gone."

70. Robert E. Cooke to Marion Fay, PhD, September 30, 1971. Robert E. Cooke Papers, file "Positions offered—Medical College of Pennsylvania," box 40JF, AMC. It is not clear in this correspondence if Eisenhower used the term "head of the hospital" explicitly or if Cooke was reading this into the letter.

71. Henry Seidel interview with John Littlefield and author, February 9, 1999.

72. John Littlefield, interview with Henry Seidel and author, August 1998.

Afterword

By Henry M. Seidel, John W. Littlefield,
and Lawrence S. Wissow
315

The Harriet Lane Home, "the birthplace of modern American pediatrics,"[1] began with a handful of physicians—scientists who were first nurtured in New Haven, Connecticut. These professionals tended the Harriet Lane Home as it thrived in its first half century. Although the connections among these men were unplanned, they were not coincidental. William Henry Welch, John Howland, Edwards Park, and Robert Cooke all attended Yale and the initial players in the Harriet Lane drama, Welch and Howland, were members of that arcane Yale society Skull and Bones, known for its exclusivity and a lifelong sense of affinity and loyalty among its members. In his biography Welch is quoted several times about this society and the strength of such relationships.[2]

The legacies of Howland, Park, and Cooke[3] can be assessed in the context of the familiar triad of academic medicine: service, teaching, and the development of new knowledge. These three men effected profound and constructive changes in the Harriet Lane Home, different in nature for each of them, and all three contributed considerably to the evolution of modern American pediatrics and helped guide the field toward its present state. Each man expanded the horizon beyond that of his predecessor: Howland focused on his wards and laboratory; Park's interest extended into the community and "social" pediatrics; and Cooke's vision encompassed the nation. Howland would probably be content with his contribution while lamenting his early death. Park and Cooke, we suspect, would probably express some frustration with their legacies, particularly if we define "service" in terms of the community and not just the individual.

Howland initiated the evolution in pediatrics that raised it from a proprietary level to respected academic scholarship. He recognized that the European model of research-oriented departments suggested the future for American medicine and that contemporary pediatrics in the United States was ready for development into an important specialty in the European mode. Johns Hopkins was the appropriate place to begin—a small, new medical school with a powerful, like-minded, forward-thinking senior faculty (especially Welch) situated in a young, research-oriented, and supportive university. Howland was fortunate because there was then widespread national concern about the quality of medical training, catalyzed by the criticisms of Abraham Flexner in his report for the Carnegie Foundation for the Advancement of Teaching. The improvements he promoted were soon backed up financially by the Rockefeller Foundation.

Howland, Park, and Cooke attracted strong colleagues, including laboratory investigators capable of making the scientific basis of pediatrics a substantial enterprise. While Park felt that Howland "did not have an imaginative or creative mind, [he] chose subjects for investigation with great intelligence and insight, as well as judgment."[4] The Harriet Lane clinic became a model for new departments of pediatrics throughout the country and members of his faculty were recruited to lead the best of those new departments.

Howland was goal-oriented and "driven to excel."[5] Would the Harriet Lane Home under Howland have evolved further if he had not died at a relatively young age? Perhaps not much. He did not often acknowledge the extraordinary talents of some of those working for him, notably Kenneth Blackfan, Grover Powers, and James Gamble, and they responded to recruitment from other institutions. There was growth but little change in the organization of his department during the fourteen years of his leadership. When Park returned in 1927, he recognized and corrected structural and functional problems in the building, honed the concept of specialty clinics, expanded social service, and encouraged interest in child welfare and "social medicine"—steps that Howland had not considered important enough to take.

When one reflects on Howland's career, one wonders if the slope of its trajectory flattened after a major "exodus" of senior faculty: Blackfan to Cincinnati in 1920; Park and Powers to Yale in 1921; and Gamble to Harvard in 1922. At that time Howland remarked to Gamble: "All the marshals are going, only Napoleon is left."[6] It was understandably demoralizing to lose a fine faculty that one had carefully chosen and nurtured, and it was hard to find the energy to rebuild such a staff a second time. Another possible factor in this exodus was that Howland's energy was gradually sapped by chronic liver disease, of which he and everyone else were quite unaware.[7]

We noted in our preface that the difficulty "town" (private practitioners) and "gown"(full-time academicians) physicians had working together constructively in the first half of the twentieth century remains a problem to this day. It was and is a barrier to the improvement of service and access to health care in Baltimore and elsewhere in the United States. It was the "town" physicians who took the first steps to establish pediatrics in this country. Many of those who were regarded as the first pediatricians in the nation and founded the American Pediatric Society participated in a fee-for-service system, including Abraham Jacobi. It was the "town" that vigorously defended this system. At first, there was no substantial "gown" community. It began at Harriet Lane with the advent of academic pediatrics under Howland. When Park, a member of the "gown" but ahead of his time, advocated change viewed by many to be "socialized medicine," he lost his role as a published commentator. In that era others of the "gown" were at best indifferent and unsupportive of Park.

Teaching, the care of sick children in the hospital, and the search for new knowledge were quite enough for Howland. He did not consider the community outside the hospital part of his responsibility. His was a culture different from that of the private practitioner. We suspect that he harbored some disdain for those outside academic medicine and failed to grasp the context within which they worked. Driven and committed to his personal goals, he isolated the pediatric "gown" and inadvertently contributed to the rift with the "town." This attitude continued throughout Cooke's era.

Howland failed to realize that new understanding of diseases and treatments and better teaching of clinical pediatrics would have diminished impact if a child's access to care was limited or even lacking. Thus he distanced his department from the "soft" interests of John Mason Knox[8] in matters involving public health and social and preventive medicine. Subsequently, these topics were emphasized in the Johns Hopkins School of Hygiene and Public Health, established in 1916 by Welch with the backing of the Rockefeller Foundation once again.[9]

Park, on the other hand, rejected the isolation of academic pediatrics from the community. He recognized that service went well beyond the care of a hospitalized child. He asked why a particular child was ill at a particular time and what might have been done to prevent it. He understood the problems of access to care. Certainly, Park built on Howland's beginnings, but he added specialty clinics for several chronic disorders, expanded the use of social workers, and introduced child-life personnel onto the wards.

And Park wanted more. Writing urgently and often, even after his retirement, he advocated change and defined the major barrier to that change: "We believe that the fundamental failure of the American Medical Association in their attitudes and policies bearing on the general problem of medical care has been its unwillingness to acknowledge the need for improvement."[10] But Park was rebuffed by a profession that viewed his proposals as threats and considered his pronouncements those of an outsider, an academic. He ultimately achieved little toward finding a unified voice. The good that evolved from his professional effort was limited by inadequate access to care for so many children.

Cooke, too, would have none of Howland's isolation. Although his early training and mentoring seemed to point him toward a career in the laboratory, the experience of caring for his two severely handicapped daughters gave him a profound sense of injustice in the world. One suspects that Cooke always had a sharp edge to his personality, but the mentally retarded—and society's negative attitudes toward them—gave him a cause. This side of Cooke was still evolving when he was recruited to Hopkins, hidden within his strong interest in physiology. It is interesting to speculate, had it emerged sooner, whether the Hopkins search committee would have found him as attractive.

Once in Baltimore, Cooke was fortunate that his cause had both an outside champion, the Kennedy family, and that the mood in the country was ripe for change. The cold war had shaken America's scientific complacency and the civil rights movement was doing the same for its social views. Cooke, like his predecessors at Harriet Lane, did not back away from developing bold plans. Unlike his predecessors, however, he had people of power and influence outside Hopkins who also wanted such plans, and he had a changing external environment and a federal government interested in supporting science, which eased his efforts and those of his contemporaries at other institutions. Cooke recognized early the importance of primary and preventive care. He encouraged the creation of comprehensive childcare clinics, institutes

NURSE ON A MANUAL ELEVATOR IN THE HARRIET LANE ON THE HOME'S LAST DAY. For ten years after the department of pediatrics had moved to the Children's Medical and Surgical Center, the hospital continued to use the Harriet Lane Home for various purposes, including a day care center on the third floor for employees' children. Helen Taussig and Edwards Park maintained offices in the building for as long as possible. It was a sad day in 1974 when this nurse closed the gate of the Inclinator elevator (a gift in 1940 from the American Legion Auxiliary) for the last time. Photo by the Barton Gillet Company of Baltimore.

for the care of handicapped children, the establishment of Head Start programs, and an institute at the National Institutes of Health that focused on children. This was probably the first concrete evidence of recognition by the federal government—six decades after von Pirquet's arrival in Baltimore—that there was a scientific basis for the practice of pediatrics.

For all his involvement on the national stage, Cooke was not enough of a politician to advance his cause either within Johns

Hopkins or the local community. He perpetuated the elitist sense of distinction between the Harriet Lane training program and other community-based programs in Baltimore, and he did not ultimately increase the sense of unity he sought with practicing pediatricians. Nor did he establish wholehearted recognition of primary care pediatrics as a legitimate academic endeavor. Though it is likely that a more acquiescent man would not have accomplished what he did nationally, he failed to find the balance between vision and politics that might have allowed him to take on the larger leadership role that he sought at Hopkins.

Perhaps the Harriet Lane during Cooke's time is a testament to how much is determined by the context of the time during which one strives. World War II and its aftermath profoundly influenced the Harriet Lane Home of the 1940s and early 1950s. The Home of the 1960s and 1970s was shaped by the brief reign of the Kennedys and their "Camelot" era and by federal support for civil rights and President Lyndon Johnson's "Great Society." Eventually, the disillusion of the Vietnam era and the country's swing back to conservatism were also part of the dynamic at the Harriet Lane. During that time a new interest in and appreciation for the importance of ethics in clinical pediatrics (which Cooke helped to initiate and eagerly embraced) contributed to the realization that medicine, while providing the expectation of a better future, has its subjective uncertainties like other human activities. Meanwhile the momentum to build a system of medical care that would serve all children and, indeed, all adults, floundered and has not since regained its forward thrust.[11]

Academic pediatrics across this country today is a tribute to its birthplace, the Harriet Lane Home. The commitment to the development of new knowledge and to teaching began with Howland in Baltimore and was sustained here and disseminated across the country by him and then by Park and Cooke, as well as by others elsewhere. The innumerable moments at the Harriet Lane that assured the success of this mission are nicely exemplified in a 1960 letter from Park to his close friend Charles Janeway at the Boston Children's Hospital. Years before, Park—as well as Howland—was interested in the role of the thymus gland and the nature of "status thymolymphaticus." As always, Park was a constant prod, never losing an opportunity to ask a question and push for answers. It was not enough to congratulate Janeway on his recent lectures on the thymus:

HELEN TAUSSIG SPEAKING AT GATHERING. In 1974 the Harriet Lane Home was razed to make way for a new facility for the treatment of cancer, but not before some of the giants of Johns Hopkins pediatrics, as well as members of the Harriet Lane Home Board of Managers, gathered in the old amphitheater to pay tribute to the great work accomplished in the building. The heat was already turned off on that cold March day, so participants huddled in their coats and listened to Taussig and others reminisce before they lifted glasses of sherry in a toast. When the building was torn down, many faculty and staff members kept bricks as mementoes.

I now wish to make a suggestion which you will say immediately dates with the time of Noah. I have not kept up with the literature and the suggestion may be absolutely obsolete. It is this: Why do you not assign one of your assistants or someone at Harvard who has had special experience in extract extraction to examine the possibility that a potent extract can be obtained from the thymus gland which will affect lymphoid propagation. It would be possible to obtain calves' thymus, which [are] very large at birth, and in a slaughterhouse pig's thymus in various embryonic stages. These glands ought to furnish abundant materials for extraction. Thymectomy in the newborn mouse supplies a wonderful end reaction, namely the virtual absence of lymphoid tissue in the intestinal tract. It would be possible to thymectomize newborn mice and follow with one abstract after another, using the plasia of lymphoid tissue in the intestinal tract as your criterion. I dare say that this has all been done as afore indicated.

I have always thought that there was some basis for thymic death, although the pathologists insist that in status lymphaticus the hyperplasia of lymphoid tissue is explained on the ground that the subject was in a normal state of nutrition. I have wondered if the thymus did not have an internal secretion and the subjects of thymic death died because of its excess. Again, do not pay any attention to this suggestion if it has already been investigated and excluded as untenable.[12]

Pure Park, this letter written fourteen years after his retirement and nine years before his death exemplifies a core tradition of the Harriet Lane Home from Howland's first day there, the persistence of the questioning life and the insistent need to try to find answers. It was a distinctive, academically grand culture.

We share some of the same regret that we're sure Park and Cooke felt. The disunion in our profession remains one of the barriers to better service for all. So does the failure to join closely the disciplines of public health and preventive care for well children with the care of the acutely ill. And so, especially, does the limited access to health care for so many children. The Harriet Lane accomplished very much indeed and gave us a pathway of effort that among other things provides a wonderful opportunity for the development of new knowledge and better understanding of disease as well as the illness that evolves from disease. It is a wonderful story and we are delighted to have the opportunity to tell at least some of it here. However, there remains a huge gap in the availability of appropriate care for so many in this country and the medical profession's protection of its turf in the past has been one of the barriers to overcoming that lack of availability. It is an ongoing fight which is making precious little if any headway in today's world. The almost 45 million people in this country who do not have access to health care deserve our constant effort. For them, so much of the new knowledge and better understanding is useless until they have that access.

Despite all of the hard work that remains to be done, the splendid level of pediatric academic excellence that now predominates in this country deserves to be acknowledged. Today—in contrast to Howland's time—most pediatricians are fine care providers, teachers, and/

or investigators. This is an excellence that is no longer localized but is widely diffused, so there is no longer a need for a single pre-eminent department. And this is as it should be.

Notes

1. Clement A. Smith, *The Children's Hospital of Boston—Built Better Than They Knew.* (Boston and Toronto: Little Brown and Company, 1983), 144.

2. Simon Flexner and James T. Flexner, *William Henry Welch and the Heroic Age of American Medicine* (Baltimore: Johns Hopkins University Press, 1993), 44–46, 51, 64–65, 174–75.

3. Although the tenure of Francis Schwentker began with promise, it was, in effect, a transition between the eras of Edwards Park and Robert Cooke.

4. Edwards A. Park, "John Howland Award Address," *Pediatrics* 10 (1952): 95.

5. Ibid., 107.

6. Edwards A. Park, draft memorandum, Harriet Lane Home Collection, RG 4, series C, box 17, folder 29, Alan Mason Chesney Medical Archives, The Johns Hopkins Medical Institutions, Baltimore, MD.

7. Edwards A. Park, "John Howland Award Address,"107. In 1952 Park offered his "verdict of time" as to the influence of Howland's contributions to American pediatrics in comparison to those of Abraham Jacobi and L. Emmett Holt. Jacobi was widely regarded as the father of American pediatrics in the late nineteenth century, and L. Emmett Holt was the best known pediatrician at the beginning of the twentieth century in New York City and across the country:

> Abraham Jacobi was the pioneer. He was a man of remarkable personality, far better educated medically and culturally, when he came to this country from Austria, than his American colleagues. He had great influence in raising the level of American medicine, particularly in New York City. But in pediatrics, so far as I can tell, his merit is limited to his having been the pioneer. He was the first, I might say, to wear the pediatric uniform. If he has left a permanent imprint on pediatrics, I do not know what it is.
>
> The case of L. Emmett Holt is quite different. Holt established pediatrics in this country as a special branch of medicine, defining it and putting it in order, and he made it include the welfare of the child in health as well as in disease, a revolutionary concept, the idea that the physician is also charged with keeping the child well, coming at a time when physicians in general thought that their duties began and ended with sickness. When we say that pediatrics more than any other branch of medicine is directed toward preventive medicine, we must feel grateful to Dr. Holt for starting its flow that way.
>
> John Howland modernized pediatrics. He changed the course of pediatrics to what we know now by substituting for bedside observation and conjecture the study of disease through laboratory methods and experiments. He caused pediatrics to become a dynamic, rapidly expanding subject. He accomplished this not by scattering ideas that caused others to act, but by example. The example lay in the development of a mod-

el clinic, model from the point of view of administration, medical care, teaching, research, spirit—the Harriet Lane Home—known all over the world, and in this country extensively copied just as he left it. Moreover he created and sent out missionaries, his pupils, filled with his ideas and spirit."

8. See also chapter 3, endnote 8; Paul Harper, "John Hall Mason Knox, Jr. (1972–1951)," *Pediatric Profiles*, 155–60.

9. Adjacent to the Johns Hopkins School of Medicine and Hospital with its Harriet Lane Home is the Johns Hopkins Bloomberg School of Public Health, a large and steadily expanding institution, world-famous for its faculty, research, and leadership. One might hope and expect there to be a close relationship between these two highly respected schools, both involved in health care, but in practice this is not the case. In regard to pediatrics this separation might have begun with Howland. But overall the most likely reason is the different viewpoints of the two schools—one focused especially on individual sick human beings and the other on the epidemiology of diseases and the prevention and treatment of medical problems threatening large populations, such as malnutrition and infections such as malaria, tuberculosis, pneumonias, measles, and the HIV virus. Clearly, among these subjects there should be much of potential interest and relevance to academic medicine as well as to public health.

10. Edwards Park to Charles Janeway, January 10, 1949. Robert Haggerty, who is writing a biography of Janeway, provided copies of correspondence between Edwards Park and Charles Janeway to Henry Seidel.

11. Many people, in and out of the health care field, believe that the lack of universal access to health care is the major unfinished business of our medical profession. The majority of our society longs for a solution to this deficiency. Here are quotations from two prominent proponents, neither of them in the medical profession:

Cardinal Joseph Bernadin of Chicago, dying of cancer in 1995, sponsored an amendment to the Illinois State Constitution to establish health care as a fundamental right of Illinois citizens and require that the General Assembly enact a plan that enables everyone in Illinois to obtain decent heath care on a regular basis. "Health care is an essential safeguard of human life and dignity, and there is an obligation for society to ensure that every person be able to realize this right." This proposed amendment received wide support across the state and especially in Chicago, but was recently put "on hold" by the Illinois legislature. Cardinal Joseph Bernadin, "A Sign of Hope, a Pastoral Letter on Healthcare," October 1995, http://www.chausa.org/RESOURCE /BERNSIGN.ASP.

Uwe E. Reinhardt, a well-known health care economist and professor at Princeton, wrote words in 1997 equally applicable today: "Throughout the past three decades Americans been locked in a tenacious ideological debate whose essence can be distilled into the following pointed question: As a matter of national policy, and to the extent that a nation's health system can make it possible, should the child of a poor American family have the same chance of avoiding preventable illness or of being cured from a given illness as does the child of a rich American family?... The 'yeas' in all other industrial nations had won that debate hands down decades ago.... In the United States, on the other hand, the 'nays' so far have carried the day. As a matter of conscious national policy, the United States always has and still does openly countenance the practice of rationing health care for millions of American children...." Uwe E. Reinhardt, "Wanted: A Clearly Articulated Social Ethic for American Health Care," *Journal of the American Medical Association* 278 (1997): 1446.

12. Letter from Edwards Park to Charles Janeway, June 27, 1960.

Afterword

Appendix A

Floor Plans of the Harriet Lane Home during the Howland Era (1912–1926)

THESE FLOOR PLANS of the Harriet Lane Home were published by Alexander A. Weech, "The Johns Hopkins University School of Medicine Department of Pediatrics" (in *Methods and Problems in Medical Education*, Eighth Series, New York, The Rockefeller Foundation, 1927, pp. 1–12) and are reproduced here with permission from the Rockefeller Archive Center.

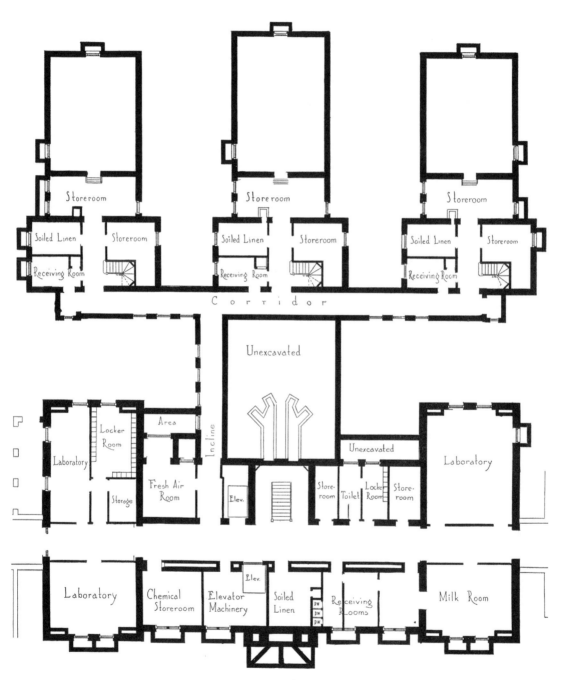

Storeroom

Storeroom

Storeroom

Soiled Linen

Storeroom

Soiled Linen

Storeroom

Soiled Linen

Storeroom

Receiving Room

Receiving Room

Receiving Room

C o r r i d o r

Unexcavated

Area

Locker Room

Laboratory

Incline

Unexcavated

Laboratory

Fresh Air Room

Storage

Elev.

Store-room

Toilet

Locker Room

Store-room

Laboratory

Chemical Storeroom

Elevator Machinery

Elev.

Soiled Linen

DW
DW
DW

Receiving Rooms

Milk Room

BASEMENT   FLOOR   PLAN

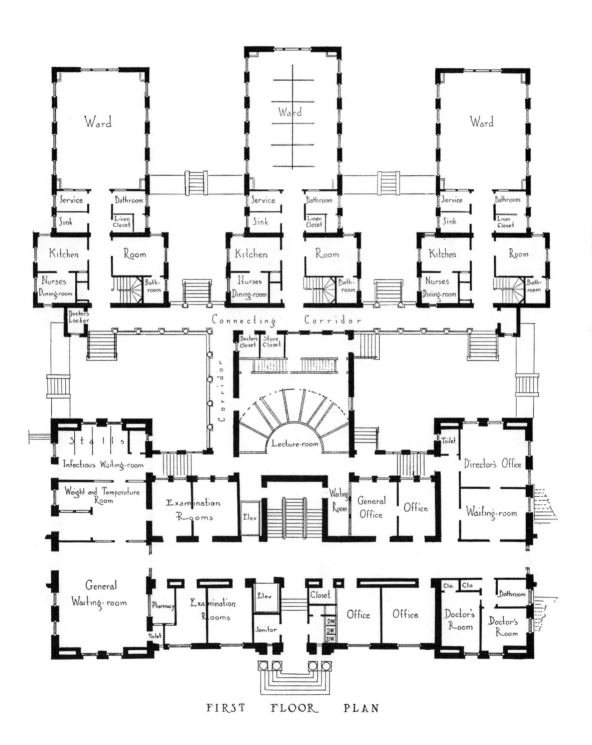

FIRST FLOOR PLAN

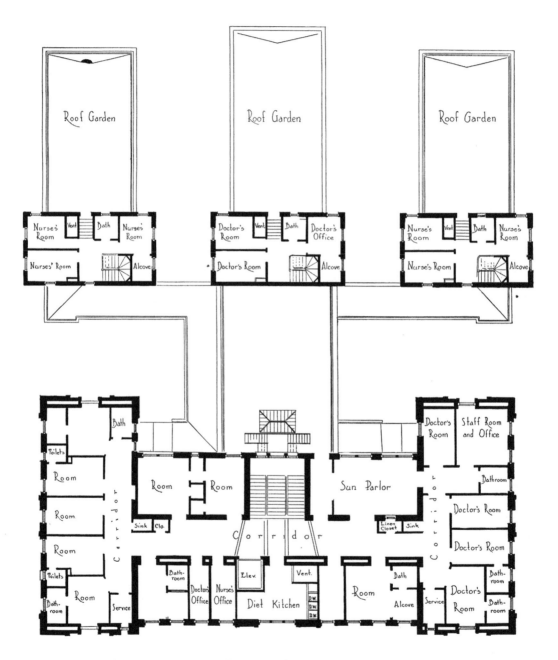

SECOND FLOOR PLAN

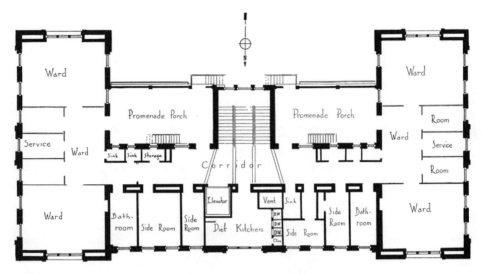

THIRD FLOOR PLAN

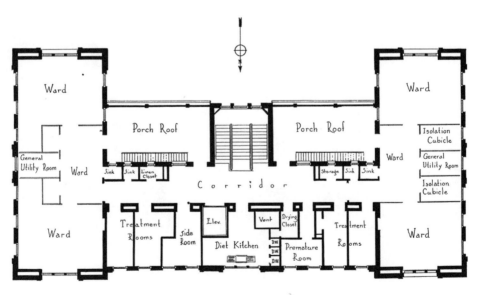

FOURTH FLOOR PLAN

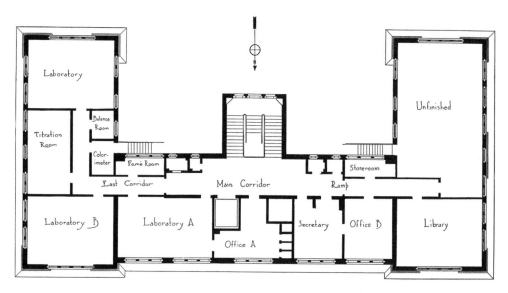

Laboratory

Titration Room

Balance Room

Color-imeter

Fume Room

East Corridor

Main Corridor

Ramp

Storeroom

Unfinished

Laboratory B

Laboratory A

Office A

Secretary

Office B

Library

FIFTH FLOOR PLAN

Appendix B

Excerpt from John Howland's Description of the Harriet Lane Home

ON NOVEMBER 20, 1912, there was a formal ceremony to open the Harriet Lane Home. L. Emmett Holt Sr., John Howland's mentor, gave the keynote address and Howland gave a short speech thereafter. There is no record of Howland's remarks on this occasion but he might well have used parts of his detailed description of the home (particularly the final two paragraphs), which he published soon after the event in the *Johns Hopkins Alumni Magazine*.[1] What follows is an excerpt of this essay.

THE FOUR BUILDINGS which comprise the Home are situated on the south side of a quadrangle formed by the main hospital, and immediately west of the new Phipps Psychiatric Clinic.[2] There is a main building, five stories high, which faces north on the lawn, and three pavilions, each two stories, placed immediately behind it. All four buildings are built of brick, with stone facings, and presenting a simple but attractive exterior. The main building contains the wards, etc., for the care of patients with diseases of a non-infectious nature. The east pavilion is devoted to the treatment of diphtheria, the west pavilion to scarlet fever, while the middle pavilion is set apart for the temporary observation of newly admitted cases of questionable diagnosis before their final distribution in the hospital. By means of this observation pavilion, it is hoped that the main hospital may be kept free from epidemics.

The pavilions are small buildings essentially of the same construction. The centrally placed observation pavilion is continuous with the main building, which is prolonged backward in its middle part to meet it, but the laterally placed pavilions for scarlet fever and diphtheria are separated from the main building, and also from the observation pavilion by a space of 25 feet. Each pavilion is built in such a way as to contain one small ward (capacity ten beds), one room and bed for a private patient, a diet kitchen, two rooms for the care and disinfection of excreta, a history room, and a nurses' dining-room, while on the second floor are bedrooms for three nurses, and a roof garden. It is to be noted that this arrangement makes it possible for nurses in charge of children suffering from the easily communicable infectious diseases to remain in complete isolation within their respective pavilions, since each pavilion is complete in itself. The internal construction of the three pavilions differs in one particular—while the wards of the pavilions for diphtheria and scarlet fever are large open rooms, the ward in the observation pavilion is occupied in its central two-thirds by a double row of ten cubicles, placed back to back. The walls forming these cubicles are thin, of solid construction below, glass above, about 6½ feet high. Each cubicle is large enough to contain one child's bed, and to allow passageway at the side of it for the nurse. By this arrangement, each patient in a cubicle is separated from neighboring patients, yet all patients are in one room, and since the partitions above the levels of the beds are of glass, all patients are in plain view of any one nurse, no matter where in the ward she happens to be.

The five story main hospital building is constructed in a general way as follows: The wards lie at the east and west ends of each floor, and are connected by broad hallways, into which open a number of rooms, later to be enumerated. Each ward is designed to accommodate about fourteen patients. Opposite the entrance to the wards—that is, built against the east and west walls of the corresponding wards—are three compartments constructed in a similar way to the cubicles already described in the observation ward. The middle of these three compartments is about the size of a small room, and contains a gas range, scales, etc., and is for the use of the nurse. The two smaller compartments on either side of it are designed for patients who need close observation, or a certain degree of isolation from other patients. Since the upper two-thirds of the pavilion forming these compartments are of glass, no obstruction to the view of the ward as a whole is afforded.

Into the halls which connect the wards open a diet kitchen provided with sterilizer, refrigerator, gas range, and apparatus for keeping the food warm, sinks, etc.; a bathing and toilet room for the children, two rooms for the isolation of patients, etc. In addition to these there are on the fourth floor two rooms for the accommodation of wet nurses. On the third floor is an operating room for minor surgery, and on the second floor ten rooms for private patients. The arrangement of the fifth floor departs from the general scheme, in that at either end roof gardens replace the wards, and in connection with the roof gardens are two sun parlors, toilets, a diet kitchen, etc. The arrangement of the ground floor is also different. On this floor the out-patient department is situated, as well as offices for the director, two rooms and a bath for the resident physician, two laboratories, a clerical room, coat rooms for the students, and the amphitheatre.[3]

The Dispensary occupies about one-third of the floor, and is composed of a large waiting room, a small drug room, four medium sized rooms for the examination of cases, and a compartment with large glass windows where children are weighed and measured. In these particulars the arrangement of the out-patient department is similar to that of out-patient departments in general, but in the following important particular it differs—namely that in close connection with the main waiting room is a large room for the immediate separation of children giving evidence to the admitting officer of an acute infectious disease, and for their isolation and treatment there until a suitable disposal of them can be made. The construction of this out-patient isolation room is further modified, in that one-half of it is subdivided into four cubicles, in which patients thought to have infectious diseases of different kinds may be isolated from each other. A separate entrance and exit is provided for this isolating room.

The amphitheatre lies at a lower level than the rest of this floor, but is on the same level as the ward floors of the pavilion. It is situated in the rear part of the main building—that is, in that part of the main building which is nearest the pavilions—and communicates with the main hospital, with the dispensary and the three pavilions by what may be termed three separate routes. The idea of this arrangement is that patients from the hospital, dispensary or pavilions may be demonstrated in the amphitheatre without danger of distributing or receiving any infection. The amphitheatre seats about eighty students.

One of the most important features of the construction is that each ward is provided with an open air porch, about half as large as the ward itself. For the private patients there is a special roof garden and sun parlor. There are no door sills, the hospital beds are provided with large castors, and the elevator of the main building is large enough to take a bed. Thus it is seen that the transfer of the patient in the bed from the ward to the open air porch, or to the roof garden or the amphitheatre—in short, from any one part of the hospital to any other part is very simple.

The food is supplied from the general kitchen of the Johns Hopkins Hospital and carried underground to the basement of the Harriet Lane Home, where it is distributed by a dumb waiter system to the various diet kitchens. All dishes used in the hospital, before they are returned to the kitchen of the Johns Hopkins Hospital, are sterilized by means of the steam sterilizer with which each diet kitchen is provided. The milk laboratory is in the basement of the main building of the Harriet Lane Home, where it occupies two rooms, and is equipped with all necessary apparatus for the care and modification of milk.[4]

The interior of the main building and pavilions is very bright. The walls are finished in cream color; the woodwork in light gray. The floors of the wards and rooms are of linoleum, varnished and waxed, laid on concrete. The floors of the halls are of concrete. The windows everywhere are very numerous, so numerous that all parts of the hospital are flooded with light. Throughout the hospital is an abundance of plumbing—for example, hot and cold water are introduced into each ward at least at two points. Both wards and rooms are provided with numerous connections for electric lights—a source of great convenience for work which has to be carried out at night. Further, wherever it is necessary, there is placed a most convenient apparatus for the disposal of excreta. The excreta are first sterilized by live steam, afterwards discharged into the city sewer. A second handling of the excreta, or their treatment by antiseptic solutions is thus made unnecessary.

The affiliation of the Harriet Lane Home with the University marks a distinct advance in pediatrics in America. There has been, up to the present time, hardly any satisfactory arrangement between universities or medical schools and children's hospitals. The conditions of affairs has been in marked contrast to that obtaining on the continent of Europe, especially in Germany. In America, those appointed to teaching positions have usually brought to the university or medical school clinical facilities [outside the school], rather than received them [inside the school]. This has resulted in a lack of opportunity for study and for teaching in this branch of medicine. For this reason, the number of workers in this country in this line of work has not compared as favorably as it might with those in other countries in numbers, in en-

THE
HARRIET LANE
HOME

thusiasm, and in contributions. Furthermore there has been the advantage that in the majority of instances [abroad] the children's hospitals have not been isolated institutions, but have been part of large hospital systems where there has been an opportunity for close contact with other men in other, but allied, lines of work with different methods, different ideas, and different points of view.

This favorable system is the one which now has been adopted here. The staff of instruction of the University is the medical staff of the Home, and the Home itself is a part of the Hopkins Hospital. The establishment of this system can only work for good, and must serve as an example for other institutions to follow.

Notes

1. John Howland, "The Harriet Lane Home for Invalid Children, *Johns Hopkins Alumni Magazine*, 1 (1912–13): 115–21.

2. This clinic opened in 1913, a year after the Harriet Lane. The buildings were adjacent and their facades complementary. The Psychiatric Clinic was named after Henry A. Phipps, its major donor, who also established a tuberculosis center.

3. Edwards Park later described these administrative rooms in the west wing of the ground floor in more detail: "The west half was occupied by the group of offices for the use of the professor, his own room, an anteroom, and an adjoining one for the secretary. [There were] offices for the supervisor of nurses and a waiting room for private patients. The latter contained the portrait of Mr. Johnston, the husband of Harriet Lane, a desk belonging to Harriet Lane herself as well as a sofa and some chairs left by her to the institution." Draft memorandum, RG 4, series C, box 17, folder 29, HLH-AMC.

4. The emphasis on the "care and modification" of milk, and the ever-present worries about infectious diseases and efforts to prevent their transmission, identify the central importance of these two topics in the practice of pediatrics at that time.

Appendix C

Edwards A. Park's Description of the New York Foundling Asylum

EDITED BY JOHN W. LITTLEFIELD*

THE NEW YORK Foundling Asylum was an extraordinary place and a year there provided an indelible experience for a physician. The building was a large, rambling, red-brick structure of mid-Victorian architecture on the north side of 68th Street in Manhattan, occupying most of the block between Lexington and Third Avenue. It was under the management of the Sisters of St. Vincent de Paul. The building contained living quarters for the Sisters and a rather beautiful chapel; but the greater part was devoted to its children. It included an obstetrical division for unmarried primipara, where between two hundred and three hundred babies were born each year. Each intern rotated thorough the obstetrical division but the star attraction was pediatrics. The Asylum proclaimed its functions at the door. In the front hall, close to the entrance, stood a basket mounted on a pedestal in which anyone could deposit a baby, never to see the baby again, and no questions asked . . . When I was at the Asylum in 1908 (seven years after John Howland left) I learned that more than 40,000 babies had been left in the basket since the Asylum opened its doors. The Sisters were intensely proud of the record, often referred to it and reported enthusiastically on additions. They believed that the anonymity of their process increased the odds that they would have the opportunity to care for unwanted children. But some people disagreed and their criti-

*Alan Mason Chesney Archives, Harriet Lane Home Collection, Record Group 4, series B, box 8, folder 11, pp. 22–27. This is from a draft memorandum, 69 pages long, which is mislabeled the "Howland Period From 1912 to 1926." The memorandum covers 1873 to 1912. The description of the Asy-

cism eventually got press attention. Shortly after my time there the basket was removed and orderly procedures for admission substituted. In Howland's time, however, the basket was in full operation.

The children were housed in six large hall-like rooms called nurseries. Each accommodated sixteen mothers with their babies and thirty-six "run-arounds," children between two and four years. The mothers and babies slept together in hospital beds while the run-arounds slept on cots between the beds. Thus each nursery housed sixteen adults and fifty-two children and the total population was ninety-six mothers and three hundred and twelve children. The nurseries must not be thought of as a stationary population but rather as steadily changing as entrances ensued on exits.

A Sister was in charge of each nursery and had under her a matron, a former resident who had elected to stay as an assistant. Each nursery was organized in a unit system. A unit consisted of a mother, her own baby and two run-arounds assigned to her. Some explanation is required: an unmarried woman who gave birth in the Asylum or brought in her newborn from outside the Asylum could obtain asylum gratis for her baby and herself for two years, provided she stayed and gave her services to the Asylum for that period. This service included the care of two of the Asylum's older children. During this period she retained charge of her baby. At the end of two years she was free to leave the Asylum with her baby or, she could turn over her baby to the Asylum if she relinquished all claims to the child. If a mother was unwilling to remain at the Asylum then her newborn baby became a ward of the Asylum. There were of course other exceptional arrangements.

The splendid thing about the unit system was that it allowed the baby and mother to remain together for two years and it also provided the older children with a foster parent during that time. In addition, the Asylum performed a great service by providing a refuge for unmarried mothers and gave them time to adjust to their lives and the outside world again. The Asylum also provided a market for child adoption, where would-be parents inspected its human wares. The market also functioned in a mail-order fashion. Each spring large groups of run-arounds would be dispatched in special day coaches to various parts of the country for adoption by Catholic families. These children were chosen by mail. The prospective foster parents requested specifications in regard to sex, even color of hair, etc., and the Sisters supplied the necessary descriptions and photographs. Each run-around was provided with garments with their new name sewed on the label.

The children in the Asylum were excellently fed and one of the features unique to the Asylum was the presence of a personal touch. I do not believe that any non-Catholic asylum in New York City offered anything even remotely comparable.

In addition to the nurseries there was a hospital ward with twenty to thirty beds and accessory rooms for children when they contracted contagious diseases. The hospital ward was managed by a most remarkable Sister, Josef Angela, a great friend and admirer of Howland. When I was an intern at the Asylum, she often mentioned his name and lamented that he no longer came to see her. Under her was a matron and assistants but there were no trained nurses in the institution.

There was a large room known as the Marasmus Ward that housed fifteen to twenty babies who furnished an insoluble problem. These infants had no mothers so it was necessary to place them together in a common room; no other course seemed viable to the Sisters. The mothers in the nurseries had their own babies to tend so double assignment was not possible. The eventual mortality in the Maramus Ward was virtually one hundred percent. In my time there, only two infants in that ward survived. One survived because a nursery mother was persuaded to breast-feed one of the ward infants in addition to her own. In retrospect the causes of the mortality were the close confinement of the babies where infections were freely passed, the bad feeding procedures of the time, and the lack of individual care. A single matron was in charge with only one or, at most, two assistants. The babies received little care and few survived beyond the third month.

I am sure that the attending staff and the interns were appalled at the mortality in the Marasmus Ward. Every physician at the Asylum, attending to intern, wished and tried to solve the mortality in the Marasmus Ward, but their solutions were limited to better ways of feeding. Looking back on infant feeding at the time, the new methods of feeding were worse. The survival rates of the babies would have improved if they had been distributed to the nursery mothers for breast feeding, but the Sisters rejected this option. It would have been difficult, but it certainly could have been done to some extent. The Sisters seemed strangely insensitive to the mortality around them in the view of many of the interns and physicians at the Asylum. The Sisters pointed out that the babies were without sins and therefore bound for heaven upon death and this was a comfort to them, for if the babies lived then heaven was not assured. This religious unworldly or next-worldly attitude was an obstacle to medical reform in other ways. It would have been easier if the use of the Asylum's anonymous basket was abolished earlier but the Sisters regarded this idea as cutting off one of the most important functions of the institution. The unfortunate result of their intentions was that their Good Samaritan efforts exceeded their resources.

In the basement there was a morgue and an autopsy room with a "stand" to hold a deceased infant. This same stand, originally used by Joseph McGuire in the development of the intubation technique with the O'Dwyer tube, was still there. It was of great use in learning the art of intubation for laryngeal diphtheria, allowing practice on the dead in preparation for use on the living. Intubation for laryngeal diphtheria was a great advance at the time and saved many lives in the Asylum and elsewhere.

Index

Numbers in *italics* refer to photo captions. Page numbers preceding "n" refer to notes pages, followed by the note number. "HLH" is "Harriet Lane Home."

Morse, John Lovett, 93
Moser, Paul, 27–28

Najjar, Victor, 16on. 114, 245n. 38, 254
National Cancer Institute (NCI), 248
National Commission for the Protection
    of Human Subjects of Biomedical and
    Behavioral Research, 303–304
National Institute of Child Health and
    Human Development (NICHD), 298,
    311n. 28
National Institute of Mental Health
    (NIMH), 299
National Institutes of Health (NIH), 213,
    248, 277, 311n. 28
National Research Act of 1974, 248, 303
Neff, John, 298
Neill, Cahterine, 173, 174, *175*, 255
Nelson, Russell, 250, 251, 260, 264;
    relationship with Cooke, 262, *263*, 270,
    288, 307
New York Foundling Asylum, 52, 67n. 11,
    123, 339–42
NICHD. *See* National Institute of Child
    Health and Human Development
NIH. *See* National Institutes of Health
NIMH. *See* National Institute of Mental
    Health
Nirenberg, Marshall W., 247
Nixon, Richard, 248, 313n. 55
nurses, *56*, *62*, *141*, 235, *235*, 295; aides,
    296–97; CMSC adjustments, 296; stu-
    dents, *141*
Nyhan, Bill, 256, 28on. 49

Odell, Gerry, 256, 271
Office of Economic Opportunity (OEO),
    302, 312n. 41
Orr, William J., 87
Oski, Frank, 113, 309
Osler, William, 86, 88, 94n. 3, 117n. 20,
    214n. 2

Park, Agnes Bevan ("Moo"), 123, 128–29,
    152–53, 241
Park, Edwards A. ("Punk"), *114*, *119*,
    120–21, 153–54, 316, *319*, 320–22; bone
    studies 124–25, 138; and bronchoscopy,
    133; characteristics, 127–28; childhood,
    121–22; death, 150; disagreements with
    Howland, 134, 135–36; education, 122,
    123; financial support of, 149, 22In. 139;
    fly-fishing, 149–50, 16on. 115; HLH
    director, 166, 309; in HLH dispensary,
    74, 76–77, 82, 97n. 22, 163–65; HLH
    historian, xi–xii, xiii, xiv n. 11, 1, 47 n,
    148–49; and HLH premature nursery,
    199, 201; Harrisons' recruitment efforts,

209–13; Howland description, 47–48,
    108–109, 148; Howland's influence, 124,
    125, 129–31; impact on staff, 137–38,
    164; Janeway assistant, 74, 123; Johns
    Hopkins pediatric chair offer, 126;
    journal column, 145–48; marriage, 123,
    128–29; pediatric clinics philosophy,
    138–39; and pediatric specialization,
    133–34, 135–36, 171–72, 174, 180, 183;
    on physician continuing education,
    134; portrait, *120*; on psychiatric child
    care, 184–86; recruitment of, 240–43;
    research, 123–24; retirement, 148; on
    Schwentker, 239–40; on social aspects of
    medicine, 144–48, 171–72, 317–18; suc-
    cessor selection, 223–24, 225; teaching
    style, 130–32, *131*, 140; testimonials to,
    150–52; view of von Pirquet, 33–34, 43;
    wife's death, 152–53; writings, 23 n; Yale
    chair of pediatrics, 124, 125
Park, Marion, 121, 127
Park, Rollo, 128, 150
Park, William Edwards, 121
Park Building. *See* Edwards A. Park Build-
    ing
Parks, Marie, 305
patients, *vi*, 43n. 1, *62*, 77; disorders,
    78–79; and doctors, 76–78; racial segre-
    gation of, 59–60, 68n. 28, *169*, 262
Peabody, Francis, 158n. 81
Pearce, Richard Mills, 71, 72
Peck, Jack, 137, 233
pediatrics, ix–xi, 16, 52, 126, 317; at Bal-
    timore hospitals, 266–67; child welfare
    movements in, 107, 144–45; specializa-
    tion, 133–34, 135–36, 180, 183–84;
    training programs in, 255–56
Pediatrics, 145, 147
Perkins, Walter F., 287, 31on. 4
Phipps Building. *See* Henry A. Phipps
    Building
Phoebe R. Berman Bioethics Institute, 307
Pincoffs, Maurice, 239
Pithotomy Club, 34, 45n. 18
Powell, Gerald, 168
Powers, Grover, 80, 91, 97n. 22, 99n. 48,
    125, 145, 163, 209, 210, 287, 316; influ-
    ence on Cooke, 252–53, 267, 291
Prall, Onica, 168
premature baby care, 201–202
Price, Julian, 151, 255, 266
Proctor, Donald, 132–33

Randall, Blanchard, 19, 34–35, 45n. 20, 61
Reed, Lowell, 226
Reichelderfer, Thomas, 245n. 38
Reinhardt, Uwe E., 324n. 11
Remsen, Ira, 34, 35–37

Index